Foreword

1   On 17 June 1983, the Maritime Safety Committee (MSC) adopted, by resolution MSC.4(48), the International Code for the Construction and Equipment of Ships Carrying Dangerous Chemicals in Bulk (IBC Code). Under the provisions of chapter VII of the International Convention for the Safety of Life at Sea, 1974 (SOLAS 74), as amended, chemical tankers constructed on or after 1 July 1986 must comply with the provisions of the Code.

2   On 5 December 1985, by resolution MEPC.19(22), the IBC Code was extended by the Marine Environment Protection Committee (MEPC) to cover marine pollution aspects for the implementation of Annex II to the International Convention for the Prevention of Pollution from Ships, 1973, as modified by the Protocol of 1978 relating thereto (MARPOL 73/78). Under the provisions of Annex II to MARPOL 73/78, chemical tankers constructed on or after 1 July 1986 must comply with the provisions of the Code.

3   The revised Annex II to MARPOL 73/78, which was adopted by resolution MEPC.118(52), encompassed the development of a new pollution categorization system and criteria for assigning products to these new categories; and the revision of stripping requirements and discharge criteria. As a consequence of these revisions, it was necessary to make a number of amendments to the IBC Code. The amended IBC Code was adopted by resolutions MEPC.119(52) and MSC.176(79) in October 2004 and December 2004 respectively. Since the adoption of the amended IBC Code by these two resolutions, products contained in the Code have had their carriage requirements or product name revised in light of new information, and the evaluation and assignment of carriage requirements of new products has continued with a view for inclusion in the next set of amendments of the IBC Code. These products have also been included in chapters 17 or 18 as appropriate and are marked with a footnote (n) in this edition of the Code.

4   Under regulation 11 of Annex II to MARPOL 73/78, chemical tankers constructed before 1 July 1986 must comply with the provisions of the Code for the Construction and Equipment of Ships Carrying Dangerous Chemicals in Bulk (BCH Code). Under SOLAS 74, the BCH Code remains as a recommendation. The BCH Code is issued as a separate publication.

5   Previously, appendices II and III of Annex II to MARPOL 73/78 contained lists of products which were reproduced in chapters 17 and 18 of the IBC Code as well as chapters VI and VII of pre-1993 editions of the BCH Code. However, since 1993, the lists of products in chapters VI and VII of the BCH Code have been replaced by references to the IBC Code, and the lists of products in Annex II to MARPOL 73/78 have been deleted. As a result, the IBC Code is now the definitive source of names for products subject to Annex II to MARPOL 73/78.

6   Reference is also made to the MEPC.2/Circulars, issued annually in December. These contain, *inter alia*, details of products that have been the subject of Tripartite Agreements and are, in effect, a supplement to the IBC Code during the interim period before the entry into force of relevant amendments of the Code. Annex 1 of these circulars includes products that are expected to become new or amended entries to the IBC Code. A future amendment, shown in the Circular, serves as prior notice of the carriage conditions which will only apply to that product when the next set of amendments enter into force.

7   A number of other documents closely related to the IBC Code are annexed to this publication. A compact disc containing files for chapters 17, 18 and 19, in portable document format, is also provided with the book, so that these chapters may be searched electronically.

Contents

IBC CODE

STANDARDS AND GUIDELINES RELEVANT TO THE CODE

IBC CODE

Preamble

1 The purpose of this Code is to provide an international standard for the safe carriage, in bulk by sea, of dangerous chemicals and noxious liquid substances listed in chapter 17 of the Code. The Code prescribes the design and construction standards of ships, regardless of tonnage, involved in such carriage and the equipment they shall carry to minimize the risk to the ship, its crew and the environment, having regard to the nature of the products involved.

2 The basic philosophy of the Code is to assign, to each chemical tanker, one of the ship types according to the degree of the hazards of the products carried by such ships. Each of the products may have one or more hazardous properties, including flammability, toxicity, corrosivity and reactivity, as well as the hazard they may present to the environment.

3 Throughout the development of the Code it was recognized that it must be based upon sound naval architectural and engineering principles and the best understanding available as to the hazards of the various products covered. Furthermore, chemical tanker design technology is not only a complex technology, but is rapidly evolving and therefore the Code should not remain static. Thus, the Organization will periodically review the Code, taking into account both experience and technical developments.

4 Amendments to the Code involving requirements for new products and their conditions of carriage will be circulated as recommendations, on an interim basis, when adopted by the Maritime Safety Committee (MSC) and the Marine Environment Protection Committee (MEPC) of the Organization, in accordance with the provisions of article VIII of the International Convention for the Safety of Life at Sea, 1974 (SOLAS 74), and article 16 of the International Convention for the Prevention of Pollution from Ships, 1973, as modified by the Protocol of 1978 relating thereto (MARPOL 73/78), respectively, pending the entry into force of these amendments.

5 The Code primarily deals with ship design and equipment. In order to ensure the safe transport of the products, the total system must, however, be appraised. Other important facets of the safe transport of the products, such as training, operation, traffic control and handling in port, are being, or will be, examined further by the Organization.

6 The development of the Code has been greatly assisted by a number of organizations in consultative status such as the International Association of Classification Societies (IACS) and the International Electrotechnical Commission (IEC).

7 Chapter 16 of the Code, dealing with operational requirements of chemical tankers, highlights the regulations in other chapters that are operational in nature and mentions those other important safety features that are peculiar to chemical tanker operation.

8 The layout of the Code is in line with the International Code for the Construction and Equipment of Ships Carrying Liquefied Gases in Bulk (IGC Code), adopted by the Maritime Safety Committee at its forty-eighth session. Gas carriers may also carry in bulk liquid chemicals covered by this Code, as prescribed in the IGC Code.

9 The 1998 edition of the Code was based on the original text as adopted by MSC resolution MSC.4(48). In response to resolution 15 of the International Conference on Marine Pollution, 1973, the MEPC, at its twenty-second session, adopted, by resolution MEPC.19(22), the IBC Code extended to cover marine pollution prevention aspects for the implementation of Annex II to MARPOL 73/78.

10   This edition of the Code includes amendments adopted by the following resolutions:*

	Resolution	Adoption	Deemed acceptance	Entry into force
1	MSC.10(54)	29 April 1987	29 April 1988	30 October 1988
2	MSC.14(57) MEPC.32(27)	11 April 1989 17 March 1989	12 April 1990 12 April 1990	13 October 1990 13 October 1990
3	MSC.28(61) MEPC.55(33)	11 December 1992 30 October 1992	1 January 1994 1 January 1994	1 July 1994 1 July 1994
4	MSC.50(66) MEPC.69(38)	4 June 1996 10 July 1996	1 January 1998 1 January 1998	1 July 1998 1 July 1998
5	MSC.58(67) MEPC.73(39)	5 December 1996 10 March 1997	1 January 1998 10 January 1998	1 July 1998 10 July 1998
6	MSC.102(73)	5 December 2000	1 January 2002	1 July 2002
7	MSC.176(79) MEPC.119(52)	9 December 2004 15 October 2004	1 July 2006 1 July 2006	1 January 2007 1 January 2007

11   As from the date of entry into force of the 1983 amendments to SOLAS 74 (i.e., 1 July 1986) and the date of implementation of Annex II of MARPOL 73/78 (i.e., 6 April 1987), this Code became subject to mandatory requirements under these Conventions. Amendments to the Code, whether from the point of view of safety or of marine pollution, must therefore be adopted and brought into force in accordance with the procedures laid down in article VIII of SOLAS 74 and article 16 of MARPOL 73/78 respectively.

---

* Refer to the Foreword and, in particular, paragraph 3 thereof.

Chapter 1

General

1.1   Application

1.1.1   The Code applies to ships regardless of size, including those of less than 500 gross tonnage, engaged in the carriage of bulk cargoes of dangerous chemicals or noxious liquid substances (NLS), other than petroleum or similar flammable products as follows:

.1   products having significant fire hazards in excess of those of petroleum products and similar flammable products;

.2   products having significant hazards in addition to or other than flammability.

1.1.2   Products that have been reviewed and determined not to present safety and pollution hazards to such an extent as to warrant the application of the Code are found in chapter 18.

1.1.3   Liquids covered by the Code are those having a vapour pressure not exceeding 0.28 MPa absolute at a temperature of 37.8°C.

1.1.4   For the purpose of the 1974 SOLAS Convention, the Code applies to ships which are engaged in the carriage of products included in chapter 17 on the basis of their safety characteristics and identified as such by an entry of S or S/P in *column d*.

1.1.5   For the purposes of MARPOL 73/78, the Code applies only to NLS tankers, as defined in regulation 1.16.2 of Annex II thereof, which are engaged in the carriage of Noxious Liquid Substances identified as such by an entry of X, Y or Z in *column c* of chapter 17.

1.1.6   For a product proposed for carriage in bulk, but not listed in chapters 17 or 18, the Administration and port Administrations involved in such carriage shall prescribe the preliminary suitable conditions for the carriage, having regard to the criteria for hazard evaluation of bulk chemicals. For the evaluation of the pollution hazard of such a product and assignment of its pollution category, the procedure specified in regulation 6.3 of Annex II of MARPOL 73/78 must be followed. The Organization shall be notified of the conditions for consideration for inclusion of the product in the Code.

1.1.7   Unless expressly provided otherwise, the Code applies to ships, the keels of which are laid or which are at the stage where:

.1   construction identifiable with the ship begins; and

.2   assembly has commenced comprising at least 50 tonnes or 1% of the estimated mass of all structural material, whichever is less;

on or after 1 July 1986.

1.1.8   A ship, irrespective of the date of construction, which is converted to a chemical tanker on or after 1 July 1986 shall be treated as a chemical tanker constructed on the date on which such conversion commences. This conversion provision does not apply to the modification of a ship referred to in regulation 1.14 of Annex II of MARPOL 73/78.

1.1.9   Where reference is made in the Code to a paragraph, all the provisions of the subparagraphs of that designation shall apply.

1.2 Hazards

Hazards of products covered by the Code include:

1.2.1 *Fire hazard*, defined by flashpoint, explosive/flammability limits/range and autoignition temperature of the chemical.

1.2.2 *Health hazard*, defined by:

.1 corrosive effects on the skin in the liquid state; or

.2 acute toxic effect, taking into account values of:

LD_{50} (oral): a dose which is lethal to 50% of the test subjects when administered orally;

LD_{50} (dermal): a dose which is lethal to 50% of the test subjects when administered to the skin;

LC_{50} (inhalation): the concentration which is lethal by inhalation to 50% of the test subjects; or

.3 Other health effects such as carcinogenicity and sensitization.

1.2.3 *Reactivity hazard*, defined by reactivity:

.1 with water;

.2 with air;

.3 with other products; or

.4 of the product itself (e.g., polymerization).

1.2.4 *Marine pollution hazard*, as defined by:

.1 bioaccumulation;

.2 lack of ready biodegradibility;

.3 acute toxicity to aquatic organisms;

.4 chronic toxicity to aquatic organisms;

.5 long-term human health effects; and

.6 physical properties resulting in the product floating or sinking and so adversely affecting marine life.

1.3 Definitions

The following definitions apply unless expressly provided otherwise. (Additional definitions are given in individual chapters).

1.3.1 *Accommodation spaces* are those spaces used for public spaces, corridors, lavatories, cabins, offices, hospitals, cinemas, games and hobbies rooms, barber shops, pantries containing no cooking appliances and similar spaces. *Public spaces* are those portions of the accommodation spaces which are used for halls, dining rooms, lounges and similar permanently enclosed spaces.

1.3.2 *Administration* means the Government of the State whose flag the ship is entitled to fly. For *Administration (Port)* see *Port Administration*.

1.3.3 *Anniversary date* means the day and the month of each year which will correspond to the date of expiry of the International Certificate of Fitness for the Carriage of Dangerous Chemicals in Bulk.

1.3.4 *Boiling point* is the temperature at which a product exhibits a vapour pressure equal to the atmospheric pressure.

1.3.5 *Breadth (B)* means the maximum breadth of the ship, measured amidships to the moulded line of the frame in a ship with a metal shell and to the outer surface of the hull in a ship with a shell of any other material. The breadth (B) shall be measured in metres.

1.3.6 *Cargo area* is that part of the ship that contains cargo tanks, slop tanks, cargo pump-rooms including pump-rooms, cofferdams, ballast or void spaces adjacent to cargo tanks or slop tanks and also deck areas throughout the entire length and breadth of the part of the ship over the above-mentioned spaces. Where independent tanks are installed in hold spaces, cofferdams, ballast or void spaces at the after end of the aftermost hold space or at the forward end of the forward-most hold space are excluded from the cargo area.

1.3.7 *Cargo pump-room* is a space containing pumps and their accessories for the handling of the products covered by the Code.

1.3.8 *Cargo service spaces* are spaces within the cargo area used for workshops, lockers and store-rooms of more than 2 m^2 in area, used for cargo-handling equipment.

1.3.9 *Cargo tank* is the envelope designed to contain the cargo.

1.3.10 *Chemical tanker* is a cargo ship constructed or adapted and used for the carriage in bulk of any liquid product listed in chapter 17.

1.3.11 *Cofferdam* is the isolating space between two adjacent steel bulkheads or decks. This space may be a void space or a ballast space.

1.3.12 *Control stations* are those spaces in which ship's radio or main navigating equipment or the emergency source of power is located or where the fire-recording or fire-control equipment is centralized. This does not include special fire-control equipment which can be most practically located in the cargo area.

1.3.13 *Dangerous chemicals* means any liquid chemicals designated as presenting a safety hazard, based on the safety criteria for assigning products to chapter 17.

1.3.14 *Density* is the ratio of the mass to the volume of a product, expressed in terms of kilograms per cubic metre. This applies to liquids, gases and vapours.

1.3.15 *Explosive/flammability limits/range* are the conditions defining the state of fuel–oxidant mixture at which application of an adequately strong external ignition source is only just capable of producing flammability in a given test apparatus.

1.3.16 *Flashpoint* is the temperature in degrees Celsius at which a product will give off enough flammable vapour to be ignited. Values given in the Code are those for a "closed-cup test" determined by an approved flashpoint apparatus.

1.3.17 *Hold space* is the space enclosed by the ship's structure in which an independent cargo tank is situated.

1.3.18 *Independent* means that a piping or venting system, for example, is in no way connected to another system and that there are no provisions available for the potential connection to other systems.

1.3.19 *Length (L)* means 96% of the total length on a waterline at 85% of the least moulded depth measured from the top of the keel, or the length from the foreside of the stem to the axis of the rudder stock on that waterline, if that be greater. In ships designed with a rake of keel, the waterline on which this length is measured shall be parallel to the designed waterline. The length (L) shall be measured in metres.

1.3.20 *Machinery spaces of category A* are those spaces and trunks to such spaces which contain:

.1 internal-combustion machinery used for main propulsion; or

.2 internal-combustion machinery used for purposes other than main propulsion where such machinery has in the aggregate a total power output of not less than 375 kW; or

.3 any oil-fired boiler or oil fuel unit or any oil-fired equipment other than boilers, such as inert gas generators, incinerators, etc.

1.3.21 *Machinery spaces* are all machinery spaces of category A and all other spaces containing propelling machinery, boilers, oil fuel units, steam and internal-combustion engines, generators and major electrical machinery, oil filling station, refrigerating, stabilizing, ventilation and air-conditioning machinery, and similar spaces, and trunks to such spaces.

1.3.22 *MARPOL* means the International Convention for the Prevention of Pollution from Ships, 1973, as modified by the Protocol of 1978 relating thereto, as amended.

1.3.23 *Noxious Liquid Substance* means any substance indicated in the Pollution Category column of chapters 17 or 18 of the International Bulk Chemical Code, or the current MEPC.2/Circular or provisionally assessed under the provisions of regulation 6.3 of MARPOL Annex II as falling into categories X, Y or Z.

1.3.24 *Oil fuel unit* is the equipment used for the preparation of oil fuel for delivery to an oil-fired boiler, or equipment used for the preparation for delivery of heated oil to an internal-combustion engine, and includes any oil pressure pumps, filters and heaters dealing with oil at a gauge pressure of more than 0.18 MPa.

1.3.25 *Organization* is the International Maritime Organization (IMO).

1.3.26 *Permeability* of a space means the ratio of the volume within that space which is assumed to be occupied by water to the total volume of that space.

1.3.27 *Port Administration* means the appropriate authority of the country in the port of which the ship is loading or unloading.

1.3.28 *Products* is the collective term used to cover both Noxious Liquid Substances and Dangerous Chemicals.

1.3.29 *Pump-room* is a space, located in the cargo area, containing pumps and their accessories for the handling of ballast and oil fuel.

1.3.30 *Recognized standards* are applicable international or national standards acceptable to the Administration or standards laid down and maintained by an organization which complies with the standards adopted by the Organization and which is recognized by the Administration.

1.3.31 *Reference temperature* is the temperature at which the vapour pressure of the cargo corresponds to the set pressure of the pressure-relief valve.

1.3.32 *Separate* means that a cargo piping system or cargo vent system, for example, is not connected to another cargo piping or cargo vent system.

1.3.33 *Service spaces* are those spaces used for galleys, pantries containing cooking appliances, lockers, mail and specie rooms, store-rooms, workshops other than those forming part of the machinery spaces and similar spaces and trunks to such spaces.

1.3.34 *SOLAS* means the International Convention for the Safety of Life at Sea, 1974, as amended.

1.3.35 *Vapour pressure* is the equilibrium pressure of the saturated vapour above a liquid expressed in pascals (Pa) at a specified temperature.

1.3.36 *Void space* is an enclosed space in the cargo area external to a cargo tank, other than a hold space, ballast space, oil fuel tank, cargo pump-room, pump-room, or any space in normal use by personnel.

1.4 Equivalents

1.4.1 Where the Code requires that a particular fitting, material, appliance, apparatus, item of equipment or type thereof shall be fitted or carried in a ship, or that any particular provision shall be made, or any procedure or arrangement shall be complied with, the Administration may allow any other fitting, material, appliance, apparatus, item of equipment or type thereof to be fitted or carried, or any other provision, procedure or arrangement to be made in that ship, if it is satisfied by trial thereof or otherwise that such fitting, material, appliance, apparatus, item of equipment or type thereof or that any particular provision, procedure or arrangement is at least as effective as that required by the Code. However, the Administration may not allow operational methods or procedures to be made an alternative to a particular fitting, material, appliance, apparatus, item of equipment, or type thereof, which are prescribed by the Code, unless such substitution is specifically allowed by the Code.

1.4.2 When the Administration allows any fitting, material, appliance, apparatus, item of equipment, or type thereof, or provision, procedure, or arrangement, or novel design or application to be substituted, it shall communicate to the Organization the particulars thereof, together with a report on the evidence submitted, so that the Organization may circulate the same to other Contracting Governments to SOLAS and Parties to MARPOL for the information of their officers.

1.5 Surveys and certification

1.5.1 Survey procedure

1.5.1.1 The survey of ships, so far as regards the enforcement of the provisions of the regulations and granting of exemptions therefrom, shall be carried out by officers of the Administration. The

Administration may, however, entrust the surveys either to surveyors nominated for the purpose or to organizations recognized by it.

1.5.1.2 The recognized organization, referred to in regulation 8.2.1 of MARPOL Annex II, shall comply with the guidelines adopted by the Organization by resolution A.739(18), as may be amended by the Organization, and the specification adopted by the Organization by resolution A.789(19), as may be amended by the Organization, provided that such amendments are adopted, brought into force and take effect in accordance with the provisions of article 16 of MARPOL and article VIII of SOLAS concerning the amendment procedures applicable to this Code.

1.5.1.3 The Administration nominating surveyors or recognizing organizations to conduct surveys shall, as a minimum, empower any nominated surveyor or recognized organization to:

.1 require repairs to a ship; and

.2 carry out surveys if requested by the appropriate authorities of a port State.

The Administration shall notify the Organization of the specific responsibilities and conditions of the authority delegated to nominated surveyors or recognized organizations for circulation to the Contracting Governments.

1.5.1.4 When a nominated surveyor or recognized organization determines that the condition of a ship or its equipment does not correspond substantially with the particulars of the International Certificate of Fitness for the Carriage of Dangerous Chemicals in Bulk, or is such that the ship is not fit to proceed to sea without danger to the ship, or persons on board, or without presenting unreasonable threat of harm to the marine environment, such surveyor or organization shall immediately ensure that corrective action is taken and shall, in due course, notify the Administration. If such corrective action is not taken the Certificate shall be withdrawn and the Administration shall be notified immediately. If the ship is in a port of another Contracting Government, the appropriate authorities of the port State shall also be notified immediately. When an officer of the Administration, a nominated surveyor or a recognized organization has notified the appropriate authorities of the port State, the Government of the port State concerned shall give such officer, surveyor or organization any necessary assistance to carry out their obligations under this paragraph. When applicable, the Government of the port State concerned shall take such steps as will ensure that the ship does not sail until it can proceed to sea or leave the port for the purpose of proceeding to the nearest appropriate repair yard available without danger to the ship or persons on board or without presenting an unreasonable threat of harm to the marine environment.

1.5.1.5 In every case, the Administration shall guarantee the completeness and efficiency of the survey, and shall undertake to ensure the necessary arrangements to satisfy this obligation.

1.5.2 Survey requirements

1.5.2.1 The structure, equipment, fittings, arrangements and material (other than items in respect of which a Cargo Ship Safety Construction Certificate, Cargo Ship Safety Equipment Certificate and Cargo Ship Safety Radio Certificate or Cargo Ship Safety Certificate are issued) of a chemical tanker shall be subjected to the following surveys:

.1 An initial survey before the ship is put in service or before the International Certificate of Fitness for the Carriage of Dangerous Chemicals in Bulk is issued for the first time, which shall include a complete examination of its structure, equipment, fittings, arrangements and material in so far as the ship is covered by the Code. This survey shall be such as to ensure that the structure, equipment, fittings, arrangements and material fully comply with the applicable provisions of the Code.

.2 A renewal survey at intervals specified by the Administration, but not exceeding 5 years, except where 1.5.6.2.2, 1.5.6.5, 1.5.6.6 or 1.5.6.7 is applicable. The renewal survey shall be such as to ensure that the structure, equipment, fittings, arrangements and material fully comply with the applicable provisions of the Code.

.3 An intermediate survey within 3 months before or after the second anniversary date or within 3 months before or after the third anniversary date of the Certificate, which shall take the place of one of the annual surveys specified in 1.5.2.1.4. The intermediate survey shall be such as to ensure that the safety equipment, and other equipment, and associated pump and piping systems fully comply with the applicable provisions of the Code and are in good working order. Such intermediate surveys shall be endorsed on the Certificate issued under 1.5.4 or 1.5.5.

.4 An annual survey within 3 months before or after each anniversary date of the Certificate, including a general inspection of the structure, equipment, fittings, arrangements and material referred to in 1.5.2.1.1 to ensure that they have been maintained in accordance with 1.5.3 and that they remain satisfactory for the service for which the ship is intended. Such annual surveys shall be endorsed on the Certificate issued under 1.5.4 or 1.5.5.

.5 An additional survey, either general or partial according to the circumstances, shall be made when required after an investigation prescribed in 1.5.3.3, or whenever any important repairs or renewals are made. Such a survey shall ensure that the necessary repairs or renewals have been effectively made, that the material and workmanship of such repairs or renewals are satisfactory; and that the ship is fit to proceed to sea without danger to the ship or persons on board or without presenting unreasonable threat of harm to the marine environment.

1.5.3 Maintenance of conditions after survey

1.5.3.1 The conditions of the ship and its equipment shall be maintained to conform with the provisions of the Code to ensure that the ship will remain fit to proceed to sea without danger to the ship or persons on board or without presenting an unreasonable threat of harm to the marine environment.

1.5.3.2 After any survey of the ship under 1.5.2 has been completed, no change shall be made in the structure, equipment, fittings, arrangements and material covered by the survey, without the sanction of the Administration, except by direct replacement.

1.5.3.3 Whenever an accident occurs to a ship or a defect is discovered, either of which affects the safety of the ship or the efficiency or completeness of its life-saving appliances or other equipment covered by the Code, the master or owner of the ship shall report at the earliest opportunity to the Administration, the nominated surveyor or recognized organization responsible for issuing the Certificate, who shall cause investigations to be initiated to determine whether a survey, as required by 1.5.2.1.5, is necessary. If the ship is in a port of another Contracting Government, the master or owner shall also report immediately to the appropriate authorities of the port State and the nominated surveyor or recognized organization shall ascertain that such a report has been made.

1.5.4 Issue or endorsement of International Certificate of Fitness

1.5.4.1 An International Certificate of Fitness for the Carriage of Dangerous Chemicals in Bulk shall be issued after an initial or renewal survey to a chemical tanker engaged in international voyages which complies with the relevant provisions of the Code.

1.5.4.2 Such a Certificate shall be drawn up in the form corresponding to the model given in the appendix. If the language used is not English, French or Spanish, the text shall include the translation into one of these languages.

1.5.4.3 The Certificate issued under provisions of this section shall be available on board for examination at all times.

1.5.5 Issue or endorsement of International Certificate of Fitness by another Government

1.5.5.1 A Government that is both a Contracting Government to the 1974 SOLAS Convention and a Party to MARPOL 73/78 may, at the request of another such Government, cause a ship entitled to fly the flag of the other State to be surveyed and, if satisfied that the provisions of the Code are complied with, issue or authorize the issue of the International Certificate of Fitness for the Carriage of Dangerous Chemicals in Bulk to the ship, and, where appropriate, endorse or authorize the endorsement of the Certificate on board the ship in accordance with the Code. Any Certificate so issued shall contain a statement to the effect that it has been issued at the request of the Government of the State whose flag the ship is entitled to fly.

1.5.6 Duration and validity of International Certificate of Fitness

1.5.6.1 An International Certificate of Fitness for the Carriage of Dangerous Chemicals in Bulk shall be issued for a period specified by the Administration which shall not exceed 5 years.

1.5.6.2.1 Notwithstanding the provisions of 1.5.6.1, when the renewal survey is completed within 3 months before the expiry date of the existing Certificate, the new Certificate shall be valid from the date of completion of the renewal survey to a date not exceeding 5 years from the date of expiry of the existing Certificate.

1.5.6.2.2 When the renewal survey is completed after the expiry date of the existing Certificate, the new Certificate shall be valid from the date of completion of the renewal survey to a date not exceeding 5 years from the date of expiry of the existing Certificate.

1.5.6.2.3 When the renewal survey is completed more than 3 months before the expiry date of the existing Certificate, the new Certificate shall be valid from the date of completion of the renewal survey to a date not exceeding 5 years from the date of completion of the renewal survey.

1.5.6.3 If a Certificate is issued for a period of less than 5 years, the Administration may extend the validity of the Certificate beyond the expiry date to the maximum period specified in 1.5.6.1, provided that the surveys referred to in 1.5.2.1.3 and 1.5.2.1.4, applicable when a Certificate is issued for a period of 5 years, are carried out as appropriate.

1.5.6.4 If a renewal survey has been completed and a new Certificate cannot be issued or placed on board the ship before the expiry date of the existing Certificate, the person or organization authorized by the Administration may endorse the existing Certificate. Such a Certificate shall be accepted as valid for a further period which shall not exceed 5 months from the expiry date.

1.5.6.5 If a ship, at the time when a Certificate expires, is not in a port in which it is to be surveyed, the Administration may extend the period of validity of the Certificate but this extension shall be granted only for the purpose of allowing the ship to complete its voyage to the port in which it is to be surveyed, and then only in cases where it appears proper and reasonable to do so.

1.5.6.6 A Certificate, issued to a ship engaged on short voyages which has not been extended under the foregoing provisions of this section, may be extended by the Administration for a period of grace of up to one month from the date of expiry stated on it. When the renewal survey is completed, the new Certificate shall be valid to a date not exceeding 5 years from the date of expiry of the existing Certificate before the extension was granted.

1.5.6.7 In special circumstances, as determined by the Administration, a new Certificate need not be dated from the date of expiry of the existing Certificate as required by 1.5.6.2.2, 1.5.6.5 or 1.5.6.6. In these special circumstances, the new Certificate shall be valid to a date not exceeding 5 years from the date of completion of the renewal survey.

1.5.6.8 If an annual or intermediate survey is completed before the period specified in 1.5.2, then:

.1 the anniversary date shown on the Certificate shall be amended by endorsement to a date which shall not be more than 3 months later than the date on which the survey was completed;

.2 the subsequent annual or intermediate survey required by 1.5.2 shall be completed at the intervals prescribed by that section using the new anniversary date; and

.3 the expiry date may remain unchanged provided one or more annual or intermediate surveys, as appropriate, are carried out so that the maximum intervals between the surveys prescribed by 1.5.2 are not exceeded.

1.5.6.9 A Certificate issued under 1.5.4 or 1.5.5 shall cease to be valid in any of the following cases:

.1 if the relevant surveys are not completed within the periods specified under 1.5.2;

.2 if the Certificate is not endorsed in accordance with 1.5.2.1.3 or 1.5.2.1.4;

.3 upon transfer of the ship to the flag of another State. A new certificate shall only be issued when the Government issuing the new Certificate is fully satisfied that the ship is in compliance with the requirements of 1.5.3.1 and 1.5.3.2. In the case of a transfer between Governments that are both a Contracting Government to the 1974 SOLAS Convention and a Party to MARPOL 73/78, if requested within 3 months after the transfer has taken place, the Government of the State whose flag the ship was formerly entitled to fly shall, as soon as possible, transmit to the Administration copies of the Certificate carried by the ship before the transfer and, if available, copies of the relevant survey reports.

Chapter 2

Ship survival capability and location of cargo tanks

2.1 General

2.1.1 Ships, subject to the Code, shall survive the normal effects of flooding following assumed hull damage caused by some external force. In addition, to safeguard the ship and the environment, the cargo tanks of certain types of ships shall be protected from penetration in the case of minor damage to the ship resulting, for example, from contact with a jetty or tug, and given a measure of protection from damage in the case of collision or stranding, by locating them at specified minimum distances inboard from the ship's shell plating. Both the assumed damage and the proximity of the cargo tanks to the ship's shell shall be dependent upon the degree of hazard presented by the products to be carried.

2.1.2 Ships subject to the Code shall be designed to one of the following standards:

.1 A type 1 ship is a chemical tanker intended to transport chapter 17 products with very severe environmental and safety hazards which require maximum preventive measures to preclude an escape of such cargo.

.2 A type 2 ship is a chemical tanker intended to transport chapter 17 products with appreciably severe environmental and safety hazards which require significant preventive measures to preclude an escape of such cargo.

.3 A type 3 ship is a chemical tanker intended to transport chapter 17 products with sufficiently severe environmental and safety hazards which require a moderate degree of containment to increase survival capability in a damaged condition.

Thus, a type 1 ship is a chemical tanker intended for the transportation of products considered to present the greatest overall hazard and type 2 and type 3 for products of progressively lesser hazards. Accordingly, a type 1 ship shall survive the most severe standard of damage and its cargo tanks shall be located at the maximum prescribed distance inboard from the shell plating.

2.1.3 The ship type required for individual products is indicated in *column e* in the table of chapter 17.

2.1.4 If a ship is intended to carry more than one product listed in chapter 17, the standard of damage shall correspond to that product having the most stringent ship type requirement. The requirements for the location of individual cargo tanks, however, are those for ship types related to the respective products intended to be carried.

2.2 Freeboard and intact stability

2.2.1 Ships subject to the Code may be assigned the minimum freeboard permitted by the International Convention on Load Lines in force. However, the draught associated with the assignment shall not be greater than the maximum draught otherwise permitted by this Code.

2.2.2 The stability of the ship in all seagoing conditions shall be to a standard which is acceptable to the Administration.

2.2.3 When calculating the effect of free surfaces of consumable liquids for loading conditions it shall be assumed that, for each type of liquid, at least one transverse pair or a single centre tank has a free surface and the tank or combination of tanks to be taken into account shall be those where the effect of free surfaces is the greatest. The free surface effect in undamaged compartments shall be calculated by a method acceptable to the Administration.

2.2.4 Solid ballast shall not normally be used in double-bottom spaces in the cargo area. Where, however, because of stability considerations, the fitting of solid ballast in such spaces becomes unavoidable, then its disposition shall be governed by the need to ensure that the impact loads resulting from bottom damage are not directly transmitted to the cargo tank structure.

2.2.5 The master of the ship shall be supplied with a loading and stability information booklet. This booklet shall contain details of typical service and ballast conditions, provisions for evaluating other conditions of loading and a summary of the ship's survival capabilities. In addition, the booklet shall contain sufficient information to enable the master to load and operate the ship in a safe and seaworthy manner.

2.3 Shipside discharges below the freeboard deck

2.3.1 The provision and control of valves fitted to discharges led through the shell from spaces below the freeboard deck or from within the superstructures and deck-houses on the freeboard deck fitted with weathertight doors shall comply with the requirements of the relevant regulation of the International Convention on Load Lines in force, except that the choice of valves shall be limited to:

.1 one automatic non-return valve with a positive means of closing from above the freeboard deck; or

.2 where the vertical distance from the summer load waterline to the inboard end of the discharge pipe exceeds 0.01L, two automatic non-return valves without positive means of closing, provided that the inboard valve is always accessible for examination under service conditions.

2.3.2 For the purpose of this chapter, "summer load line" and "freeboard deck" have the meanings as defined in the International Convention on Load Lines in force.

2.3.3 The automatic non-return valves referred to in 2.3.1.1 and 2.3.1.2 shall be fully effective in preventing admission of water into the ship, taking into account the sinkage, trim and heel in survival requirements in 2.9, and shall comply with recognized standards.

2.4 Conditions of loading

Damage survival capability shall be investigated on the basis of loading information submitted to the Administration for all anticipated conditions of loading and variations in draught and trim. Ballast conditions where the chemical tanker is not carrying products covered by the Code, or is carrying only residues of such products, need not be considered.

2.5 Damage assumptions

2.5.1 The assumed maximum extent of damage shall be:

.1	**Side damage:**		
.1.1	Longitudinal extent:	$1/3L^{2/3}$ or 14.5 m, whichever is less	
.1.2	Transverse extent:	$B/5$ or 11.5 m, whichever is less (measured inboard from the ship's side at right angles to the centreline at the level of the summer load line)	
.1.3	Vertical extent:	upwards without limit (measured from the moulded line of the bottom shell plating at centreline)	
.2	**Bottom damage:**	**For 0.3L from the forward perpendicular of the ship**	**Any other part of the ship**
.2.1	Longitudinal extent:	$1/3L^{2/3}$ or 14.5 m, whichever is less	$1/3L^{2/3}$ or 5 m, whichever is less
.2.2	Transverse extent:	$B/6$ or 10 m, whichever is less	$B/6$ or 5 m, whichever is less
.2.3	Vertical extent:	$B/15$ or 6 m, whichever is less [measured from the moulded line of the bottom shell plating at centreline (see 2.6.2)]	$B/15$ or 6 m, whichever is less [measured from the moulded line of the bottom shell plating at centreline (see 2.6.2)]

2.5.2   If any damage of a lesser extent than the maximum damage specified in 2.5.1 would result in a more severe condition, such damage shall be considered.

2.6   Location of cargo tanks

2.6.1   Cargo tanks shall be located at the following distances inboard:

.1   *Type 1 ships:* from the side shell plating, not less than the transverse extent of damage specified in 2.5.1.1.2, and from the moulded line of the bottom shell plating at centreline, not less than the vertical extent of damage specified in 2.5.1.2.3, and nowhere less than 760 mm from the shell plating. This requirement does not apply to the tanks for diluted slops arising from tank washing.

.2   *Type 2 ships:* from the moulded line of the bottom shell plating at centreline, not less than the vertical extent of damage specified in 2.5.1.2.3, and nowhere less than 760 mm from the shell plating. This requirement does not apply to the tanks for diluted slops arising from tank washing.

.3   *Type 3 ships:* no requirement.

2.6.2   Except for type 1 ships, suction wells installed in cargo tanks may protrude into the vertical extent of bottom damage specified in 2.5.1.2.3 provided that such wells are as small as practicable and the protrusion below the inner bottom plating does not exceed 25% of the depth of the double bottom or 350 mm, whichever is less. Where there is no double bottom, the protrusion of the suction well of independent tanks below the upper limit of bottom damage shall not exceed 350 mm. Suction wells installed in accordance with this paragraph may be ignored in determining the compartments affected by damage.

2.7   Flooding assumptions

2.7.1   The requirements of 2.9 shall be confirmed by calculations which take into consideration the design characteristics of the ship; the arrangements, configuration and contents of the damaged compartments; the distribution, relative densities and the free surface effects of liquids; and the draught and trim for all conditions of loading.

2.7.2   The permeabilities of spaces assumed to be damaged shall be as follows:

Spaces	Permeabilities
Appropriated to stores	0.60
Occupied by accommodation	0.95
Occupied by machinery	0.85
Voids	0.95
Intended for consumable liquids	0 to 0.95*
Intended for other liquids	0 to 0.95*

2.7.3   Wherever damage penetrates a tank containing liquids it shall be assumed that the contents are completely lost from that compartment and replaced by salt water up to the level of the final plane of equilibrium.

2.7.4   Every watertight division within the maximum extent of damage defined in 2.5.1 and considered to have sustained damage in positions given in 2.8.1 shall be assumed to be penetrated. Where damage less than the maximum is being considered in accordance with 2.5.2, only watertight divisions or combinations of watertight divisions within the envelope of such lesser damage shall be assumed to be penetrated.

2.7.5   The ship shall be so designed as to keep unsymmetrical flooding to the minimum consistent with efficient arrangements.

---

* The permeability of partially filled compartments shall be consistent with the amount of liquid carried in the compartment.

2.7.6 Equalization arrangements requiring mechanical aids such as valves or cross-levelling pipes, if fitted, shall not be considered for the purpose of reducing an angle of heel or attaining the minimum range of residual stability to meet the requirements of 2.9 and sufficient residual stability shall be maintained during all stages where equalization is used. Spaces which are linked by ducts of large cross-sectional area may be considered to be common.

2.7.7 If pipes, ducts, trunks or tunnels are situated within the assumed extent of damage penetration, as defined in 2.5, arrangements shall be such that progressive flooding cannot thereby extend to compartments other than those assumed to be flooded for each case of damage.

2.7.8 The buoyancy of any superstructure directly above the side damage shall be disregarded. The unflooded parts of superstructures beyond the extent of damage, however, may be taken into consideration provided that:

.1 they are separated from the damaged space by watertight divisions and the requirements of 2.9.3 in respect of these intact spaces are complied with; and

.2 openings in such divisions are capable of being closed by remotely operated sliding watertight doors and unprotected openings are not immersed within the minimum range of residual stability required in 2.9; however, the immersion of any other openings capable of being closed weathertight may be permitted.

2.8 Standard of damage

2.8.1 Ships shall be capable of surviving the damage indicated in 2.5 with the flooding assumptions in 2.7 to the extent determined by the ship's type according to the following standards:

.1 A type 1 ship shall be assumed to sustain damage anywhere in its length.

.2 A type 2 ship of more than 150 m in length shall be assumed to sustain damage anywhere in its length.

.3 A type 2 ship of 150 m in length or less shall be assumed to sustain damage anywhere in its length except involving either of the bulkheads bounding a machinery space located aft.

.4 A type 3 ship of more than 225 m in length shall be assumed to sustain damage anywhere in its length.

.5 A type 3 ship of 125 m in length or more but not exceeding 225 m in length shall be assumed to sustain damage anywhere in its length except involving either of the bulkheads bounding a machinery space located aft.

.6 A type 3 ship below 125 m in length shall be assumed to sustain damage anywhere in its length except involving damage to the machinery space when located aft. However, the ability to survive the flooding of the machinery space shall be considered by the Administration.

2.8.2 In the case of small type 2 and type 3 ships which do not comply in all respects with the appropriate requirements of 2.8.1.3 and 2.8.1.6, special dispensation may only be considered by the Administration provided that alternative measures can be taken which maintain the same degree of safety. The nature of the alternative measures shall be approved and clearly stated and be available to the port Administration. Any such dispensation shall be duly noted on the International Certificate of Fitness referred to in 1.5.4.

2.9 Survival requirements

2.9.1 Ships subject to the Code shall be capable of surviving the assumed damage specified in 2.5 to the standard provided in 2.8 in a condition of stable equilibrium and shall satisfy the following criteria.

2.9.2 In any stage of flooding:

.1 the waterline, taking into account sinkage, heel and trim, shall be below the lower edge of any opening through which progressive flooding or downflooding may take place. Such openings shall include air pipes and openings which are closed by means of weathertight doors or hatch covers and may exclude those openings closed by means of watertight manhole covers and watertight flush scuttles, small watertight cargo tank hatch covers which maintain the high integrity of the deck, remotely operated watertight sliding doors, and sidescuttles of the non-opening type;

.2 the maximum angle of heel due to unsymmetrical flooding shall not exceed 25°, except that this angle may be increased to 30° if no deck immersion occurs;

.3 the residual stability during intermediate stages of flooding shall be to the satisfaction of the Administration. However, it shall never be significantly less than that required by 2.9.3.

2.9.3   At final equilibrium after flooding:

.1 the righting-lever curve shall have a minimum range of 20° beyond the position of equilibrium in association with a maximum residual righting lever of at least 0.1 m within the 20° range; the area under the curve within this range shall not be less than 0.0175 m radians. Unprotected openings shall not be immersed within this range unless the space concerned is assumed to be flooded. Within this range, the immersion of any of the openings listed in 2.9.2.1 and other openings capable of being closed weathertight may be permitted; and

.2 the emergency source of power shall be capable of operating.

Chapter 3

Ship arrangements

3.1 Cargo segregation

3.1.1 Unless expressly provided otherwise, tanks containing cargo or residues of cargo subject to the Code shall be segregated from accommodation, service and machinery spaces and from drinking water and stores for human consumption by means of a cofferdam, void space, cargo pump-room, pump-room, empty tank, oil fuel tank or other similar space.

3.1.2 Cargo piping shall not pass through any accommodation, service or machinery space other than cargo pump-rooms or pump-rooms.

3.1.3 Cargoes, residues of cargoes or mixtures containing cargoes, which react in a hazardous manner with other cargoes, residues or mixtures, shall:

.1 be segregated from such other cargoes by means of a cofferdam, void space, cargo pump-room, pump-room, empty tank, or tank containing a mutually compatible cargo;

.2 have separate pumping and piping systems which shall not pass through other cargo tanks containing such cargoes, unless encased in a tunnel; and

.3 have separate tank venting systems.

3.1.4 If cargo piping systems or cargo ventilation systems are to be separated, this separation may be achieved by the use of design or operational methods. Operational methods shall not be used within a cargo tank and shall consist of one of the following types:

.1 removing spool-pieces or valves and blanking the pipe ends;

.2 arrangement of two spectacle flanges in series, with provisions for detecting leakage into the pipe between the two spectacle flanges.

3.1.5 Cargoes subject to the Code shall not be carried in either the fore or aft peak tank.

3.2 Accommodation, service and machinery spaces and control stations

3.2.1 No accommodation or service spaces or control stations shall be located within the cargo area except over a cargo pump-room recess or pump-room recess that complies with SOLAS regulations II-2/ 4.5.1 to 4.5.2.4 and no cargo or slop tank shall be aft of the forward end of any accommodation.

3.2.2 In order to guard against the danger of hazardous vapours, due consideration shall be given to the location of air intakes and openings into accommodation, service and machinery spaces and control stations in relation to cargo piping and cargo vent systems.

3.2.3 Entrances, air inlets and openings to accommodation, service and machinery spaces and control stations shall not face the cargo area. They shall be located on the end bulkhead not facing the cargo area and/or on the outboard side of the superstructure or deck-house at a distance of at least 4% of the length (*L*) of the ship but not less than 3 m from the end of the superstructure or deck-house facing the cargo area. This distance, however, need not exceed 5 m. No doors shall be permitted within the limits mentioned above, except that doors to those spaces not having access to accommodation and service spaces and control stations, such as cargo control stations and store-rooms, may be fitted. Where such doors are fitted, the boundaries of the space shall be insulated to "A-60" standard. Bolted plates for removal of machinery may be fitted within the limits specified above. Wheelhouse doors and wheelhouse windows may be located within the limits specified above so long as they are so designed that a rapid and efficient gas- and vapour-tightening of the wheelhouse can be ensured. Windows and sidescuttles facing the cargo area and on the sides of the superstructures and deck-houses within the limits specified above shall be of the fixed (non-opening) type. Such sidescuttles in the first tier on the main deck shall be fitted with inside covers of steel or equivalent material.

3.3 Cargo pump-rooms

3.3.1 Cargo pump-rooms shall be so arranged as to ensure:

.1 unrestricted passage at all times from any ladder platform and from the floor; and

.2 unrestricted access to all valves necessary for cargo handling for a person wearing the required personnel protective equipment.

3.3.2 Permanent arrangements shall be made for hoisting an injured person with a rescue line while avoiding any projecting obstacles.

3.3.3 Guard railings shall be installed on all ladders and platforms.

3.3.4 Normal access ladders shall not be fitted vertical and shall incorporate platforms at suitable intervals.

3.3.5 Means shall be provided to deal with drainage and any possible leakage from cargo pumps and valves in cargo pump-rooms. The bilge system serving the cargo pump-room shall be operable from outside the cargo pump-room. One or more slop tanks for storage of contaminated bilge water or tank washings shall be provided. A shore connection with a standard coupling or other facilities shall be provided for transferring contaminated liquids to onshore reception facilities.

3.3.6 Pump discharge pressure gauges shall be provided outside the cargo pump-room.

3.3.7 Where machinery is driven by shafting passing through a bulkhead or deck, gastight seals with efficient lubrication or other means of ensuring the permanence of the gas seal shall be fitted in way of the bulkhead or deck.

3.4 Access to spaces in the cargo area

3.4.1 Access to cofferdams, ballast tanks, cargo tanks and other spaces in the cargo area shall be direct from the open deck and such as to ensure their complete inspection. Access to double-bottom spaces may be through a cargo pump-room, pump-room, deep cofferdam, pipe tunnel or similar compartments, subject to consideration of ventilation aspects.

3.4.2 For access through horizontal openings, hatches or manholes, the dimensions shall be sufficient to allow a person wearing a self-contained air-breathing apparatus and protective equipment to ascend or descend any ladder without obstruction and also to provide a clear opening to facilitate the hoisting of an injured person from the bottom of the space. The minimum clear opening shall be not less than 600 mm by 600 mm.

3.4.3 For access through vertical openings, or manholes providing passage through the length and breadth of the space, the minimum clear opening shall be not less than 600 mm by 800 mm at a height of not more than 600 mm from the bottom shell plating unless gratings or other footholds are provided.

3.4.4 Smaller dimensions may be approved by the Administration in special circumstances, if the ability to traverse such openings or to remove an injured person can be proved to the satisfaction of the Administration.

3.5 Bilge and ballast arrangements

3.5.1 Pumps, ballast lines, vent lines and other similar equipment serving permanent ballast tanks shall be independent of similar equipment serving cargo tanks and of cargo tanks themselves. Discharge arrangements for permanent ballast tanks sited immediately adjacent to cargo tanks shall be outside machinery spaces and accommodation spaces. Filling arrangements may be in the machinery spaces provided that such arrangements ensure filling from tank deck level and non-return valves are fitted.

3.5.2 Filling of ballast in cargo tanks may be arranged from deck level by pumps serving permanent ballast tanks, provided that the filling line has no permanent connection to cargo tanks or piping and that non-return valves are fitted.

3.5.3   Bilge pumping arrangements for cargo pump-rooms, pump-rooms, void spaces, slop tanks, double-bottom tanks and similar spaces shall be situated entirely within the cargo area except for void spaces, double-bottom tanks and ballast tanks where such spaces are separated from tanks containing cargo or residues of cargo by a double bulkhead.

3.6   Pump and pipeline identification

Provisions shall be made for the distinctive marking of pumps, valves and pipelines to identify the service and tanks which they serve.

3.7   Bow or stern loading and unloading arrangements

3.7.1   Cargo piping may be fitted to permit bow or stern loading and unloading. Portable arrangements shall not be permitted.

3.7.2   Bow or stern loading and unloading lines shall not be used for the transfer of products required to be carried in type 1 ships. Bow and stern loading and unloading lines shall not be used for the transfer of cargoes emitting toxic vapours required to comply with 15.12.1, unless specifically approved by the Administration.

3.7.3   In addition to 5.1, the following provisions apply:

.1   The piping outside the cargo area shall be fitted at least 760 mm inboard on the open deck. Such piping shall be clearly identified and fitted with a shutoff valve at its connection to the cargo piping system within the cargo area. At this location, it shall also be capable of being separated by means of a removable spool-piece and blank flanges when not in use.

.2   The shore connection shall be fitted with a shutoff valve and a blank flange.

.3   The piping shall be full-penetration butt-welded, and fully radiographed. Flange connections in the piping shall only be permitted within the cargo area and at the shore connection.

.4   Spray shields shall be provided at the connections specified in 3.7.3.1 as well as collecting trays of sufficient capacity, with means for the disposal of drainage.

.5   The piping shall be self-draining to the cargo area and preferably into a cargo tank. Alternative arrangements for draining the piping may be accepted by the Administration.

.6   Arrangements shall be made to allow such piping to be purged after use and maintained gas-safe when not in use. The vent pipes connected with the purge shall be located in the cargo area. The relevant connections to the piping shall be provided with a shutoff valve and blank flange.

3.7.4   Entrances, air inlets and openings to accommodation, service and machinery spaces and control stations shall not face the cargo shore-connection location of bow or stern loading and unloading arrangements. They shall be located on the outboard side of the superstructure or deck-house at a distance of at least 4% of the length of the ship but not less than 3 m from the end of the house facing the cargo shore-connection location of the bow or stern loading and unloading arrangements. This distance, however, need not exceed 5 m. Sidescuttles facing the shore-connection location and on the sides of the superstructure or deck-house within the distance mentioned above shall be of the fixed (non-opening) type. In addition, during the use of the bow or stern loading and unloading arrangements, all doors, ports and other openings on the corresponding superstructure or deck-house side shall be kept closed. Where, in the case of small ships, compliance with 3.2.3 and this paragraph is not possible, the Administration may approve relaxations from the above requirements.

3.7.5   Air pipes and other openings to enclosed spaces not listed in 3.7.4 shall be shielded from any spray which may come from a burst hose or connection.

3.7.6   Escape routes shall not terminate within the coamings required by 3.7.7 or within a distance of 3 m beyond the coamings.

3.7.7   Continuous coamings of suitable height shall be fitted to keep any spills on deck and away from the accommodation and service areas.

3.7.8   Electrical equipment within the coamings required by 3.7.7 or within a distance of 3 m beyond the coamings shall be in accordance with the requirements of chapter 10.

3.7.9   Fire-fighting arrangements for the bow or stern loading and unloading areas shall be in accordance with 11.3.16.

3.7.10   Means of communication between the cargo control station and the cargo shore-connection location shall be provided and certified safe, if necessary. Provision shall be made for the remote shutdown of cargo pumps from the cargo shore-connection location.

Chapter 4

Cargo containment

4.1 Definitions

4.1.1 *Independent tank* means a cargo-containment envelope which is not contiguous with, or part of, the hull structure. An independent tank is built and installed so as to eliminate whenever possible (or in any event to minimize) its stressing as a result of stressing or motion of the adjacent hull structure. An independent tank is not essential to the structural completeness of the ship's hull.

4.1.2 *Integral tank* means a cargo-containment envelope which forms part of the ship's hull and which may be stressed in the same manner and by the same loads which stress the contiguous hull structure and which is normally essential to the structural completeness of the ship's hull.

4.1.3 *Gravity tank* means a tank having a design pressure not greater than 0.07 MPa gauge at the top of the tank. A gravity tank may be independent or integral. A gravity tank shall be constructed and tested according to recognized standards, taking account of the temperature of carriage and relative density of the cargo.

4.1.4 *Pressure tank* means a tank having a design pressure greater than 0.07 MPa gauge. A pressure tank shall be an independent tank and shall be of a configuration permitting the application of pressure-vessel design criteria according to recognized standards.

4.2 Tank type requirements for individual products

Requirements for both installation and design of tank types for individual products are shown in *column f* in the table of chapter 17.

Chapter 5

Cargo transfer

5.1 Piping scantlings

5.1.1 Subject to the conditions stated in 5.1.4, the wall thickness (t) of pipes shall not be less than:

$$t = \frac{t_0 + b + c}{1 - \frac{a}{100}} \text{ (mm)}$$

where:

$t_0 = $ theoretical thickness

$$t_0 = PD/(2Ke + P) \text{ (mm)}$$

with

$P = $ design pressure (MPa) referred to in 5.1.2

$D = $ outside diameter (mm)

$K = $ allowable stress (N/mm^2) referred to in 5.1.5

$e = $ efficiency factor equal to 1.0 for seamless pipes and for longitudinally or spirally welded pipes, delivered by approved manufacturers of welded pipes, which are considered equivalent to seamless pipes when non-destructive testing on welds is carried out in accordance with recognized standards. In other cases, an efficiency factor of less than 1.0, in accordance with recognized standards, may be required depending on the manufacturing process.

$b = $ allowance for bending (mm). The value of b shall be chosen so that the calculated stress in the bend, due to internal pressure only, does not exceed the allowable stress. Where such justification is not given, b shall be not less than:

$$b = \frac{Dt_0}{2.5r} \text{ (mm)}$$

with

$r = $ mean radius of the bend (mm)

$c = $ corrosion allowance (mm). If corrosion or erosion is expected, the wall thickness of piping shall be increased over that required by the other design requirements

$a = $ negative manufacturing tolerance for thickness (%).

5.1.2 The design pressure P in the formula for t_0 in 5.1.1 is the maximum gauge pressure to which the system may be subjected in service, taking into account the highest set pressure on any relief valve on the system.

5.1.3 Piping and piping-system components which are not protected by a relief valve, or which may be isolated from their relief valve, shall be designed for at least the greatest of:

.1 for piping systems or components, which may contain some liquid, the saturated vapour pressure at 45°C;

.2 the pressure setting of the associated pump discharge relief valve;

.3 the maximum possible total pressure head at the outlet of the associated pumps when a pump discharge relief valve is not installed.

5.1.4 The design pressure shall not be less than 1 MPa gauge except for open-ended lines, where it shall be not less than 0.5 MPa gauge.

5.1.5 For pipes, the allowable stress K to be considered in the formula for t_0 in 5.1.1 is the lower of the following values:

$$\frac{R_m}{A} \text{ or } \frac{R_e}{B}$$

where:

R_m = specified minimum tensile strength at ambient temperature (N/mm^2)

R_e = specified minimum yield stress at ambient temperature (N/mm^2). If the stress–strain curve does not show a defined yield stress, the 0.2% proof stress applies.

A and B shall have values of at least $A = 2.7$ and $B = 1.8$.

5.1.6.1 The minimum wall thickness shall be in accordance with recognized standards.

5.1.6.2 Where necessary for mechanical strength to prevent damage, collapse, excessive sag or buckling of pipes due to weight of pipes and content and to superimposed loads from supports, ship deflection or other causes, the wall thickness shall be increased over that required by 5.1.1 or, if this is impracticable or would cause excessive local stresses, these loads shall be reduced, protected against or eliminated by other design methods.

5.1.6.3 Flanges, valves and other fittings shall be in accordance with recognized standards, taking into account the design pressure defined under 5.1.2.

5.1.6.4 For flanges not complying with a standard, the dimensions for flanges and associated bolts shall be to the satisfaction of the Administration.

5.2 Piping fabrication and joining details

5.2.1 The requirements of this section apply to piping inside and outside the cargo tanks. However, relaxations from these requirements may be accepted in accordance with recognized standards for open-ended piping and for piping inside cargo tanks except for cargo piping serving other cargo tanks.

5.2.2 Cargo piping shall be joined by welding except:

.1 for approved connections to shutoff valves and expansion joints; and

.2 for other exceptional cases specifically approved by the Administration.

5.2.3 The following direct connections of pipe lengths without flanges may be considered:

.1 Butt-welded joints with complete penetration at the root may be used in all applications.

.2 Slip-on welded joints with sleeves and related welding having dimensions in accordance with recognized standards shall only be used for pipes with an external diameter of 50 mm or less. This type of joint shall not be used when crevice corrosion is expected to occur.

.3 Screwed connections, in accordance with recognized standards, shall only be used for accessory lines and instrumentation lines with external diameters of 25 mm or less.

5.2.4 Expansion of piping shall normally be allowed for by the provision of expansion loops or bends in the piping system.

.1 Bellows, in accordance with recognized standards, may be specially considered.

.2 Slip joints shall not be used.

5.2.5 Welding, post-weld heat treatment and non-destructive testing shall be performed in accordance with recognized standards.

5.3 Flange connections

5.3.1 Flanges shall be of the welded-neck, slip-on or socket-welded type. However, socket-welded-type flanges shall not be used in nominal size above 50 mm.

5.3.2 Flanges shall comply with recognized standards as to their type, manufacture and test.

5.4 Test requirements for piping

5.4.1 The test requirements of this section apply to piping inside and outside cargo tanks. However, relaxations from these requirements may be accepted in accordance with recognized standards for piping inside tanks and open-ended piping.

5.4.2 After assembly, each cargo piping system shall be subject to a hydrostatic test to at least 1.5 times the design pressure. When piping systems or parts of systems are completely manufactured and equipped with all fittings, the hydrostatic test may be conducted prior to installation aboard the ship. Joints welded on board shall be hydrostatically tested to at least 1.5 times the design pressure.

5.4.3 After assembly on board, each cargo piping system shall be tested for leaks to a pressure depending on the method applied.

5.5 Piping arrangements

5.5.1 Cargo piping shall not be installed under deck between the outboard side of the cargo-containment spaces and the skin of the ship unless clearances required for damage protection (see 2.6) are maintained; but such distances may be reduced where damage to the pipe would not cause release of cargo provided that the clearance required for inspection purposes is maintained.

5.5.2 Cargo piping located below the main deck may run from the tank it serves and penetrate tank bulkheads or boundaries common to longitudinally or transversally adjacent cargo tanks, ballast tanks, empty tanks, pump-rooms or cargo pump-rooms provided that inside the tank it serves it is fitted with a stop valve operable from the weather deck and provided cargo compatibility is assured in the event of piping failure. As an exception, where a cargo tank is adjacent to a cargo pump-room, the stop valve operable from the weather deck may be situated on the tank bulkhead on the cargo pump-room side, provided an additional valve is fitted between the bulkhead valve and the cargo pump. A totally enclosed hydraulically operated valve located outside the cargo tank may, however, be accepted, provided that the valve is:

.1 designed to preclude the risk of leakage;

.2 fitted on the bulkhead of the cargo tank which it serves;

.3 suitably protected against mechanical damage;

.4 fitted at a distance from the shell as required for damage protection; and

.5 operable from the weather deck.

5.5.3 In any cargo pump-room where a pump serves more than one tank, a stop valve shall be fitted in the line to each tank.

5.5.4 Cargo piping installed in pipe tunnels shall also comply with the requirements of 5.5.1 and 5.5.2. Pipe tunnels shall satisfy all tank requirements for construction, location and ventilation and electrical hazard requirements. Cargo compatibility shall be assured in the event of a piping failure. The tunnel shall not have any other openings except to the weather deck and cargo pump-room or pump-room.

5.5.5 Cargo piping passing through bulkheads shall be so arranged as to preclude excessive stresses at the bulkhead and shall not utilize flanges bolted through the bulkhead.

5.6 Cargo-transfer control systems

5.6.1 For the purpose of adequately controlling the cargo, cargo-transfer systems shall be provided with:

.1 one stop valve capable of being manually operated on each tank filling and discharge line, located near the tank penetration; if an individual deepwell pump is used to discharge the contents of a cargo tank, a stop valve is not required on the discharge line of that tank;

.2 one stop valve at each cargo-hose connection;

.3 remote shutdown devices for all cargo pumps and similar equipment.

5.6.2 The controls necessary during transfer or transport of cargoes covered by the Code other than in cargo pump-rooms which have been dealt with elsewhere in the Code shall not be located below the weather deck.

5.6.3   For certain products, additional cargo-transfer control requirements are shown in *column o* in the table of chapter 17.

5.7   Ship's cargo hoses

5.7.1   Liquid and vapour hoses used for cargo transfer shall be compatible with the cargo and suitable for the cargo temperature.

5.7.2   Hoses subject to tank pressure or the discharge pressure of pumps shall be designed for a bursting pressure not less than 5 times the maximum pressure the hose will be subjected to during cargo transfer.

5.7.3   For cargo hoses installed on board ships on or after 1 July 2002, each new type of cargo hose, complete with end-fittings, shall be prototype-tested at a normal ambient temperature with 200 pressure cycles from zero to at least twice the specified maximum working pressure. After this cycle pressure test has been carried out, the prototype test shall demonstrate a bursting pressure of at least 5 times its specified maximum working pressure at the extreme service temperature. Hoses used for prototype testing shall not be used for cargo service. Thereafter, before being placed in service, each new length of cargo hose produced shall be hydrostatically tested at ambient temperature to a pressure not less than 1.5 times its specified maximum working pressure but not more than two-fifths of its bursting pressure. The hose shall be stencilled or otherwise marked with the date of testing, its specified maximum working pressure and, if used in services other than the ambient temperature services, its maximum and minimum service temperature, as applicable. The specified maximum working pressure shall not be less than 1 MPa gauge.

Chapter 6

Materials of construction, protective linings and coatings

6.1   Structural materials used for tank construction, together with associated piping, pumps, valves, vents and their jointing materials, shall be suitable at the temperature and pressure for the cargo to be carried in accordance with recognized standards. Steel is assumed to be the normal material of construction.

6.2   The shipyard is responsible for providing compatibility information to the ship operator and/or master. This must be done in a timely manner before delivery of the ship or on completion of a relevant modification of the material of construction.

6.3   Where applicable, the following should be taken into account in selecting the material of construction:

    .1 notch ductility at the operating temperature;

    .2 corrosive effect of the cargo; and

    .3 possibility of hazardous reactions between the cargo and the material of construction.

6.4   The shipper of the cargo is responsible for providing compatibility information to the ship operator and/or master. This must be done in a timely manner before transportation of the product. The cargo shall be compatible with all materials of construction such that:

    .1 no damage to the integrity of the materials of construction is incurred; and/or

    .2 no hazardous, or potentially hazardous, reaction is created.

6.5   When a product is submitted to IMO for evaluation, and where compatibility of the product with materials referred to in paragraph 6.1 renders special requirements, the BLG Product Data Reporting Form shall provide information on the required materials of construction. These requirements shall be reflected in chapter 15 and consequentially be referred to in *column o* of chapter 17. The reporting form shall also indicate if no special requirements are necessary. The producer of the product is responsible for providing the correct information.

Chapter 7

Cargo temperature control

7.1 General

7.1.1 When provided, any cargo heating or cooling systems shall be constructed, fitted and tested to the satisfaction of the Administration. Materials used in the construction of temperature-control systems shall be suitable for use with the product intended to be carried.

7.1.2 Heating or cooling media shall be of a type approved for use with the specific cargo. Consideration shall be given to the surface temperature of heating coils or ducts to avoid dangerous reactions from localized overheating or overcooling of cargo. (See also 15.13.6.)

7.1.3 Heating or cooling systems shall be provided with valves to isolate the system for each tank and to allow manual regulation of flow.

7.1.4 In any heating or cooling system, means shall be provided to ensure that, when in any condition other than empty, a higher pressure can be maintained within the system than the maximum pressure head that could be exerted by the cargo tank contents on the system.

7.1.5 Means shall be provided for measuring the cargo temperature.

   .1 The means for measuring the cargo temperature shall be of restricted or closed type, respectively, when a restricted or closed gauging device is required for individual substances, as shown in *column j* in the table of chapter 17.

   .2 A restricted temperature-measuring device is subject to the definition for a restricted gauging device in 13.1.1.2 (e.g., a portable thermometer lowered inside a gauge tube of the restricted type).

   .3 A closed temperature-measuring device is subject to the definition for a closed gauging device in 13.1.1.3 (e.g., a remote-reading thermometer of which the sensor is installed in the tank).

   .4 When overheating or overcooling could result in a dangerous condition, an alarm system which monitors the cargo temperature shall be provided. (See also operational requirements in 16.6.)

7.1.6 When products for which 15.12, 15.12.1 or 15.12.3 are listed in *column o* in the table of chapter 17 are being heated or cooled, the heating or cooling medium shall operate in a circuit:

   .1 which is independent of other ship's services, except for another cargo heating or cooling system, and which does not enter the machinery space; or

   .2 which is external to the tank carrying toxic products; or

   .3 where the medium is sampled to check for the presence of cargo before it is recirculated to other services of the ship or into the machinery space. The sampling equipment shall be located within the cargo area and be capable of detecting the presence of any toxic cargo being heated or cooled. Where this method is used, the coil return shall be tested not only at the commencement of heating or cooling of a toxic product, but also on the first occasion the coil is used subsequent to having carried an unheated or uncooled toxic cargo.

7.2 Additional requirements

For certain products, additional requirements contained in chapter 15 are shown in *column o* in the table of chapter 17.

Chapter 8

Cargo tank venting and gas-freeing arrangements

8.1   Application

8.1.1   Unless expressly provided otherwise, this chapter applies to ships constructed on or after 1 January 1994.

8.1.2   Ships constructed before 1 January 1994 shall comply with the requirements of chapter 8 of this Code which were in force prior to the said date.

8.1.3   For the purpose of this regulation, the term ''ship constructed'' is as defined in SOLAS regulation II-1/1.3.1.

8.1.4   Ships constructed on or after 1 July 1986 but before 1 January 1994 which fully comply with the requirements of the Code applicable at that time may be regarded as complying with the requirements of SOLAS regulations II-2/4.5.3, 4.5.6 to 4.5.8, 4.5.10 and 11.6.

8.1.5   For ships to which the Code applies, the requirements of this chapter shall apply in lieu of SOLAS regulations II-2/4.5.3 and 4.5.6.

8.1.6   Ships constructed on or after 1 July 1986, but before 1 July 2002, shall comply with the requirements of 8.3.3.

8.2   Cargo tank venting

8.2.1   All cargo tanks shall be provided with a venting system appropriate to the cargo being carried and these systems shall be independent of the air pipes and venting systems of all other compartments of the ship. Tank venting systems shall be designed so as to minimize the possibility of cargo vapour accumulating about the decks, entering accommodation, service and machinery spaces and control stations and, in the case of flammable vapours, entering or collecting in spaces or areas containing sources of ignition. Tank venting systems shall be arranged to prevent entrance of water into the cargo tanks and, at the same time, vent outlets shall direct the vapour discharge upwards in the form of unimpeded jets.

8.2.2   The venting systems shall be connected to the top of each cargo tank and as far as practicable the cargo vent lines shall be self-draining back to the cargo tanks under all normal operational conditions of list and trim. Where it is necessary to drain venting systems above the level of any pressure/vacuum valve, capped or plugged drain cocks shall be provided.

8.2.3   Provision shall be made to ensure that the liquid head in any tank does not exceed the design head of the tank. Suitable high-level alarms, overflow control systems or spill valves, together with gauging and tank filling procedures, may be accepted for this purpose. Where the means of limiting cargo tank overpressure includes an automatic closing valve, the valve shall comply with the appropriate provisions of 15.19.

8.2.4   Tank venting systems shall be designed and operated so as to ensure that neither pressure nor vacuum created in the cargo tanks during loading or unloading exceeds tank design parameters. The main factors to be considered in the sizing of a tank venting system are as follows:

  .1   design loading and unloading rate;

  .2   gas evolution during loading: this shall be taken account of by multiplying the maximum loading rate by a factor of at least 1.25;

  .3   density of the cargo vapour mixture;

.4 pressure loss in vent piping and across valves and fittings; and

.5 pressure/vacuum settings of relief devices.

8.2.5 Tank vent piping connected to cargo tanks of corrosion-resistant material, or to tanks which are lined or coated to handle special cargoes as required by the Code, shall be similarly lined or coated or constructed of corrosion-resistant material.

8.2.6 The master shall be provided with the maximum permissible loading and unloading rates for each tank or group of tanks consistent with the design of the venting systems.

8.3 Types of tank venting systems

8.3.1 An open tank venting system is a system which offers no restriction except for friction losses to the free flow of cargo vapours to and from the cargo tanks during normal operations. An open venting system may consist of individual vents from each tank, or such individual vents may be combined into a common header or headers, with due regard to cargo segregation. In no case shall shutoff valves be fitted either to the individual vents or to the header.

8.3.2 A controlled tank venting system is a system in which pressure- and vacuum-relief valves or pressure/vacuum valves are fitted to each tank to limit the pressure or vacuum in the tank. A controlled venting system may consist of individual vents from each tank or such individual vents on the pressure side only as may be combined into a common header or headers, with due regard to cargo segregation. In no case shall shutoff valves be fitted either above or below pressure- or vacuum-relief valves or pressure/vacuum valves. Provision may be made for bypassing a pressure- or vacuum-relief valve or pressure/vacuum valve under certain operating conditions provided that the requirement of 8.3.6 is maintained and that there is suitable indication to show whether or not the valve is bypassed.

8.3.3 Controlled tank venting systems shall consist of a primary and a secondary means of allowing full flow relief of vapour to prevent over-pressure or under-pressure in the event of failure of one means. Alternatively, the secondary means may consist of pressure sensors fitted in each tank with a monitoring system in the ship's cargo control room or position from which cargo operations are normally carried out. Such monitoring equipment shall also provide an alarm facility which is activated by detection of over-pressure or under-pressure conditions within a tank.

8.3.4 The position of vent outlets of a controlled tank venting system shall be arranged:

.1 at a height of not less than 6 m above the weather deck or above a raised walkway if fitted within 4 m of the raised walkway; and

.2 at a distance of at least 10 m measured horizontally from the nearest air intake or opening to accommodation, service and machinery spaces and ignition sources.

8.3.5 The vent outlet height referred to in 8.3.4.1 may be reduced to 3 m above the deck or a raised walkway, as applicable, provided that high-velocity venting valves of an approved type, directing the vapour/air mixture upwards in an unimpeded jet with an exit velocity of at least 30 m/s, are fitted.

8.3.6 Controlled tank venting systems fitted to tanks to be used for cargoes having a flashpoint not exceeding 60°C (closed-cup test) shall be provided with devices to prevent the passage of flame into the cargo tanks. The design, testing and locating of the devices shall comply with the requirements of the Administration, which shall contain at least the standards adopted by the Organization.

8.3.7 In designing venting systems and in the selection of devices to prevent the passage of flame for incorporation into the tank venting system, due attention shall be paid to the possibility of the blockage of these systems and fittings by, for example, the freezing of cargo vapour, polymer build-up, atmospheric dust or icing up in adverse weather conditions. In this context it shall be noted that flame arresters and flame screens are more susceptible to blockage. Provisions shall be made such that the system and fittings may be inspected, operationally checked, cleaned or renewed as applicable.

8.3.8 Reference in 8.3.1 and 8.3.2 to the use of shutoff valves in the venting lines shall be interpreted to extend to all other means of stoppage, including spectacle blanks and blank flanges.

8.4 Venting requirements for individual products

Venting requirements for individual products are shown in *column g*, and additional requirements in *column o* in the table of chapter 17.

8.5 Cargo tank gas-freeing

8.5.1 The arrangements for gas-freeing cargo tanks used for cargoes other than those for which open venting is permitted shall be such as to minimize the hazards due to the dispersal of flammable or toxic vapours in the atmosphere and to flammable or toxic vapour mixtures in a cargo tank. Accordingly, gas-freeing operations shall be carried out such that vapour is initially discharged:

.1 through the vent outlets specified in 8.3.4 and 8.3.5; or

.2 through outlets at least 2 m above the cargo tank deck level with a vertical exit velocity of at least 30 m/s maintained during the gas-freeing operation; or

.3 through outlets at least 2 m above the cargo tank deck level with a vertical exit velocity of at least 20 m/s which are protected by suitable devices to prevent the passage of flame.

When the flammable vapour concentration at the outlets has been reduced to 30% of the lower flammable limit and, in the case of a toxic product, the vapour concentration does not present a significant health hazard, gas-freeing may thereafter be continued at cargo tank deck level.

8.5.2 The outlets referred to in 8.5.1.2 and 8.5.1.3 may be fixed or portable pipes.

8.5.3 In designing a gas-freeing system in conformity with 8.5.1, particularly in order to achieve the required exit velocities of 8.5.1.2 and 8.5.1.3, due consideration shall be given to the following:

.1 materials of construction of system;

.2 time to gas-free;

.3 flow characteristics of fans to be used;

.4 the pressure losses created by ducting, piping, cargo tank inlets and outlets;

.5 the pressure achievable in the fan driving medium (e.g., water or compressed air); and

.6 the densities of the cargo vapour/air mixtures for the range of cargoes to be carried.

Chapter 9

Environmental control

9.1 General

9.1.1 Vapour spaces within cargo tanks and, in some cases, spaces surrounding cargo tanks may require to have specially controlled atmospheres.

9.1.2 There are four different types of control for cargo tanks, as follows:

.1 *Inerting:* by filling the cargo tank and associated piping systems and, where specified in chapter 15, the spaces surrounding the cargo tanks, with a gas or vapour which will not support combustion and which will not react with the cargo, and maintaining that condition.

.2 *Padding:* by filling the cargo tank and associated piping systems with a liquid, gas or vapour which separates the cargo from the air, and maintaining that condition.

.3 *Drying:* by filling the cargo tank and associated piping systems with moisture-free gas or vapour with a dewpoint of −40°C or below at atmospheric pressure, and maintaining that condition.

.4 *Ventilation:* forced or natural.

9.1.3 Where inerting or padding of cargo tanks is required:

.1 An adequate supply of inert gas for use in filling and discharging the cargo tanks shall be carried or shall be manufactured on board unless a shore supply is available. In addition, sufficient inert gas shall be available on the ship to compensate for normal losses during transportation.

.2 The inert gas system on board the ship shall be able to maintain a pressure of at least 0.007 MPa gauge within the containment system at all times. In addition, the inert gas system shall not raise the cargo tank pressure to more than the tank's relief-valve setting.

.3 Where padding is used, similar arrangements for supply of the padding medium shall be made as required for inert gas in 9.1.3.1 and 9.1.3.2.

.4 Means shall be provided for monitoring ullage spaces containing a gas blanket to ensure that the correct atmosphere is being maintained.

.5 Inerting or padding arrangements or both, where used with flammable cargoes, shall be such as to minimize the creation of static electricity during the admission of the inerting medium.

9.1.4 Where drying is used and dry nitrogen is used as the medium, similar arrangements for supply of the drying agent shall be made to those required in 9.1.3. Where drying agents are used as the drying medium on all air inlets to the tank, sufficient medium shall be carried for the duration of the voyage, taking into consideration the diurnal temperature range and the expected humidity.

9.2 Environmental control requirements for individual products

The required types of environmental control for certain products are shown in *column h* in the table of chapter 17.

Chapter 10

Electrical installations

10.1 General

10.1.1 The provisions of this chapter are applicable to ships carrying cargoes which are inherently, or due to their reaction with other substances, flammable or corrosive to the electrical equipment, and shall be applied in conjunction with applicable electrical requirements of part D of chapter II-1 of SOLAS.

10.1.2.1 Electrical installations shall be such as to minimize the risk of fire and explosion from flammable products.*

10.1.2.2 Where the specific cargo is liable to damage the materials normally used in electrical apparatus, due consideration shall be given to the particular characteristics of the materials chosen for conductors, insulation, metal parts, etc. As far as necessary, these components shall be protected to prevent contact with gases or vapours liable to be encountered.

10.1.3 The Administration shall take appropriate steps to ensure uniformity in the implementation and the application of the provisions of this chapter in respect of electrical installations.

10.1.4 Electrical equipment, cables and wiring shall not be installed in the hazardous locations unless it conforms with the standards not inferior to those acceptable to the Organization.* However, for locations not covered by such standards, electrical equipment, cables and wiring which do not conform to the standards may be installed in hazardous locations based on a risk assessment to the satisfaction of the Administration, to ensure that an equivalent level of safety is assured.

10.1.5 Where electrical equipment is installed in hazardous locations, as permitted in this chapter, it shall be to the satisfaction of the Administration and certified by the relevant authorities recognized by the Administration for operation in the flammable atmosphere concerned, as indicated in *column i* in the table of chapter 17.

10.1.6 For guidance, indication is given if the flashpoint of a substance is in excess of 60°C. In the case of a heated cargo, carriage conditions might need to be established and the requirements for cargoes having a flashpoint not exceeding 60°C applied.

10.2 Bonding

Independent cargo tanks shall be electrically bonded to the hull. All gasketed cargo-pipe joints and hose connections shall be electrically bonded.

10.3 Electrical requirements for individual products

Electrical requirements for individual products are shown in *column i* in the table of chapter 17.

---

* Reference is made to the recommendations published by the International Electrotechnical Commission, in particular to Publication IEC 60092-502: 1999.

Chapter 11

*Fire protection and fire extinction**

11.1 Application

11.1.1 The requirements for tankers in SOLAS chapter II-2 shall apply to ships covered by the Code, irrespective of tonnage, including ships of less than 500 gross tonnage, except that:

   .1 regulations 4.5.5, 10.8 and 10.9 shall not apply;

   .2 regulation 4.5.1.2 (i.e., the requirements for location of the main cargo control station) need not apply;

   .3 regulations 10.2, 10.4, and 10.5 shall apply as they would apply to cargo ships of 2,000 tons gross tonnage and over;

   .4 the provisions of 11.3 shall apply in lieu of regulation 10.8; and

   .5 the provisions of 11.2 shall apply in lieu of regulation 10.9.

11.1.2 Notwithstanding the provisions of 11.1.1, ships engaged solely in the carriage of products which are non-flammable (entry "NF" in *column i* of the table of minimum requirements) need not comply with requirements for tankers specified in SOLAS chapter II-2, provided that they comply with the requirements for cargo ships of that chapter, except that regulation 10.7 need not apply to such ships and 11.2 and 11.3, hereunder, need not apply.

11.1.3 For ships engaged solely in the carriage of products with a flashpoint of 60°C and above (entry "Yes" in *column i* of the table of minimum requirements), the requirements of SOLAS chapter II-2 may apply as specified in regulation II-2/1.6.4 in lieu of the provisions of this chapter.

11.2 Cargo pump-rooms

11.2.1 The cargo pump-room of any ship shall be provided with a fixed carbon dioxide fire-extinguishing system as specified in SOLAS regulation II-2/10.9.1.1. A notice shall be exhibited at the controls stating that the system is only to be used for fire-extinguishing and not for inerting purposes, due to the electrostatic ignition hazard. The alarms referred to in SOLAS regulation II-2/10.9.1.1.1 shall be safe for use in a flammable cargo vapour/air mixture. For the purpose of this requirement, an extinguishing system shall be provided which would be suitable for machinery spaces. However, the amount of gas carried shall be sufficient to provide a quantity of free gas equal to 45% of the gross volume of the cargo pump-room in all cases.

11.2.2 Cargo pump-rooms of ships which are dedicated to the carriage of a restricted number of cargoes shall be protected by an appropriate fire-extinguishing system approved by the Administration.

11.2.3 If cargoes are to be carried which are not suited to extinguishment by carbon dioxide or equivalent media, the cargo pump-room shall be protected by a fire-extinguishing system consisting of either a fixed pressure water spray or high-expansion foam system. The International Certificate of Fitness for the Carriage of Dangerous Chemicals in Bulk shall reflect this conditional requirement.

11.3 Cargo area

11.3.1 Every ship shall be provided with a fixed deck foam system in accordance with the requirements of 11.3.2 to 11.3.12.

---

* Refer to MSC-MEPC.2/Circ.4 on the Early Application of the amendments to the fire proctection requirements of the revised IBC Code.

11.3.2 Only one type of foam concentrate shall be supplied, and it shall be effective for the maximum possible number of cargoes intended to be carried. For other cargoes for which foam is not effective or is incompatible, additional arrangements to the satisfaction of the Administration shall be provided. Regular protein foam shall not be used.

11.3.3 The arrangements for providing foam shall be capable of delivering foam to the entire cargo tanks deck area as well as into any cargo tank, the deck of which is assumed to be ruptured.

11.3.4 The deck foam system shall be capable of simple and rapid operation. The main control station for the system shall be suitably located outside of the cargo area, adjacent to the accommodation spaces and readily accessible and operable in the event of fires in the areas protected.

11.3.5 The rate of supply of foam solution shall be not less than the greatest of the following:

.1 2 ℓ/min per square metre of the cargo tanks deck area, where "cargo tanks deck area" means the maximum breadth of the ship times the total longitudinal extent of the cargo tank spaces;

.2 20 ℓ/min per square metre of the horizontal sectional area of the single tank having the largest such area;

.3 10 ℓ/min per square metre of the area protected by the largest monitor, such area being entirely forward of the monitor, but not less than 1,250 ℓ/min. For ships less than 4,000 tonnes deadweight, the minimum capacity of the monitor shall be to the satisfaction of the Administration.

11.3.6 Sufficient foam concentrate shall be supplied to ensure at least 30 min of foam generation when using the highest of the solution rates stipulated in 11.3.5.1, 11.3.5.2 and 11.3.5.3.

11.3.7 Foam from the fixed foam system shall be supplied by means of monitors and foam applicators. At least 50% of the foam rate required in 11.3.5.1 or 11.3.5.2 shall be delivered from each monitor. The capacity of any monitor shall be at least 10 ℓ/min of foam solution per square metre of deck area protected by that monitor, such area being entirely forward of the monitor. Such capacity shall be not less than 1,250 ℓ/min. For ships less than 4,000 tonnes deadweight, the minimum capacity of the monitor shall be to the satisfaction of the Administration.

11.3.8 The distance from the monitor to the farthest extremity of the protected area forward of that monitor shall be not more than 75% of the monitor throw in still air conditions.

11.3.9 A monitor and hose connection for a foam applicator shall be situated both port and starboard at the poop front or accommodation spaces facing the cargo area.

11.3.10 Applicators shall be provided for flexibility of action during fire-fighting operations and to cover areas screened from the monitors. The capacity of any applicator shall be not less than 400 ℓ/min and the applicator throw in still air conditions shall be not less than 15 m. The number of foam applicators provided shall be not less than four. The number and disposition of foam main outlets shall be such that foam from at least two applicators can be directed to any part of the cargo tanks deck area.

11.3.11 Valves shall be provided in the foam main, and in the fire main where this is an integral part of the deck foam system, immediately forward of any monitor position to isolate damaged sections of those mains.

11.3.12 Operation of a deck foam system at its required output shall permit the simultaneous use of the minimum required number of jets of water at the required pressure from the fire main.

11.3.13 Ships which are dedicated to the carriage of a restricted number of cargoes shall be protected by alternative provisions to the satisfaction of the Administration when they are just as effective for the products concerned as the deck foam system required for the generality of flammable cargoes.

11.3.14 Suitable portable fire-extinguishing equipment for the products to be carried shall be provided and kept in good operating order.

11.3.15 Where flammable cargoes are to be carried, all sources of ignition shall be excluded from hazardous locations unless such sources conform with 10.1.4.

11.3.16 Ships fitted with bow or stern loading and unloading arrangements shall be provided with one additional foam monitor meeting the requirements of 11.3.7 and one additional applicator meeting the requirements of 11.3.10. The additional monitor shall be located to protect the bow or stern loading and unloading arrangements. The area of the cargo line forward or aft of the cargo area shall be protected by the above-mentioned applicator.

11.4 Special requirements

All fire-extinguishing media determined to be effective for each product are listed in *column l* in the table of chapter 17.

Chapter 12

Mechanical ventilation in the cargo area

For ships to which the Code applies, the requirements of this chapter replace the requirements of SOLAS regulations II-2/4.5.2.6 and 4.5.4.

However, for products addressed under paragraphs 11.1.2 and 11.1.3, except acids and products for which paragraph 15.17 applies, SOLAS regulations II-2/4.5.2.6 and 4.5.4 may apply in lieu of the provisions of this chapter.

12.1 Spaces normally entered during cargo-handling operations

12.1.1 Cargo pump-rooms and other enclosed spaces which contain cargo-handling equipment and similar spaces in which work is performed on the cargo shall be fitted with mechanical ventilation systems, capable of being controlled from outside such spaces.

12.1.2 Provision shall be made to ventilate such spaces prior to entering the compartment and operating the equipment and a warning notice requiring the use of such ventilation shall be placed outside the compartment.

12.1.3 Mechanical ventilation inlets and outlets shall be arranged to ensure sufficient air movement through the space to avoid the accumulation of toxic or flammable vapours or both (taking into account their vapour densities) and to ensure sufficient oxygen to provide a safe working environment, but in no case shall the ventilation system have a capacity of less than 30 changes of air per hour, based upon the total volume of the space. For certain products, increased ventilation rates for cargo pump-rooms are prescribed in 15.17.

12.1.4 Ventilation systems shall be permanent and shall normally be of the extraction type. Extraction from above and below the floor plates shall be possible. In rooms housing motors driving cargo pumps, the ventilation shall be of the positive-pressure type.

12.1.5 Ventilation exhaust ducts from spaces within the cargo area shall discharge upwards in locations at least 10 m in the horizontal direction from ventilation intakes and openings to accommodation, service and machinery spaces and control stations and other spaces outside the cargo area.

12.1.6 Ventilation intakes shall be so arranged as to minimize the possibility of recycling hazardous vapours from any ventilation discharge opening.

12.1.7 Ventilation ducts shall not be led through accommodation, service and machinery spaces or other similar spaces.

12.1.8 Electric motors driving fans shall be placed outside the ventilation ducts if the carriage of flammable products is intended. Ventilation fans and fan ducts, in way of fans only, for hazardous locations referred to in chapter 10 shall be of non-sparking construction, defined as:

.1 impellers or housing of non-metallic construction, due regard being paid to the elimination of static electricity;

.2 impellers and housing of non-ferrous materials;

.3 impellers and housing of austenitic stainless steel; and

.4 ferrous impellers and housing with not less than 13 mm design tip clearance.

Any combination of an aluminium or a magnesium alloy fixed or rotating component and a ferrous fixed or rotating component, regardless of tip clearance, is considered a sparking hazard and shall not be used in these places.

12.1.9   Sufficient spare parts shall be carried for each type of fan on board required by this chapter.

12.1.10   Protection screens of not more than 13 mm square mesh shall be fitted in outside openings of ventilation ducts.

12.2   Pump-rooms and other enclosed spaces normally entered

Pump-rooms and other enclosed spaces normally entered which are not covered by 12.1.1 shall be fitted with mechanical ventilation systems, capable of being controlled from outside such spaces and complying with the requirements of 12.1.3, except that the capacity shall not be less than 20 changes of air per hour, based upon the total volume of the space. Provision shall be made to ventilate such spaces prior to personnel entering.

12.3   Spaces not normally entered

Double bottoms, cofferdams, duct keels, pipe tunnels, hold spaces and other spaces where cargo may accumulate shall be capable of being ventilated to ensure a safe environment when entry into the spaces is necessary. Where a permanent ventilation system is not provided for such spaces, approved means of portable mechanical ventilation shall be provided. Where necessary, owing to the arrangement of spaces, for instance hold spaces, essential ducting for ventilation shall be permanently installed. For permanent installations the capacity of eight air changes per hour shall be provided and for portable systems the capacity of 16 air changes per hour. Fans or blowers shall be clear of personnel access openings, and shall comply with 12.1.8.

Chapter 13

Instrumentation

13.1 Gauging

13.1.1 Cargo tanks shall be fitted with one of the following types of gauging devices:

.1 *Open device:* which makes use of an opening in the tanks and may expose the gauger to the cargo or its vapour. An example of this is the ullage opening.

.2 *Restricted device:* which penetrates the tank and which, when in use, permits a small quantity of cargo vapour or liquid to be exposed to the atmosphere. When not in use, the device is completely closed. The design shall ensure that no dangerous escape of tank contents (liquid or spray) can take place in opening the device.

.3 *Closed device:* which penetrates the tank, but which is part of a closed system and keeps tank contents from being released. Examples are the float-type systems, electronic probe, magnetic probe and protected sight-glass. Alternatively, an *indirect device* which does not penetrate the tank shell and which is independent of the tank may be used. Examples are weighing of cargo, pipe flowmeter.

13.1.2 Gauging devices shall be independent of the equipment required under 15.19.

13.1.3 Open gauging and restricted gauging shall be allowed only where:

.1 open venting is allowed by the Code; or

.2 means are provided for relieving tank pressure before the gauge is operated.

13.1.4 Types of gauging for individual products are shown in *column j* in the table of chapter 17.

13.2 Vapour detection

13.2.1 Ships carrying toxic or flammable products or both shall be equipped with at least two instruments designed and calibrated for testing for the specific vapours in question. If such instruments are not capable of testing for both toxic concentrations and flammable concentrations, then two separate sets of instruments shall be provided.

13.2.2 Vapour-detection instruments may be portable or fixed. If a fixed system is installed, at least one portable instrument shall be provided.

13.2.3 When toxic-vapour-detection equipment is not available for some products which require such detection, as indicated in *column k* in the table of chapter 17, the Administration may exempt the ship from the requirement, provided an appropriate entry is made on the International Certificate of Fitness for the Carriage of Dangerous Chemicals in Bulk. When granting such an exemption, the Administration shall recognize the necessity for additional breathing-air supply and an entry shall be made on the International Certificate of Fitness for the Carriage of Dangerous Chemicals in Bulk drawing attention to the provisions of 14.2.4 and 16.4.2.2.

13.2.4 Vapour-detection requirements for individual products are shown in *column k* in the table of chapter 17.

Chapter 14

Personnel protection

14.1 Protective equipment

14.1.1 For the protection of crew members who are engaged in loading and discharging operations, the ship shall have on board suitable protective equipment consisting of large aprons, special gloves with long sleeves, suitable footwear, coveralls of chemical-resistant material, and tight-fitting goggles or face shields or both. The protective clothing and equipment shall cover all skin so that no part of the body is unprotected.

14.1.2 Work clothes and protective equipment shall be kept in easily accessible places and in special lockers. Such equipment shall not be kept within accommodation spaces, with the exception of new, unused equipment and equipment which has not been used since undergoing a thorough cleaning process. The Administration may, however, approve storage rooms for such equipment within accommodation spaces if adequately segregated from living spaces such as cabins, passageways, dining rooms, bathrooms, etc.

14.1.3 Protective equipment shall be used in any operation which may entail danger to personnel.

14.2 Safety equipment

14.2.1 Ships carrying cargoes for which 15.12, 15.12.1 or 15.12.3 is listed in *column o* in the table of chapter 17 shall have on board sufficient but not less than three complete sets of safety equipment, each permitting personnel to enter a gas-filled compartment and perform work there for at least 20 min. Such equipment shall be in addition to that required by SOLAS regulation II-2/10.10.

14.2.2 One complete set of safety equipment shall consist of:

.1 one self-contained air-breathing apparatus (not using stored oxygen);

.2 protective clothing, boots, gloves and tight-fitting goggles;

.3 fireproof lifeline with belt resistant to the cargoes carried; and

.4 explosion-proof lamp.

14.2.3 For the safety equipment required in 14.2.1, all ships shall carry either:

.1 one set of fully charged spare air bottles for each breathing apparatus;

.2 a special air compressor suitable for the supply of high-pressure air of the required purity;

.3 a charging manifold capable of dealing with sufficient spare air bottles for the breathing apparatus; or

.4 fully charged spare air bottles with a total free air capacity of at least 6,000 ℓ for each breathing apparatus on board in excess of the requirements of SOLAS regulation II-2/10.10.

14.2.4 A cargo pump-room on ships carrying cargoes which are subject to the requirements of 15.18 or cargoes for which in *column k* in the table of chapter 17 toxic-vapour-detection equipment is required but is not available shall have either:

.1 a low-pressure line system with hose connections suitable for use with the breathing apparatus required by 14.2.1. This system shall provide sufficient high-pressure air capacity to supply, through pressure-reduction devices, enough low-pressure air to enable two men to work in a gas-dangerous space for at least 1 h without using the air bottles of the breathing apparatus. Means shall be provided for recharging the fixed air bottles and the breathing apparatus air bottles from a special air compressor suitable for the supply of high-pressure air of the required purity; or

.2 an equivalent quantity of spare bottled air in lieu of the low-pressure air line.

14.2.5   At least one set of safety equipment as required by 14.2.2 shall be kept in a suitable clearly marked locker in a readily accessible place near the cargo pump-room. The other sets of safety equipment shall also be kept in suitable, clearly marked, easily accessible places.

14.2.6   The breathing apparatus shall be inspected at least once a month by a responsible officer, and the inspection recorded in the ship's log-book. The equipment shall be inspected and tested by an expert at least once a year.

14.3   Emergency equipment

14.3.1   Ships carrying cargoes for which "Yes" is indicated in *column n* of chapter 17 shall be provided with suitable respiratory and eye protection sufficient for every person on board for emergency escape purposes, subject to the following:

   .1   filter-type respiratory protection is unacceptable;

   .2   self-contained breathing apparatus shall have at least a duration of service of 15 min;

   .3   emergency escape respiratory protection shall not be used for fire-fighting or cargo-handling purposes and shall be marked to that effect.

14.3.2   The ship shall have on board medical first-aid equipment, including oxygen resuscitation equipment and antidotes for cargoes to be carried, based on the guidelines developed by the Organization.*

14.3.3   A stretcher which is suitable for hoisting an injured person up from spaces such as the cargo pump-room shall be placed in a readily accessible location.

14.3.4   Suitably marked decontamination showers and an eyewash shall be available on deck in convenient locations. The showers and eyewash shall be operable in all ambient conditions.

---

* Reference is made to the Medical First Aid Guide for Use in Accidents Involving Dangerous Goods (MFAG), which provides advice on the treatment of casualties in accordance with the symptoms exhibited as well as equipment and antidotes that may be appropriate for treating the casualty.

Chapter 15

Special requirements

15.1 General

15.1.1 The provisions of this chapter are applicable where specific reference is made in *column o* in the table of chapter 17. These requirements are additional to the general requirements of the Code.

15.2 Ammonium nitrate solution (93% or less)

15.2.1 The ammonium nitrate solution shall contain at least 7% by weight of water. The acidity (pH) of the cargo when diluted with ten parts of water to one part of cargo by weight shall be between 5.0 and 7.0. The solution shall not contain more than 10 ppm chloride ions, 10 ppm ferric ions and shall be free of other contaminants.

15.2.2 Tanks and equipment for ammonium nitrate solution shall be independent of tanks and equipment containing other cargoes or combustible products. Equipment which may, in service or when defective, release combustible products into the cargo (e.g., lubricants) shall not be used. Tanks shall not be used for seawater ballast.

15.2.3 Except where expressly approved by the Administration, ammonium nitrate solutions shall not be transported in tanks which have previously contained other cargoes unless tanks and associated equipment have been cleaned to the satisfaction of the Administration.

15.2.4 The temperature of the heat-exchanging medium in the tank heating system shall not exceed 160°C. The heating system shall be provided with a control system to keep the cargo at a bulk mean temperature of 140°C. High-temperature alarms at 145°C and 150°C and a low-temperature alarm at 125°C shall be provided. Where the temperature of the heat-exchanging medium exceeds 160°C, an alarm shall also be given. Temperature alarms and controls shall be located on the navigating bridge.

15.2.5 If the bulk mean cargo temperature reaches 145°C, a cargo sample shall be diluted with ten parts of distilled or demineralized water to one part of cargo by weight and the pH shall be determined by means of a narrow-range indicator paper or stick. Acidity measurements shall then be taken every 24 hours. If the pH is found to be below 4.2, ammonia gas shall be injected into the cargo until the pH of 5.0 is reached.

15.2.6 A fixed installation shall be provided to inject ammonia gas into the cargo. Controls for this system shall be located on the navigation bridge. For this purpose, 300 kg of ammonia per 1,000 tonnes of ammonium nitrate solution shall be available on board.

15.2.7 Cargo pumps shall be of the centrifugal deepwell type or of the centrifugal type with water-flushed seals.

15.2.8 Vent piping shall be fitted with approved weatherhoods to prevent clogging. Such weatherhoods shall be accessible for inspection and cleaning.

15.2.9 Hot work on tanks, piping and equipment which have been in contact with ammonium nitrate solution shall only be done after all traces of ammonium nitrate have been removed, inside as well as outside.

15.3 Carbon disulphide

Carbon disulphide may be carried either under a water pad or under a suitable inert gas pad as specified in the following paragraphs.

Carriage under water pad

15.3.1   Provision shall be made to maintain a water pad in the cargo tank during loading, unloading and transit. In addition, an inert-gas pad shall be maintained in the ullage space during transit.

15.3.2   All openings shall be in the top of the tank, above the deck.

15.3.3   Loading lines shall terminate near the bottom of the tank.

15.3.4   A standard ullage opening shall be provided for emergency sounding.

15.3.5   Cargo piping and vent lines shall be independent of piping and vent lines used for other cargo.

15.3.6   Pumps may be used for discharging cargo, provided they are of the deepwell or hydraulically driven submersible types. The means of driving a deepwell pump shall not present a source of ignition for carbon disulphide and shall not employ equipment that may exceed a temperature of 80°C.

15.3.7   If a cargo discharge pump is used, it shall be inserted through a cylindrical well extending from the tank top to a point near the tank bottom. A water pad shall be formed in this well before attempting pump removal unless the tank has been certified as gas-free.

15.3.8   Water or inert-gas displacement may be used for discharging cargo, provided the cargo system is designed for the expected pressure and temperature.

15.3.9   Safety relief valves shall be of stainless steel construction.

15.3.10   Because of its low ignition temperature and close clearances required to arrest its flame propagation, only intrinsically safe systems and circuits are permitted in the hazardous locations.

Carriage under suitable inert gas pad

15.3.11   Carbon disulphide shall be carried in independent tanks with a design pressure of not less than 0.06 MPa gauge.

15.3.12   All openings shall be located on the top of the tank, above the deck.

15.3.13   Gaskets used in the containment system shall be of a material which does not react with, or dissolve in, carbon disulphide.

15.3.14   Threaded joints shall not be permitted in the cargo containment system, including the vapour lines.

15.3.15   Prior to loading, the tank(s) shall be inerted with suitable inert gas until the oxygen level is 2% by volume or lower. Means shall be provided to automatically maintain a positive pressure in the tank using suitable inert gas during loading, transport and discharge. The system shall be able to maintain this positive pressure between 0.01 and 0.02 MPa, and shall be remotely monitored and fitted with over-/under-pressure alarms.

15.3.16   Hold spaces surrounding an independent tank carrying carbon disulphide shall be inerted by a suitable inert gas until the oxygen level is 2% or less. Means shall be provided to monitor and maintain this condition throughout the voyage. Means shall also be provided to sample these spaces for carbon disulphide vapour.

15.3.17   Carbon disulphide shall be loaded, transported and discharged in such a manner that venting to the atmosphere does not occur. If carbon disulphide vapour is returned to shore during loading or to the ship during discharge, the vapour-return system shall be independent of all other containment systems.

15.3.18   Carbon disulphide shall be discharged only by submerged deepwell pumps or by a suitable inert gas displacement. The submerged deepwell pumps shall be operated in a way that prevents heat build-up in the pump. The pump shall also be equipped with a temperature sensor in the pump housing with remote readout and alarm in the cargo control room. The alarm shall be set at 80°C. The pump shall also be fitted with an automatic shut-down device to be activated if the tank pressure falls below atmospheric pressure during the discharge.

15.3.19   Air shall not be allowed to enter the cargo tank, cargo pump or lines while carbon disulphide is contained in the system.

15.3.20   No other cargo handling, tank cleaning or deballasting shall take place concurrent with loading or discharge of carbon disulphide.

15.3.21 A water spray system of sufficient capacity shall be provided to blanket effectively the area surrounding the loading manifold, the exposed deck piping associated with product handling and the tank domes. The arrangement of piping and nozzles shall be such as to give a uniform distribution rate of 10 $\ell/m^2/min$. Remote manual operation shall be arranged such that remote starting of pumps supplying the water-spray system and remote operation of any normally closed valves in the system can be carried out from a suitable location outside the cargo area adjacent to the accommodation spaces and readily accessible and operable in the event of fire in the areas protected. The water-spray system shall be capable of both local and remote manual operation, and the arrangement shall ensure that any spilled cargo is washed away. Additionally, a water hose with pressure to the nozzle when atmospheric temperature permits, shall be connected ready for immediate use during loading and unloading operations.

15.3.22 No cargo tanks shall be more than 98% liquid-full at the reference temperature (*R*).

15.3.23 The maximum volume (V_L) of cargo to be loaded in a tank shall be:

$$V_L = 0.98V \frac{\rho_R}{\rho_L}$$

where:

V = volume of the tank

ρ_R = density of cargo at the reference temperature (*R*)

ρ_L = density of cargo at the loading temperature

R = reference temperature

15.3.24 The maximum allowable tank filling limits for each cargo tank shall be indicated for each loading temperature which may be applied, and for the applicable maximum reference temperature, on a list approved by the Administration. A copy of the list shall be permanently kept on board by the master.

15.3.25 Zones on open deck, or semi-enclosed spaces on open deck within three metres of a tank outlet, gas or vapour outlet, cargo pipe flange or cargo valve of a tank certified to carry carbon disulphide, shall comply with the electrical equipment requirements specified for carbon disulphide in *column i*, chapter 17. Also, within the specified zone, no other heat sources, like steam piping, with surface temperatures in excess of 80°C shall be allowed.

15.3.26 Means shall be provided to ullage and sample the cargo without opening the tank or disturbing the positive suitable inert gas blanket.

15.3.27 The product shall be transported only in accordance with a cargo handling plan that has been approved by the Administration. Cargo handling plans shall show the entire cargo piping system. A copy of the approved cargo handling plan shall be available on board. The International Certificate of Fitness for the Carriage of Dangerous Chemicals in Bulk shall be endorsed to include reference to the approved cargo handling plan.

15.4 Diethyl ether

15.4.1 Unless inerted, natural ventilation shall be provided for the voids around the cargo tanks while the vessel is under way. If a mechanical ventilation system is installed, all blowers shall be of non-sparking construction. Mechanical ventilation equipment shall not be located in the void spaces surrounding the cargo tanks.

15.4.2 Pressure-relief-valve settings shall not be less than 0.02 MPa gauge for gravity tanks.

15.4.3 Inert-gas displacement may be used for discharging cargo from pressure tanks provided the cargo system is designed for the expected pressure.

15.4.4 In view of the fire hazard, provision shall be made to avoid any ignition source or heat generation or both in the cargo area.

15.4.5 Pumps may be used for discharging cargo, provided that they are of a type designed to avoid liquid pressure against the shaft gland or are of a hydraulically operated submerged type and are suitable for use with the cargo.

15.4.6 Provision shall be made to maintain the inert-gas pad in the cargo tank during loading, unloading and transit.

15.5   Hydrogen peroxide solutions

15.5.1   Hydrogen peroxide solutions over 60% but not over 70% by mass

15.5.1.1 Hydrogen peroxide solutions over 60% but not over 70% by mass shall be carried in dedicated ships only and no other cargoes shall be carried.

15.5.1.2 Cargo tanks and associated equipment shall be either pure aluminium (99.5%) or solid stainless steel (304L, 316, 316L or 316Ti), and passivated in accordance with approved procedures. Aluminium shall not be used for piping on deck. All non-metallic materials of construction for the containment system shall neither be attacked by hydrogen peroxide nor contribute to its decomposition.

15.5.1.3 Pump-rooms shall not be used for cargo-transfer operations.

15.5.1.4 Cargo tanks shall be separated by cofferdams from oil fuel tanks or any other space containing flammable or combustible materials.

15.5.1.5 Tanks intended for the carriage of hydrogen peroxide shall not be used for seawater ballast.

15.5.1.6 Temperature sensors shall be installed at the top and bottom of the tank. Remote temperature readouts and continuous monitoring shall be located on the navigating bridge. If the temperature in the tanks rises above 35°C, visible and audible alarms shall be activated on the navigating bridge.

15.5.1.7 Fixed oxygen monitors (or gas-sampling lines) shall be provided in void spaces adjacent to tanks to detect leakage of the cargo into these spaces. Remote readouts, continuous monitoring (if gas-sampling lines are used, intermittent sampling is satisfactory) and visible and audible alarms similar to those for the temperature sensors shall also be located on the navigating bridge. The visible and audible alarms shall be activated if the oxygen concentration in these void spaces exceeds 30% by volume. Two portable oxygen monitors shall also be available as back-up systems.

15.5.1.8 As a safeguard against uncontrolled decomposition, a cargo-jettisoning system shall be installed to discharge the cargo overboard. The cargo shall be jettisoned if the temperature rise of the cargo exceeds a rate of 2°C per hour over a 5-hour period or when the temperature in the tank exceeds 40°C.

15.5.1.9 Cargo tank venting systems shall have pressure/vacuum-relief valves for normal controlled venting, and rupture discs or a similar device for emergency venting, should tank pressure rise rapidly as a result of uncontrolled decomposition. Rupture discs shall be sized on the basis of tank design pressure, tank size and anticipated decomposition rate.

15.5.1.10 A fixed water-spray system shall be provided for diluting and washing away any concentrated hydrogen peroxide solution spilled on deck. The areas covered by the water-spray shall include the manifold/hose connections and the tank tops of those tanks designated for carrying hydrogen peroxide solutions. The minimum application rate shall satisfy the following criteria:

.1   The product shall be diluted from the original concentration to 35% by mass within 5 minutes of the spill.

.2   The rate and estimated size of the spill shall be based upon maximum anticipated loading and discharge rates, the time required to stop flow of cargo in the event of tank overfill or a piping/hose failure, and the time necessary to begin application of dilution water with actuation at the cargo control location or on the navigating bridge.

15.5.1.11 Only those hydrogen peroxide solutions which have a maximum decomposition rate of 1% per year at 25°C shall be carried. Certification from the shipper that the product meets this standard shall be presented to the master and kept on board. A technical representative of the manufacturer shall be on board to monitor the transfer operations and have the capability to test the stability of the hydrogen peroxide. He shall certify to the master that the cargo has been loaded in a stable condition.

15.5.1.12 Protective clothing that is resistant to hydrogen peroxide solutions shall be provided for each crew member involved in cargo-transfer operations. Protective clothing shall include non-flammable coveralls, suitable gloves, boots and eye protection.

15.5.2 Hydrogen peroxide solutions over 8% but not over 60% by mass

15.5.2.1 The ship's shell plating shall not form any boundaries of tanks containing this product.

15.5.2.2 Hydrogen peroxide shall be carried in tanks thoroughly and effectively cleaned of all traces of previous cargoes and their vapours or ballast. Procedures for inspection, cleaning, passivation and loading of tanks shall be in accordance with MSC/Circ.394. A certificate shall be on board the vessel indicating that the procedures in the circular have been followed. The passivation requirement may be waived by an Administration for domestic shipments of short duration. Particular care in this respect is essential to ensure the safe carriage of hydrogen peroxide:

.1 When hydrogen peroxide is carried, no other cargoes shall be carried simultaneously.

.2 Tanks which have contained hydrogen peroxide may be used for other cargoes after cleaning in accordance with the procedures outlined in MSC/Circ.394.

.3 Consideration in design shall provide minimum internal tank structure, free draining, no entrapment and ease of visual inspection.

15.5.2.3 Cargo tanks and associated equipment shall be either pure aluminium (99.5%) or solid stainless steel of types suitable for use with hydrogen peroxide (e.g., 304, 304L, 316, 316L, 316Ti). Aluminium shall not be used for piping on deck. All non-metallic materials of construction for the containment system shall neither be attacked by hydrogen peroxide nor contribute to its decomposition.

15.5.2.4 Cargo tanks shall be separated by a cofferdam from fuel oil tanks or any other space containing materials incompatible with hydrogen peroxide.

15.5.2.5 Temperature sensors shall be installed at the top and bottom of the tank. Remote temperature readouts and continuous monitoring shall be located on the navigating bridge. If the temperature in the tank rises above 35°C, visible and audible alarms shall activate on the navigating bridge.

15.5.2.6 Fixed oxygen monitors (or gas-sampling lines) shall be provided in void spaces adjacent to tanks to detect leakage of the cargo into these spaces. The enhancement of flammability by oxygen enrichment shall be recognized. Remote readouts, continuous monitoring (if gas-sampling lines are used, intermittent sampling is satisfactory) and visible and audible alarms similar to those for the temperature sensors shall also be located on the navigating bridge. The visible and audible alarms shall activate if the oxygen concentration in these void spaces exceeds 30% by volume. Two portable oxygen monitors shall also be available as back-up systems.

15.5.2.7 As a safeguard against uncontrolled decomposition, a cargo-jettisoning system shall be installed to discharge the cargo overboard. The cargo shall be jettisoned if the temperature rise of the cargo exceeds a rate of 2°C per hour over a 5-hour period or when the temperature in the tank exceeds 40°C.

15.5.2.8 Cargo tank venting systems with filtration shall have pressure/vacuum-relief valves for normal controlled venting, and a device for emergency venting, should tank pressure rise rapidly as a result of an uncontrolled decomposition rate, as stipulated in 15.5.2.7. These venting systems shall be designed in such a manner that there is no introduction of seawater into the cargo tank even under heavy sea conditions. Emergency venting shall be sized on the basis of tank design pressure and tank size.

15.5.2.9 A fixed water-spray system shall be provided for diluting and washing away any concentrated solution spilled on deck. The areas covered by the water-spray shall include the manifold/hose connections and the tank tops of those tanks designated for the carriage of hydrogen peroxide solutions. The minimum application rate shall satisfy the following criteria:

.1 The product shall be diluted from the original concentration to 35% by mass within 5 minutes of the spill.

.2 The rate and estimated size of the spill shall be based upon maximum anticipated loading and discharge rates, the time required to stop flow of the cargo in the event of tank overfill or a piping/hose failure, and the time necessary to begin application of dilution water with actuation at the cargo control location or on the navigating bridge.

15.5.2.10 Only those hydrogen peroxide solutions which have a maximum decomposition rate of 1% per year at 25°C shall be carried. Certification from the shipper that the product meets this standard shall be presented to the master and kept on board. A technical representative of the manufacturer shall be on board to monitor the transfer operations and have the capability to test the stability of the hydrogen peroxide. He shall certify to the master that the cargo has been loaded in a stable condition.

15.5.2.11 Protective clothing that is resistant to hydrogen peroxide shall be provided for each crew member involved in cargo-transfer operations. Protective clothing shall include coveralls that are non-flammable, suitable gloves, boots and eye protection.

15.5.2.12 During transfer of hydrogen peroxide, the related piping system shall be separated from all other systems. Cargo hoses used for transfer of hydrogen peroxide shall be marked "FOR HYDROGEN PEROXIDE TRANSFER ONLY".

15.5.3 **Procedures for inspection, cleaning, passivation and loading of tanks for the carriage of hydrogen peroxide solutions 8–60%, which have contained other cargoes, or for the carriage of other cargoes after the carriage of hydrogen peroxide**

15.5.3.1 Tanks having contained cargoes other than hydrogen peroxide shall be inspected, cleaned and passivated before re-use for the transport of hydrogen peroxide solutions. The procedures for inspection and cleaning, as given in 15.5.3.2 to 15.5.3.8 below, apply to both stainless steel and pure aluminium tanks (see 15.5.2.2). Procedures for passivation are given in 15.5.3.9 for stainless steel and 15.5.3.10 for aluminium. Unless otherwise specified, all steps apply to the tanks and to all associated equipment having been in contact with the other cargo.

15.5.3.2 After unloading the previous cargo, the tank shall be rendered safe and inspected for any residues, scale and rust.

15.5.3.3 Tanks and associated equipment shall be washed with clean filtered water. The water to be used shall at least have the quality of potable water with a low chlorine content.

15.5.3.4 Trace residues and vapours of the previous cargo shall be removed by steaming of tank and equipment.

15.5.3.5 Tank and equipment are washed again with clean water (quality as above) and dried, using filtered, oil-free air.

15.5.3.6 The atmosphere in the tank shall be sampled and investigated for the presence of organic vapours and oxygen concentration.

15.5.3.7 The tank shall be checked again by visual inspection for residues of the previous cargo, scale and rust as well as for any smell of the previous cargo.

15.5.3.8 If inspection or measurements indicate the presence of residues of the previous cargo or its vapours, actions described in 15.5.3.3 to 15.5.3.5 shall be repeated.

15.5.3.9 Tank and equipment made from stainless steel which have contained other cargoes than hydrogen peroxide or which have been under repair shall be cleaned and passivated, regardless of any previous passivation, according to the following procedure:

.1 New welds and other repaired parts shall be cleaned and finished using stainless steel wire brush, chisel, sandpaper or buff. Rough surfaces shall be given a smooth finish. A final polishing is necessary.

.2 Fatty and oily residues shall be removed by the use of appropriate organic solvents or detergent solutions in water. The use of chlorine-containing compounds shall be avoided as they can seriously interfere with passivation.

.3 The residues of the degreasing agent shall be removed, followed by a washing with water.

.4 In the next step, scale and rust shall be removed by the application of acid (e.g., a mixture of nitric and hydrofluoric acids), followed again by a washing with clean water.

.5 All the metal surfaces which can come into contact with hydrogen peroxide shall be passivated by the application of nitric acid of a concentration between 10 and 35% by mass. The nitric acid must be free from heavy metals, other oxidizing agents or hydrogen fluoride. The passivation process shall continue for 8 to 24 h, depending upon the concentration of acid, the ambient temperature and other factors. During this time a continuous contact between the surfaces to be passivated and the nitric acid shall be ensured. In the case of large surfaces this may be achieved by recirculating the acid. Hydrogen gas may be evolved in the passivation process, leading to the presence of an explosive atmosphere in the tanks. Therefore, appropriate measures must be taken to avoid the build-up or the ignition of such an atmosphere.

.6 After passivation, the surfaces shall be thoroughly washed with clean filtered water. The washing process shall be repeated until the effluent water has the same pH value as the incoming water.

.7 Surfaces treated according to the above steps may cause some decomposition when coming into contact with hydrogen peroxide for the first time. This decomposition will cease after a short time (usually within two or three days). Therefore an additional flushing with hydrogen peroxide for a period of at least two days is recommended.

.8 Only degreasing agents and acid cleaning agents which have been recommended for this purpose by the manufacturer of the hydrogen peroxide shall be used in the process.

15.5.3.10 Tanks and equipment made from aluminium and which have contained cargoes other than hydrogen peroxide, or which have been under repair, shall be cleaned and passivated. The following is an example of a recommended procedure:

.1 The tank shall be washed with a solution of a sulphonated detergent in hot water, followed by a washing with water.

.2 The surface shall then be treated for 15 to 20 minutes with a solution of sodium hydroxide of a concentration of 7% by mass or treated for a longer period with a less concentrated solution (e.g., for 12 h with 0.4 to 0.5% sodium hydroxide). To prevent excessive corrosion at the bottom of the tank when treating with more concentrated solutions of sodium hydroxide, water shall be added continuously to dilute the sodium hydroxide solution which collects there.

.3 The tank shall be thoroughly washed with clean, filtered water. As soon as possible after washing, the surface shall be passivated by the application of nitric acid of a concentration between 30 and 35% by mass. The passivation process shall continue for 16 to 24 h. During this time a continuous contact between the surfaces to be passivated and the nitric acid shall be ensured.

.4 After passivation the surfaces shall be thoroughly washed with clean, filtered water. The washing process shall be repeated until the effluent water has the same pH value as the incoming water.

.5 A visual inspection shall be made to ensure that all surfaces have been treated. It is recommended that an additional flushing is carried out for a minimum of 24 h with dilute hydrogen peroxide solution of a concentration approximately 3% by mass.

15.5.3.11 The concentration and stability of the hydrogen peroxide solution to be loaded shall be determined.

15.5.3.12 The hydrogen peroxide is loaded under intermittent visual supervision of the interior of the tank from an appropriate opening.

15.5.3.13 If substantial bubbling is observed which does not disappear within 15 minutes after the completion of loading, the contents of the tank shall be unloaded and disposed of in an environmentally safe manner. The tank and equipment shall then be repassivated as described above.

15.5.3.14 The concentration and stability of the hydrogen peroxide solution shall be determined again. If the same values are obtained within the limits of error as in 15.5.3.10, the tank is considered to be properly passivated and the cargo ready for shipment.

15.5.3.15 Actions described in 15.5.3.2 to 15.5.3.8 shall be carried out under the supervision of the master or shipper. Actions described in 15.5.3.9 to 15.5.3.14 shall be carried out under the on-site supervision and responsibility of a representative of the hydrogen peroxide manufacturer or under supervision and responsibility of another person familiar with the safety-relevant properties of hydrogen peroxide.

15.5.3.16 The following procedure shall be applied when tanks having contained hydrogen peroxide solution are to be used for other products (unless otherwise specified, all steps apply to the tanks and to all associated equipment having been in contact with hydrogen peroxide):

.1 Hydrogen peroxide cargo residue shall be drained as completely as possible from tanks and equipment.

.2 Tanks and equipment shall be rinsed with clean water, and subsequently thoroughly washed with clean water.

.3 The interior of the tank shall be dried and inspected for any residues.

Steps .1 to .3, in 15.5.3.16, shall be carried out under the supervision of the master or the shipper. Step .3 in 15.5.3.16 shall be carried out by a person familiar with the safety-relevant properties of the chemical to be transported and of hydrogen peroxide.

SPECIAL CAUTIONS: 1 Hydrogen peroxide decomposition may enrich the atmosphere with oxygen and appropriate precautions shall be observed.

2 Hydrogen gas may be evolved in the passivation processes described in 15.5.3.9.5, 15.5.3.10.2 and 15.5.3.10.4, leading to the presence of an explosive atmosphere in the tank. Therefore, appropriate measures must be taken to avoid the build-up or the ignition of such an atmosphere.

15.6   Motor fuel anti-knock compounds (containing lead alkyls)

15.6.1   Tanks used for these cargoes shall not be used for the transportation of any other cargo except those commodities to be used in the manufacture of motor fuel anti-knock compounds containing lead alkyls.

15.6.2   If a cargo pump-room is located on deck level according to 15.18, the ventilation arrangements shall be in compliance with 15.17.

15.6.3   Entry into cargo tanks used for the transportation of these cargoes is not permitted unless approved by the Administration.

15.6.4   Air analysis shall be made for lead content to determine if the atmosphere is satisfactory prior to allowing personnel to enter the cargo pump-room or void spaces surrounding the cargo tank.

15.7   Phosphorus, yellow or white

15.7.1   Phosphorus shall, at all times, be loaded, carried and discharged under a water pad of 760 mm minimum depth. During discharge operations, arrangements shall be made to ensure that water occupies the volume of phosphorus discharged. Any water discharged from a phosphorus tank shall be returned only to a shore installation.

15.7.2   Tanks shall be designed and tested to a minimum equivalent water head of 2.4 m above the top of the tank, under designed loading conditions, taking into account the depth, relative density and method of loading and discharge of the phosphorus.

15.7.3   Tanks shall be so designed as to minimize the interfacial area between the liquid phosphorus and its water pad.

15.7.4   A minimum ullage space of 1% shall be maintained above the water pad. The ullage space shall be filled with inert gas or naturally ventilated by two cowled standpipes terminating at different heights but at least 6 m above the deck and at least 2 m above the pump-house top.

15.7.5   All openings shall be at the top of cargo tanks, and fittings and joints attached thereto shall be of materials resistant to phosphorus pentoxide.

15.7.6   Phosphorus shall be loaded at a temperature not exceeding 60°C.

15.7.7   Tank heating arrangements shall be external to tanks and have a suitable method of temperature control to ensure that the temperature of the phosphorus does not exceed 60°C. A high-temperature alarm shall be fitted.

15.7.8   A water drench system acceptable to the Administration shall be installed in all void spaces surrounding the tanks. The system shall operate automatically in the event of an escape of phosphorus.

15.7.9   Void spaces referred to in 15.7.8 shall be provided with effective means of mechanical ventilation which shall be capable of being sealed off quickly in an emergency.

15.7.10   Loading and discharge of phosphorus shall be governed by a central system on the ship which, in addition to incorporating high-level alarms, shall ensure that no overflow of tanks is possible and that such operations can be stopped quickly in an emergency from either ship or shore.

15.7.11 During cargo transfer, a water hose on deck shall be connected to a water supply and kept flowing throughout the operation so that any spillage of phosphorus may be washed down with water immediately.

15.7.12 Ship-to-shore loading and discharge connections shall be of a type approved by the Administration.

15.8 Propylene oxide or ethylene oxide/propylene oxide mixtures with an ethylene oxide content of not more than 30% by mass

15.8.1 Products transported under the provisions of this section shall be acetylene-free.

15.8.2 Unless cargo tanks are properly cleaned, these products shall not be carried in tanks which have contained as one of the three previous cargoes any products known to catalyse polymerization, such as:

    .1 mineral acids (e.g., sulphuric, hydrochloric, nitric);

    .2 carboxylic acids and anhydrides (e.g., formic, acetic);

    .3 halogenated carboxylic acids (e.g., chloracetic);

    .4 sulphonic acids (e.g., benzenesulphonic);

    .5 caustic alkalis (e.g., sodium hydroxide, potassium hydroxide);

    .6 ammonia and ammonia solutions;

    .7 amines and amine solutions; and

    .8 oxidizing substances.

15.8.3 Before loading, tanks shall be thoroughly and effectively cleaned, to remove all traces of previous cargoes from tanks and associated pipework, except where the immediately prior cargo has been propylene oxide or ethylene oxide/propylene oxide mixtures. Particular care shall be taken in the case of ammonia in tanks made of steel other than stainless steel.

15.8.4 In all cases, the effectiveness of cleaning procedures for tanks and associated pipework shall be checked by suitable testing or inspection, to ascertain that no traces of acidic or alkaline materials remain that might create a hazardous situation in the presence of these products.

15.8.5 Tanks shall be entered and inspected prior to each initial loading of these products to ensure freedom from contamination, heavy rust deposits and visible structural defects. When cargo tanks are in continuous service for these products, such inspections shall be performed at intervals of not more than two years.

15.8.6 Tanks for the carriage of these products shall be of steel or stainless steel construction.

15.8.7 Tanks for the carriage of these products may be used for other cargoes after thorough cleaning of tanks and associated pipework systems by washing or purging.

15.8.8 All valves, flanges, fittings and accessory equipment shall be of a type suitable for use with the products and shall be constructed of steel or stainless steel in accordance with recognized standards. Discs or disc faces, seats and other wearing parts of valves shall be made of stainless steel containing not less than 11% chromium.

15.8.9 Gaskets shall be constructed of materials which do not react with, dissolve in, or lower the autoignition temperature of these products and which are fire-resistant and possess adequate mechanical behaviour. The surface presented to the cargo shall be polytetrafluoroethylene (PTFE), or materials giving a similar degree of safety by their inertness. Spirally wound stainless steel, with a filler of PTFE or similar fluorinated polymer, may be accepted.

15.8.10 Insulation and packing, if used, shall be of a material which does not react with, dissolve in, or lower the autoignition temperature of these products.

15.8.11 The following materials are generally found unsatisfactory for gaskets, packing and similar uses in containment systems for these products and would require testing before being approved by the Administration:

    .1 neoprene or natural rubber, if it comes into contact with the products;

    .2 asbestos, or binders used with asbestos;

    .3 materials containing oxides of magnesium, such as mineral wools.

15.8.12   Threaded joints shall not be permitted in the cargo liquid and vapour lines.

15.8.13   Filling and discharge piping shall extend to within 100 mm of the bottom of the tank or any sump pit.

15.8.14.1   The containment system for a tank containing these products shall have a valved vapour-return connection.

15.8.14.2   The products shall be loaded and discharged in such a manner that venting of the tanks to atmosphere does not occur. If vapour return to shore is used during tank loading, the vapour-return system connected to a containment system for the product shall be independent of all other containment systems.

15.8.14.3   During discharge operations, the pressure in the cargo tank must be maintained above 0.007 MPa gauge.

15.8.15   The cargo may be discharged only by deepwell pumps, hydraulically operated submerged pumps, or inert-gas displacement. Each cargo pump shall be arranged to ensure that the product does not heat significantly if the discharge line from the pump is shut off or otherwise blocked.

15.8.16   Tanks carrying these products shall be vented independently of tanks carrying other products. Facilities shall be provided for sampling the tank contents without opening the tank to atmosphere.

15.8.17   Cargo hoses used for transfer of these products shall be marked "FOR ALKYLENE OXIDE TRANSFER ONLY".

15.8.18   Cargo tanks, void spaces and other enclosed spaces adjacent to an integral gravity cargo tank carrying propylene oxide shall either contain a compatible cargo (those cargoes specified in 15.8.2 are examples of substances considered incompatible) or be inerted by injection of a suitable inert gas. Any hold space in which an independent cargo tank is located shall be inerted. Such inerted spaces and tanks shall be monitored for these products and oxygen. The oxygen content of these spaces shall be maintained below 2%. Portable sampling equipment is satisfactory.

15.8.19   In no case shall air be allowed to enter the cargo pump or piping system while these products are contained within the system.

15.8.20   Prior to disconnecting shore-lines, the pressure in liquid and vapour lines shall be relieved through suitable valves installed at the loading header. Liquid and vapour from these lines shall not be discharged to atmosphere.

15.8.21   Propylene oxide may be carried in pressure tanks or in independent or integral gravity tanks. Ethylene oxide/propylene oxide mixtures shall be carried in independent gravity tanks or pressure tanks. Tanks shall be designed for the maximum pressure expected to be encountered during loading, conveying and discharging cargo.

15.8.22.1   Tanks for the carriage of propylene oxide with a design pressure less than 0.06 MPa gauge and tanks for the carriage of ethylene oxide/propylene oxide mixtures with a design pressure of less than 0.12 MPa gauge shall have a cooling system to maintain the cargo below the reference temperature.

15.8.22.2   The refrigeration requirement for tanks with a design pressure less than 0.06 MPa gauge may be waived by the Administration for ships operating in restricted areas or on voyages of restricted duration, and account may be taken in such cases of any insulation of the tanks. The area and times of year for which such carriage would be permitted shall be included in the conditions of carriage of the International Certificate of Fitness for the Carriage of Dangerous Chemicals in Bulk.

15.8.23.1   Any cooling system shall maintain the liquid temperature below the boiling temperature at the containment pressure. At least two complete cooling plants, automatically regulated by variations within the tanks, shall be provided. Each cooling plant shall be complete with the necessary auxiliaries for proper operation. The control system shall also be capable of being manually operated. An alarm shall be provided to indicate malfunctioning of the temperature controls. The capacity of each cooling system shall be sufficient to maintain the temperature of the liquid cargo below the reference temperature of the system.

15.8.23.2   An alternative arrangement may consist of three cooling plants, any two of which shall be sufficient to maintain the liquid temperature below the reference temperature.

15.8.23.3 Cooling media which are separated from the products by a single wall only shall be non-reactive with the products.

15.8.23.4 Cooling systems requiring compression of the products shall not be used.

15.8.24 Pressure-relief-valve settings shall not be less than 0.02 MPa gauge and for pressure tanks not greater than 0.7 MPa gauge for the carriage of propylene oxide and not greater than 0.53 MPa gauge for the carriage of propylene oxide/ethylene oxide mixtures.

15.8.25.1 The piping system for tanks to be loaded with these products shall be separated (as defined in 3.1.4) from piping systems for all other tanks, including empty tanks. If the piping system for the tanks to be loaded is not independent (as defined in 1.3.18), the required piping separation shall be accomplished by the removal of spool-pieces, valves, or other pipe section and the installation of blank flanges at these locations. The required separation applies to all liquid and vapour piping, liquid and vapour vent lines and any other possible connections, such as common inert-gas supply lines.

15.8.25.2 These products may be transported only in accordance with cargo-handling plans that have been approved by the Administration. Each intended loading arrangement shall be shown on a separate cargo-handling plan. Cargo-handling plans shall show the entire cargo piping system and the locations for installation of blank flanges needed to meet the above piping separation requirements. A copy of each approved cargo-handling plan shall be maintained on board the ship. The International Certificate of Fitness for the Carriage of Dangerous Chemicals in Bulk shall be endorsed to include reference to the approved cargo-handling plans.

15.8.25.3 Before each initial loading of these products and before every subsequent return to such service, certification verifying that the required piping separation has been achieved shall be obtained from a responsible person acceptable to the port Administration and carried on board the ship. Each connection between a blank flange and a pipeline flange shall be fitted with a wire and seal by the responsible person to ensure that inadvertent removal of the blank flange is impossible.

15.8.26.1 No cargo tanks shall be more than 98% liquid-full at the reference temperature.

15.8.26.2 The maximum volume to which a cargo tank shall be loaded is:

$$V_L = 0.98V \frac{\rho_R}{\rho_L}$$

where

V_L = maximum volume to which the tank may be loaded

V = volume of the tank

ρ_R = density of cargo at the reference temperature

ρ_L = density of cargo at the loading temperature and pressure

15.8.26.3 The maximum allowable tank filling limits for each cargo tank shall be indicated for each loading temperature which may be applied and for the applicable maximum reference temperature, on a list to be approved by the Administration. A copy of the list shall be permanently kept on board by the master.

15.8.27 The cargo shall be carried under a suitable protective padding of nitrogen gas. An automatic nitrogen make-up system shall be installed to prevent the tank pressure falling below 0.007 MPa gauge in the event of product temperature fall due to ambient conditions or maloperation of refrigeration systems. Sufficient nitrogen shall be available on board to satisfy the demand of the automatic pressure control. Nitrogen of commercially pure quality (99.9% by volume) shall be used for padding. A battery of nitrogen bottles connected to the cargo tanks through a pressure-reduction valve satisfies the intention of the expression "automatic" in this context.

15.8.28 The cargo tank vapour space shall be tested prior to and after loading to ensure that the oxygen content is 2% by volume or less.

15.8.29 A water-spray system of sufficient capacity shall be provided to blanket effectively the area surrounding the loading manifold, the exposed deck piping associated with product handling, and the tank domes. The arrangement of piping and nozzles shall be such as to give a uniform distribution rate of 10 ℓ/m^2/min. Remote manual operation shall be arranged such that remote starting of pumps supplying the water-spray system and remote operation of any normally closed valves in the system can be carried out from a suitable location outside the cargo area, adjacent to the accommodation spaces and readily accessible and operable in the event of fire in the areas protected. The water-spray system shall be capable of both local and remote manual operation, and the arrangement shall ensure that any spilled cargo is washed away. Additionally, a water hose with pressure to the nozzle, when atmospheric temperatures permit, shall be connected ready for immediate use during loading and unloading operations.

15.8.30 A remotely operated, controlled closing-rate, shutoff valve shall be provided at each cargo-hose connection used during cargo transfer.

15.9 Sodium chlorate solution (50% or less by mass)

15.9.1 Tanks and associated equipment which have contained this product may be used for other cargoes after thorough cleaning by washing or purging.

15.9.2 In the event of spillage of this product, all spilled liquid shall be thoroughly washed away without delay. To minimize fire risk, spillage shall not be allowed to dry out.

15.10 Sulphur (molten)

15.10.1 Cargo tank ventilation shall be provided to maintain the concentration of hydrogen sulphide below one half of its lower explosive limit throughout the cargo tank vapour space for all conditions of carriage (i.e., below 1.85% by volume).

15.10.2 Where mechanical ventilation systems are used for maintaining low gas concentrations in cargo tanks, an alarm system shall be provided to give warning if the system fails.

15.10.3 Ventilation systems shall be so designed and arranged as to preclude depositing of sulphur within the system.

15.10.4 Openings to void spaces adjacent to cargo tanks shall be so designed and fitted as to prevent the entry of water, sulphur or cargo vapour.

15.10.5 Connections shall be provided to permit sampling and analysing of vapour in void spaces.

15.10.6 Cargo temperature controls shall be provided to ensure that the temperature of the sulphur does not exceed 155°C.

15.10.7 Sulphur (molten) has a flashpoint above 60°C ; however, electrical equipment shall be certified safe for gases evolved.

15.11 Acids

15.11.1 The ship's shell plating shall not form any boundaries of tanks containing mineral acids.

15.11.2 Proposals for lining steel tanks and related piping systems with corrosion-resistant materials may be considered by the Administration. The elasticity of the lining shall not be less than that of the supporting boundary plating.

15.11.3 Unless constructed wholly of corrosion-resistant materials or fitted with an approved lining, the plating thickness shall take into account the corrosivity of the cargo.

15.11.4 Flanges of the loading and discharge manifold connections shall be provided with shields, which may be portable, to guard against the danger of the cargo being sprayed; and in addition, drip trays shall also be provided to guard against leakage onto the deck.

15.11.5 Because of the danger of evolution of hydrogen when these substances are being carried, the electrical arrangements shall comply with 10.1.4. The certified safe type equipment shall be suitable for use in hydrogen/air mixtures. Other sources of ignition shall not be permitted in such spaces.

15.11.6 Substances subjected to the requirements of this section shall be segregated from oil fuel tanks, in addition to the segregation requirements in 3.1.1.

15.11.7 Provision shall be made for suitable apparatus to detect leakage of cargo into adjacent spaces.

15.11.8 The cargo pump-room bilge pumping and drainage arrangements shall be of corrosion-resistant materials.

15.12   Toxic products

15.12.1 Exhaust openings of tank vent systems shall be located:

.1   at a height of $B/3$ or 6 m, whichever is greater, above the weather deck or, in the case of a deck tank, the access gangway;

.2   not less than 6 m above the fore-and-aft gangway, if fitted within 6 m of the gangway;

.3   15 m from any opening or air intake to any accommodation and service spaces; and

.4   the vent height may be reduced to 3 m above the deck or fore-and-aft gangway, as applicable, provided high-velocity vent valves of an approved type, directing the vapour/air mixture upwards in an unimpeded jet with an exit velocity of at least 30 m/s, are fitted.

15.12.2 Tank venting systems shall be provided with a connection for a vapour-return line to the shore installation.

15.12.3 Products shall:

.1   not be stowed adjacent to oil fuel tanks;

.2   have separate piping systems; and

.3   have tank vent systems separate from tanks containing non-toxic products.

15.12.4 Cargo tank relief-valve settings shall be a minimum of 0.02 MPa gauge.

15.13   Cargoes protected by additives

15.13.1 Certain cargoes with a reference in *column o* in the table of chapter 17, by the nature of their chemical make-up, tend, under certain conditions of temperature, exposure to air or contact with a catalyst, to undergo polymerization, decomposition, oxidation or other chemical changes. Mitigation of this tendency is carried out by introducing small amounts of chemical additives into the liquid cargo or controlling the cargo tank environment.

15.13.2 Ships carrying these cargoes shall be so designed as to eliminate from the cargo tanks and cargo-handling system any material of construction or contaminants which could act as a catalyst or destroy the inhibitor.

15.13.3 Care shall be taken to ensure that these cargoes are sufficiently protected to prevent deleterious chemical change at all times during the voyage. Ships carrying such cargoes shall be provided with a certificate of protection from the manufacturer, and kept during the voyage, specifying:

.1   the name and amount of additive present;

.2   whether the additive is oxygen-dependent;

.3   date additive was put in the product and duration of effectiveness;

.4   any temperature limitations qualifying the additive's effective lifetime; and

.5   the action to be taken should the length of voyage exceed the effective lifetime of the additives.

15.13.4 Ships using the exclusion of air as the method of preventing oxidation of the cargo shall comply with 9.1.3.

15.13.5 A product containing an oxygen-dependent additive shall be carried without inertion (in tanks of a size not greater than 3,000 m^3). Such cargoes shall not be carried in a tank requiring inertion under the requirements of SOLAS chapter II-2.*

15.13.6 Venting systems shall be of a design that eliminates blockage from polymer build-up. Venting equipment shall be of a type that can be checked periodically for adequacy of operation.

---

* For equivalency arrangements for the carriage of styrene monomer, see MSC/Circ.879 as amended by MSC/Circ.879/Corr.1.

15.13.7 Crystallization or solidification of cargoes normally carried in the molten state can lead to depletion of inhibitor in parts of the tank's contents. Subsequent remelting can thus yield pockets of uninhibited liquid, with the accompanying risk of dangerous polymerization. To prevent this, care shall be taken to ensure that at no time are such cargoes allowed to crystallize or solidify, either wholly or partially, in any part of the tank. Any required heating arrangements shall be such as to ensure that in no part of the tank does cargo become overheated to such an extent that any dangerous polymerization can be initiated. If the temperature from steam coils would induce overheating, an indirect low-temperature heating system shall be used.

15.14 Cargoes with a vapour pressure greater than 0.1013 MPa absolute at 37.8°C

15.14.1 For a cargo referenced in *column o* in the table of chapter 17 to this section, a mechanical refrigeration system shall be provided unless the cargo system is designed to withstand the vapour pressure of the cargo at 45°C. Where the cargo system is designed to withstand the vapour pressure of the cargo at 45°C, and no refrigeration system is provided, a notation shall be made in the conditions of carriage on the International Certificate of Fitness for the Carriage of Dangerous Chemicals in Bulk to indicate the required relief-valve setting for the tanks.

15.14.2 A mechanical refrigeration system shall maintain the liquid temperature below the boiling temperature at the cargo tank design pressure.

15.14.3 When ships operate in restricted areas and at restricted times of the year, or on voyages of limited duration, the Administration involved may agree to waive requirements for a refrigeration system. A notation of any such agreement, listing geographic area restrictions and times of the year, or voyage duration limitations, shall be included in the conditions of carriage on the International Certificate of Fitness for the Carriage of Dangerous Chemicals in Bulk.

15.14.4 Connections shall be provided for returning expelled gases to shore during loading.

15.14.5 Each tank shall be provided with a pressure gauge which indicates the pressure in the vapour space above the cargo.

15.14.6 Where the cargo needs to be cooled, thermometers shall be provided at the top and bottom of each tank.

15.14.7.1 No cargo tanks shall be more than 98% liquid-full at the reference temperature (R).

15.14.7.2 The maximum volume (V_L) of cargo to be loaded in a tank shall be:

$$V_L = 0.98V \frac{\rho_R}{\rho_L}$$

where

V = volume of the tank

ρ_R = density of cargo at the reference temperature (R)

ρ_L = density of cargo at the loading temperature

15.14.7.3 The maximum allowable tank filling limits for each cargo tank shall be indicated for each loading temperature which may be applied, and for the applicable maximum reference temperature, on a list approved by the Administration. A copy of the list shall be permanently kept on board by the master.

15.15 Cargoes with low ignition temperature and wide flammability range

Deleted.

15.16 Cargo contamination

15.16.1 *Deleted.*

15.16.2 Where *column o* in the table of chapter 17 refers to this section, water shall not be allowed to contaminate this cargo. In addition, the following provisions apply:

.1 Air inlets to pressure/vacuum-relief valves of tanks containing the cargo shall be situated at least 2 m above the weather deck.

.2 Water or steam shall not be used as the heat-transfer media in a cargo temperature control system required by chapter 7.

.3 The cargo shall not be carried in cargo tanks adjacent to permanent ballast or water tanks unless the tanks are empty and dry.

.4 The cargo shall not be carried in tanks adjacent to slop tanks or cargo tanks containing ballast or slops or other cargoes containing water which may react in a dangerous manner. Pumps, pipes or vent lines serving such tanks shall be separate from similar equipment serving tanks containing the cargo. Pipelines from slop tanks or ballast lines shall not pass through tanks containing the cargo unless encased in a tunnel.

15.17 Increased ventilation requirements

For certain products, the ventilation system as described in 12.1.3 shall have a minimum capacity of at least 45 changes of air per hour, based upon the total volume of space. The ventilation system exhaust ducts shall discharge at least 10 m away from openings into accommodation spaces, work areas or other similar spaces, and intakes to ventilation systems, and at least 4 m above the tank deck.

15.18 Special cargo pump-room requirements

For certain products, the cargo pump-room shall be located on the deck level or cargo pumps shall be located in the cargo tank. The Administration may give special consideration to cargo pump-rooms below deck.

15.19 Overflow control

15.19.1 The provisions of this section are applicable where specific reference is made in *column o* in the table of chapter 17, and are in addition to the requirements for gauging devices.

15.19.2 In the event of a power failure on any system essential for safe loading, an alarm shall be given to the operators concerned.

15.19.3 Loading operations shall be terminated at once in the event of any system essential for safe loading becoming inoperative.

15.19.4 Level alarms shall be capable of being tested prior to loading.

15.19.5 The high-level alarm system required under 15.19.6 shall be independent of the overflow-control system required by 15.19.7 and shall be independent of the equipment required by 13.1.

15.19.6 Cargo tanks shall be fitted with a visual and audible high-level alarm which complies with 15.19.1 to 15.19.5 and which indicates when the liquid level in the cargo tank approaches the normal full condition.

15.19.7 A tank overflow-control system required by this section shall:

.1 come into operation when the normal tank loading procedures fail to stop the tank liquid level exceeding the normal full condition;

.2 give a visual and audible tank-overflow alarm to the ship's operator; and

.3 provide an agreed signal for sequential shutdown of onshore pumps or valves or both and of the ship's valves. The signal, as well as the pump and valve shutdown, may be dependent on operator's intervention. The use of shipboard automatic closing valves shall be permitted only when specific approval has been obtained from the Administration and the port State authority concerned.

15.19.8 The loading rate (*LR*) of the tank shall not exceed:

$$LR = \frac{3600U}{t} \ (\text{m}^3/\text{h})$$

where

U = ullage volume (m^3) at operating signal level;

t = time(s) needed from the initiating signal to fully stopping the cargo flow into the tank, being the sum of times needed for each step in sequential operations such as operator's responses to signals, stopping pumps and closing valves;

and shall also take into account the pipeline system design pressure.

15.20 Alkyl (C₇–C₉) nitrates, all isomers

15.20.1 The carriage temperature of the cargo shall be maintained below 100°C to prevent the occurrence of a self-sustaining, exothermic decomposition reaction.

15.20.2 The cargo may not be carried in independent pressure vessels permanently affixed to the vessel's deck unless:

  .1 the tanks are sufficiently insulated from fire; and

  .2 the vessel has a water deluge system for the tanks such that the cargo temperature is maintained below 100°C and the temperature rise in the tanks does not exceed 1.5°C per hour for a fire of 650°C.

15.21 Temperature sensors

Temperature sensors shall be used to monitor the cargo pump temperature to detect overheating due to pump failures.

Chapter 16

Operational requirements

16.1 Maximum allowable quantity of cargo per tank

16.1.1 The quantity of a cargo required to be carried in a type 1 ship shall not exceed 1,250 m³ in any one tank.

16.1.2 The quantity of cargo required to be carried in a type 2 ship shall not exceed 3,000 m³ in any one tank.

16.1.3 Tanks carrying liquids at ambient temperatures shall be so loaded as to avoid the tank becoming liquid-full during the voyage, having due regard to the highest temperature which the cargo may reach.

16.2 Cargo information

16.2.1 A copy of this Code, or national regulations incorporating the provisions of this Code, shall be on board every ship covered by this Code.

16.2.2 Any cargo offered for bulk shipment shall be indicated in the shipping documents by the product name under which it is listed in chapter 17 or 18 of the Code or the latest edition of MEPC.2/Circ. or under which it has been provisionally assessed. Where the cargo is a mixture, an analysis indicating the dangerous components contributing significantly to the total hazard of the product shall be provided, or a complete analysis if this is available. Such an analysis shall be certified by the manufacturer or by an independent expert acceptable to the Administration.

16.2.3.1 Information shall be on board, and available to all concerned, giving the necessary data for the safe carriage of the cargo in bulk. Such information shall include a cargo stowage plan, to be kept in an accessible place, indicating all cargo on board, including, for each dangerous chemical carried:

    .1 a full description of the physical and chemical properties, including reactivity, necessary for the safe containment of the cargo;

    .2 action to be taken in the event of spills or leaks;

    .3 countermeasures against accidental personal contact;

    .4 fire-fighting procedures and fire-fighting media; and

    .5 procedures for cargo transfer, tank cleaning, gas-freeing and ballasting.

16.2.3.2 For those cargoes required to be stabilized or inhibited, the cargo shall be refused if the appropriate certificate required by 16.2.3.7 is not supplied.

16.2.4 If sufficient information, necessary for the safe transportation of the cargo, is not available, the cargo shall be refused.

16.2.5 Cargoes which evolve highly toxic imperceptible vapours shall not be transported unless perceptible additives are introduced into the cargo.

16.2.6 Where *column o* in the table of chapter 17 refers to this paragraph, the cargo's viscosity at 20°C shall be specified on a shipping document, and if the cargo's viscosity exceeds 50 mPa·s at 20°C, the temperature at which the cargo has a viscosity of 50 mPa·s shall be specified in the shipping document.

16.2.7 *Deleted.*

16.2.8 *Deleted.*

16.2.9 Where *column o* in the table of chapter 17 refers to this paragraph, the cargo's melting point shall be indicated in the shipping document.

16.3 Personnel training

16.3.1 All personnel shall be adequately trained in the use of protective equipment and have basic training in the procedures appropriate to their duties necessary under emergency conditions.

16.3.2 Personnel involved in cargo operations shall be adequately trained in handling procedures.

16.3.3 Officers shall be trained in emergency procedures to deal with conditions of leakage, spillage or fire involving the cargo and a sufficient number of them shall be instructed and trained in essential first aid for cargoes carried, based on the guidelines developed by the Organization.*

16.4 Opening of and entry into cargo tanks

16.4.1 During handling and carriage of cargoes producing flammable and/or toxic vapours or when ballasting after the discharge of such cargo, or when loading or unloading cargo, cargo tank lids shall always be kept closed. With any hazardous cargo, cargo tank lids, ullage and sighting ports and tank washing access covers shall be open only when necessary.

16.4.2 Personnel shall not enter cargo tanks, void spaces around such tanks, cargo-handling spaces or other enclosed spaces unless:

.1 the compartment is free of toxic vapours and not deficient in oxygen; or

.2 personnel wear breathing apparatus and other necessary protective equipment, and the entire operation is under the close supervision of a responsible officer.

16.4.3 Personnel shall not enter such spaces when the only hazard is of a purely flammable nature, except under the close supervision of a responsible officer.

16.5 Stowage of cargo samples

16.5.1 Samples which have to be kept on board shall be stowed in a designated space situated in the cargo area or, exceptionally, elsewhere, subject to the approval of the Administration.

16.5.2 The stowage space shall be:

.1 cell-divided in order to avoid shifting of the bottles at sea;

.2 made of material fully resistant to the different liquids intended to be stowed; and

.3 equipped with adequate ventilation arrangements.

16.5.3 Samples which react with each other dangerously shall not be stowed close to each other.

16.5.4 Samples shall not be retained on board longer than necessary.

16.6 Cargoes not to be exposed to excessive heat

16.6.1 Where the possibility exists of a dangerous reaction of a cargo, such as polymerization, decomposition, thermal instability or evolution of gas, resulting from local overheating of the cargo in either the tank or associated pipelines, such cargo shall be loaded and carried adequately segregated from other products whose temperature is sufficiently high to initiate a reaction of such cargo (see 7.1.5.4).

16.6.2 Heating coils in tanks carrying this product shall be blanked off or secured by equivalent means.

16.6.3 Heat-sensitive products shall not be carried in deck tanks which are not insulated.

16.6.4 In order to avoid elevated temperatures, this cargo shall not be carried in deck tanks.

---

* Refer to the Medical First Aid Guide for Use in Accidents Involving Dangerous Goods (MFAG), which provides advice on the treatment of casualties in accordance with the symptoms exhibited as well as equipment and antidotes that may be appropriate for treating the casualty, and to the relevant provisions of the STCW Code, parts A and B.

Chapter 17

Summary of minimum requirements

Mixtures of noxious liquid substances presenting pollution hazards only, and which are assessed or provisionally assessed under regulation 6.3 of MARPOL Annex II, may be carried under the requirements of the Code applicable to the appropriate position of the entry in this chapter for Noxious Liquid Substances, not otherwise specified (n.o.s.).

EXPLANATORY NOTES

Product name *(column a)*	The product name shall be used in the shipping document for any cargo offered for bulk shipments. Any additional name may be included in brackets after the product name. In some cases, the product names are not identical with the names given in previous issues of the Code.
UN Number *(column b)*	*Deleted*
Pollution Category *(column c)*	The letter X, Y, Z means the Pollution Category assigned to each product under MARPOL Annex II
Hazards *(column d)*	"S" means that the product is included in the Code because of its safety hazards; "P" means that the product is included in the Code because of its pollution hazards; and "S/P" means that the product is included in the Code because of both its safety and pollution hazards.

Ship type
(column e)

1:	ship type 1 (2.1.2.1)
2:	ship type 2 (2.1.2.2)
3:	ship type 3 (2.1.2.3)

Tank type
(column f)

1:	independent tank (4.1.1)
2:	integral tank (4.1.2)
G:	gravity tank (4.1.3)
P:	pressure tank (4.1.4)

Tank vents
(column g)

Cont.:	controlled venting
Open:	open venting

Tank environmental control
(column h)

Inert:	inerting (9.1.2.1)
Pad:	liquid or gas padding (9.1.2.2)
Dry:	drying (9.1.2.3)
Vent:	natural or forced ventilation (9.1.2.4)
No:	no special requirements under this Code

Electrical equipment
(column i)

Temperature classes (i')	T1 to T6	
	–	indicates no requirements
	blank	no information
Apparatus group (i'')	IIA, IIB or IIC:	
	–	indicates no requirements
	blank	no information
Flashpoint (i''')	Yes:	flashpoint exceeding 60°C (10.1.6)
	No:	flashpoint not exceeding 60°C (10.1.6)
	NF:	non-flammable product (10.1.6)

Gauging *(column j)*	O: R: C:	open gauging (13.1.1.1) restricted gauging (13.1.1.2) closed gauging (13.1.1.3)
Vapour detection *(column k)*	F: T: No:	flammable vapours toxic vapours indicates no special requirements under this Code
Fire protection *(column l)*	A: B: C: D: No:	alcohol-resistant foam or multi-purpose foam regular foam; encompasses all foams that are not of an alcohol-resistant type, including fluoro-protein and aqueous-film-forming foam (AFFF) water-spray dry chemical no special requirements under this Code
Materials of construction *(column m)*	*Deleted*	
Emergency equipment *(column n)*	Yes: No:	see 14.3.1 no special requirements under this Code
Specific and operational requirements *(column o)*	When specific reference is made to chapters 15 and/or 16, these requirements shall be additional to the requirements in any other column	

a	c	d	e	f	g	h	i'	i''	i'''	j	k	l	n	o
Acetic acid	Z	S/P	3	2G	Cont	No	T1	IIA	No	R	F	A	Yes	15.11.2, 15.11.3, 15.11.4, 15.11.6, 15.11.7, 15.11.8, 15.19.6, 16.2.9
Acetic anhydride	Z	S/P	2	2G	Cont	No	T2	IIA	No	R	F-T	A	Yes	15.11.2, 15.11.3, 15.11.4, 15.11.6, 15.11.7, 15.11.8, 15.19.6
Acetochlor (n)	X	P	2	2G	Open	No			Yes	O	No	A	No	15.19.6, 16.2.6, 16.2.9
Acetone cyanohydrin	Y	S/P	2	2G	Cont	No	T1	IIA	Yes	C	T	A	Yes	15.12, 15.13, 15.17, 15.18, 15.19, 16.6.1, 16.6.2, 16.6.3
Acetonitrile	Z	S/P	2	2G	Cont	No	T2	IIA	No	R	F-T	A	No	15.12, 15.19.6
Acetonitrile (low purity grade) (n)	Y	S/P	3	2G	Cont	No	T1	IIA	No	R	F-T	A, C	No	15.12.3, 15.12.4, 15.19.6
Acid oil mixture from soyabean, corn (maize) and sunflower oil refining (n)	Y	S/P	2	2G	Open	No	-	-	Yes	O	No	A, B, C	No	15.19.6, 16.2.6, 16.2.9
Acrylamide solution (50% or less) (n)	Y	S/P	2	2G	Open	No			NF	C	No	No	No	15.12.3, 15.13, 15.19.6, 16.2.9, 16.6.1
Acrylic acid (n)	Y	S/P	2	2G	Cont	No	T2	IIA	No	C	F-T	A	Yes	15.11.2, 15.11.3, 15.11.4, 15.11.6, 15.11.7, 15.11.8, 15.12.3, 15.12.4, 15.13, 15.17, 15.19, 16.2.9, 16.6.1
Acrylic acid	Y	S/P	2	2G	Cont	No	T2	IIA	No	R	F-T	A	No	15.13, 15.19.6, 16.2.9, 16.6.1
Acrylonitrile	Y	S/P	2	2G	Cont	No	T1	IIB	No	C	F-T	A	Yes	15.12, 15.13, 15.17, 15.19
Acrylonitrile–Styrene copolymer dispersion in polyether polyol	Y	P	3	2G	Open	No			Yes	O	No	A, B	No	15.19.6, 16.2.6
Adiponitrile	Z	S/P	3	2G	Cont	No		IIB	Yes	R	T	A	No	16.2.9
Alachlor technical (90% or more)	X	S/P	2	2G	Cont	No			Yes	O	No	A, C	No	15.19.6, 16.2.9
Alcohol (C9–C11) poly(2.5–9)ethoxylate	Y	P	3	2G	Open	No			Yes	O	No	A	No	15.19.6, 16.2.9
Alcohol (C6–C17) (secondary) poly(3–6)ethoxylates	Y	P	2	2G	Open	No			Yes	O	No	A	No	15.19.6, 16.2.9
Alcohol (C6–C17) (secondary) poly(7–12)ethoxylates	Y	P	2	2G	Open	No			Yes	O	No	A	No	15.19.6, 16.2.6, 16.2.9
Alcohol (C12–C16) poly(1–6)ethoxylates	Y	P	2	2G	Open	No			Yes	O	No	A	No	15.19.6, 16.2.9
Alcohol (C12–C16) poly(20+)ethoxylates	Y	P	3	2G	Open	No			Yes	O	No	A	No	15.19.6, 16.2.9
Alcohol (C12–C16) poly(7–19)ethoxylates	Y	P	2	2G	Open	No			Yes	O	No	A	No	15.19.6, 16.2.9
Alcohols (C13+)	Y	P	2	2G	Open	No			Yes	O	No	A, B	No	15.19.6, 16.2.9
Alcohols (C8–C11), primary, linear and essentially linear (n)	Y	S/P	2	2G	Cont	No	-	-	Yes	R	T	A, B, C	No	15.12.3, 15.2.4, 15.19.6, 16.2.6, 16.2.9

a	c	d	e	f	g	h	i'	i''	i'''	j	k	l	n	o
Alcohols (C$_{12}$–C$_{13}$), primary, linear and essentially linear (n)	Y	S/P	2	2G	Open	No	–	–	Yes	O	No	A, B, C	No	15.19.6, 16.2.6, 16.2.9
Alcohols (C$_{14}$–C$_{18}$), primary, linear and essentially linear (n)	Y	S/P	2	2G	Open	No	–	–	Yes	O	No	A, B, C	No	15.19.6, 16.2.6
Alkanes (C$_6$–C$_9$)	X	P	2	2G	Cont	No			No	R	F	A	No	15.19.6
n-Alkanes (C$_{10}$+)	Y	P	3	2G	Cont	No			No	R	F	A	No	15.19.6
n-Alkanes (C$_{10}$+) (n)	Z	P	3	2G	Cont	No			No	R	F	A, B	No	15.19.6
Alkaryl polyethers (C$_9$–C$_{20}$) (n)	Y	P	2	2G	Open	No	–	–	Yes	O	No	A, B	No	15.19.6, 16.2.6
Alkenyl (C$_{11}$+) amide (n)	X	P	2	2G	Open	No	–	–	Yes	O	No	A	No	15.19.6, 16.2.6, 16.2.9
Alkenyl (C$_{16}$–C$_{20}$) succinic anhydride	Z	S/P	3	2G	Cont	No	–	–	Yes	C	T	No	Yes	15.12, 15.17, 15.19
Alkyl acrylate–Vinylpyridine copolymer in toluene (n)	Y	P	2	2G	Cont	No			No	R	F	A	No	15.19.6, 16.2.9
Alkylaryl phosphate mixtures (more than 40% Diphenyl tolyl phosphate, less than 0.02% *ortho*-isomers)	X	S/P	1	2G	Cont	No	T1	IIA	Yes	C	T	A, B, C	No	15.12, 15.17, 15.19
Alkylated (C$_4$–C$_9$) hindered phenols	Y	S/P	2	2G	Open	No	–	–	Yes	O	No	B, D	No	15.19.6, 16.2.6, 16.2.9
Alkylbenzene, alkylindane, alkylindene mixture (each C$_{12}$–C$_{17}$)	Z	P	3	2G	Open	No	–	–	Yes	O	No	A	No	15.19.6
Alkyl benzene distillation bottoms (n)	Y	S/P	2	2G	Open	No	–	–	Yes	O	No	A, B, C	No	15.19.6, 16.2.6
Alkylbenzene mixtures (containing at least 50% of toluene) (n)	Y	S/P	3	2G	Cont	No	T1	IIA	No	C	F-T	A, B, C	No	15.12, 15.17, 15.19.6
Alkyl (C$_3$–C$_4$) benzenes (n)	Y	P	2	2G	Cont	No			No	R	F	A	No	15.19.6
Alkyl (C$_5$–C$_8$) benzenes (n)	X	P	2	2G	Open	No	–	–	Yes	O	No	A	No	15.19.6
Alkyl(C$_9$+)benzenes (n)	Y	P	3	2G	Open	No	–	–	Yes	O	No	A, B	No	
Alkyl(C$_9$+)benzenes	Z	P	3	2G	Open	No	–	–	Yes	O	No	A, B	No	
Alkyl (C$_{11}$–C$_{17}$) benzene sulphonic acid (n)	Y	P	2	2G	Open	No	–	–	Yes	O	No	A	No	15.19.6, 16.2.6
Alkylbenzene sulphonic acid, sodium salt solution (n)	Y	S/P	2	2G	Open	No			NF	O	No	No	No	15.19.6, 16.2.6, 16.2.9
Alkyl (C$_{12}$+) dimethylamine	X	S/P	1	2G	Cont	No	–	–	Yes	C	T	B, C, D	Yes	15.12, 15.17, 15.19
Alkyl dithiocarbamate (C$_{19}$–C$_{35}$)	Y	P	3	2G	Open	No	–	–	Yes	O	No	A, B	No	15.19.6, 16.2.6, 16.2.9
Alkyldithiothiadiazole (C$_6$–C$_{24}$)	Z	P	3	2G	Open	No	–	–	Yes	O	No	A	No	
Alkyldithiothiadiazole (C$_6$–C$_{24}$) (n)	Y	P	3	2G	Open	No	–	–	Yes	O	No	A	No	15.19.6, 16.2.6
Alkyl ester copolymer (C$_4$–C$_{20}$)	Y	P	2	2G	Open	No	–	–	Yes	O	No	A, B	No	15.19.6, 16.2.6, 16.2.9

a	c	d	e	f	g	h	i'	i''	i'''	j	k	l	n	o
Alkyl (C8–C10)/(C12–C14);(40% or less/60% or more) polyglucoside solution (55% or less)	Y	P	3	2G	Open	No			Yes	O	No	No	No	15.19.6, 16.2.6, 16.2.9
Alkyl (C8–C10)/(C12–C14);(50%/50%) polyglucoside solution (55% or less)	Y	P	3	2G	Open	No			Yes	O	No	No	No	16.2.6, 16.2.9
Alkyl (C8–C10)/(C12–C14);(60% or more/40% or less) polyglucoside solution (55% or less)	Y	P	3	2G	Open	No			Yes	O	No	No	No	16.2.6, 16.2.9
Alkyl (C7–C9) nitrates (n)	Y	S/P	2	2G	Open	No			Yes	O	No	A, B	No	15.19.6, 15.20, 16.6.1, 16.6.2, 16.6.3
Alkyl(C7–C11)phenol poly(4–12)ethoxylate (n)	Y	P	2	2G	Open	No			Yes	O	No	A	No	15.19.6
Alkyl (C8–C40) phenol sulphide	Z	P	3	2G	Open	No			Yes	O	No	A, B	No	
Alkyl (C8–C9) phenylamine in aromatic solvents	Y	P	2	2G	Cont	No			No	R	F	A	No	15.19.6
Alkyl (C9–C15) phenyl propoxylate	Z	P	3	2G	Open	No			Yes	O	No	A, B	No	
Alkyl (C12–C14) polyglucoside solution (55% or less)	Y	P	3	2G	Open	No			Yes	O	No	No	No	15.19.6, 16.2.9
Alkyl (C8–C10) polyglucoside solution (65% or less)	Y	P	3	2G	Open	No			Yes	O	No	No	No	16.2.9
Alkyl (C10–C20, saturated and unsaturated) phosphite	Y	P	2	2G	Open	No			Yes	O	No	A	No	16.2.9
Alkyl sulphonic acid ester of phenol	Y	P	3	2G	Open	No			Yes	O	No	A, B	No	15.19.6, 16.2.6
Allyl alcohol	Y	S/P	2	2G	Cont	No	T2	IIB	No	C	F-T	A	Yes	15.12, 15.17, 15.19
Allyl chloride	Y	S/P	2	2G	Cont	No	T2	IIA	No	C	F-T	A	Yes	15.12, 15.17, 15.19
Aluminium sulphate solution	Y	P	2	2G	Open	No			Yes	O	No	A	No	15.19.6
2-(2-Aminoethoxy)ethanol (n)	Z	S/P	3	2G	Open	No			Yes	O	No	A, D	No	15.19.6
Aminoethyldiethanolamine/Aminoethylethanolamine solution (n)	Z	P	3	2G	Open	No	-	-	Yes	O	No	A	No	16.2.9
Aminoethylethanolamine	Z	S/P	3	2G	Open	No	T2	IIA	Yes	O	No	A	No	
N-Aminoethylpiperazine (n)	Z	S/P	3	2G	Cont	No			Yes	R	T	A	No	15.19.6, 16.2.9
2-Amino-2-methyl-1-propanol	Z	P	3	2G	Open	No			Yes	O	No	A	No	
Ammonia aqueous (28% or less)	Y	S/P	2	2G	Cont	No			NF	R	T	A, B, C	Yes	15.19.6
Ammonium hydrogen phosphate solution	Z	P	3	2G	Open	No			Yes	O	No	A	No	
Ammonium lignosulphonate solutions (n)	Z	P	3	2G	Open	No			Yes	O	No	A	No	16.2.9
Ammonium nitrate solution (93% or less)	Z	S/P	2	1G	Open	No	-	-	NF	O	No	No	No	15.2, 15.11.4, 15.11.6, 15.18, 15.19.6, 16.2.9
Ammonium polyphosphate solution	Z	P	3	2G	Open	No			Yes	O	No	A	No	
Ammonium sulphate solution	Z	P	3	2G	Open	No			Yes	O	No	A	No	

a	c	d	e	f	g	h	i'	i''	i'''	j	k	l	n	o
Ammonium sulphide solution (45% or less)	Y	S/P	2	2G	Cont	No			No	C	F-T	A	Yes	15.12, 15.17, 15.19, 16.6.1, 16.6.2, 16.6.3
Ammonium thiosulphate solution (60% or less) (n)	Z	P	3	2G	Open	No			NF	O	No	No	No	16.2.9
Amyl acetate (all isomers)	Y	P	3	2G	Cont	No			No	R	F	A	No	15.19.6
n-Amyl alcohol	Z	P	3	2G	Cont	No			No	R	F	A, B	No	
Amyl alcohol, primary	Z	P	3	2G	Cont	No			No	R	F	A, B	No	
sec-Amyl alcohol	Z	P	3	2G	Cont	No			No	R	F	A, B	No	
tert-Amyl alcohol	Z	P	3	2G	Cont	No			No	R	F	A	No	
tert-Amyl methyl ether	X	P	2	2G	Cont	No			No	R	F	A	No	15.19.6
Aniline	Y	S/P	2	2G	Cont	No	T3	IIA	Yes	C	T	A	No	15.12, 15.17, 15.19
Aryl polyolefins (C$_{11}$–C$_{50}$)	Y	P	2	2G	Open	No	T1		Yes	O	No	A, B	No	15.19.6, 16.2.6, 16.2.9
Aviation alkylates (C$_8$ paraffins and iso-paraffins BPT 95–120°C)	X	P	2	2G	Cont	No			No	R	F	B	No	15.19.6
Barium long chain (C$_{11}$–C$_{50}$) alkaryl sulphonate	Y	S/P	2	2G	Open	No			Yes	O	No	A, D	No	15.12.3, 15.19, 16.2.6, 16.2.9
Benzene and mixtures having 10% benzene or more (i)	Y	S/P	3	2G	Cont	No	T1	IIA	No	C	F-T	A, B	No	15.12.1, 15.17, 15.19.6, 16.2.9
Benzene sulphonyl chloride (n)	Z	S/P	3	2G	Cont	No			Yes	R	T	A, D	No	15.19.6, 16.2.9
Benzenetricarboxylic acid, trioctyl ester	Y	P	2	2G	Open	No			Yes	O	No	A, B	No	15.19.6, 16.2.6
Benzyl acetate	Y	P	2	2G	Open	No			Yes	O	No	A	No	15.19.6
Benzyl alcohol	Y	P	3	2G	Open	No			Yes	O	No	A	No	15.19.6
Benzyl chloride (n)	Y	S/P	2	2G	Cont	No	T1	IIA	Yes	C	T	A, B	Yes	15.12, 15.13, 15.17, 15.19
Brake fluid base mix: Poly(2–8)alkylene (C$_2$–C$_3$) glycols/Polyalkylene (C$_2$–C$_{10}$) glycols monoalkyl (C$_1$–C$_4$) ethers and their borate esters (n)	Z	P	3	2G	Open	No	–	–	Yes	O	No	A	No	
Bromochloromethane	Z	S/P	3	2G	Cont	No			NF	R	T	No	No	
Butene oligomer (n)	X	P	2	2G	Open	No			Yes	O	No	A	No	15.19.6
Butyl acetate (all isomers)	Y	P	3	2G	Cont	No			No	R	F	A	No	15.19.6
Butyl acrylate (all isomers)	Y	S/P	2	2G	Cont	No	T2	IIB	No	R	F-T	A	No	15.13, 15.19.6, 16.6.1, 16.6.2
tert-Butyl alcohol	Z	P	3	2G	Cont	No			No	R	F	A	No	
Butylamine (all isomers)	Y	S/P	2	2G	Cont	No			No	R	F-T	A	Yes	15.12, 15.17, 15.19.6
Butylbenzene (all isomers)	X	P	2	2G	Cont	No			No	R	F	A	No	15.19.6
Butyl benzyl phthalate	X	P	2	2G	Open	No			Yes	O	No	A	No	15.19.6

a	c	d	e	f	g	h	i'	i''	i'''	j	k	l	n	o
Butyl butyrate (all isomers)	Y	P	3	2G	Cont	No			No	R	F	A	No	15.19.6
Butyl/Decyl/Cetyl/Eicosyl methacrylate mixture	Y	S/P	2	2G	Cont	No			Yes	R	No	A, D	No	15.13, 15.19.6, 16.6.1, 16.6.2
Butylene glycol	Z	P	3	2G	Open	No			Yes	O	No	A	No	15.19.6
1,2-Butylene oxide	Y	S/P	3	2G	Cont	Inert	T2	IIB	No	R	F	A, C	No	15.8.1 to 15.8.7, 15.8.12, 15.8.13, 15.8.16, 15.8.17, 15.8.18, 15.8.19, 15.8.21, 15.8.25, 15.8.27, 15.8.29, 15.19.6
n-Butyl ether	Y	S/P	3	2G	Cont	Inert	T4	IIB	No	R	F-T	A	No	15.4.6, 15.12, 15.19.6
Butyl methacrylate	Z	S/P	3	2G	Cont	No		IIA	No	R	F-T	A, D	No	15.13, 15.19.6, 16.6.1, 16.6.2
n-Butyl propionate	Y	P	3	2G	Cont	No			No	R	F	A	No	15.19.6
Butyraldehyde (all isomers)	Y	S/P	3	2G	Cont	No	T3	IIA	No	R	F-T	A	No	15.19.6
Butyric acid	Y	S/P	3	2G	Cont	No			Yes	R	No	A	No	15.11.2, 15.11.3, 15.11.4, 15.11.6, 15.11.7, 15.11.8, 15.19.6
gamma-Butyrolactone	Y	P	3	2G	Open	No			Yes	O	No	A, B	No	15.19.6
Calcium carbonate slurry	Z	P	3	2G	Open	No			Yes	O	No	A, B	No	
Calcium hydroxide slurry (n)	Z	P	3	2G	Open	No	-	-	Yes	O	No	A	No	16.2.9
Calcium hypochlorite solution (15% or less)	Y	S/P	2	2G	Cont	No			NF	R	No	No	No	15.19.6
Calcium hypochlorite solution (more than 15%)	X	S/P	1	2G	Cont	No			NF	R	No	No	No	15.19, 16.2.9
Calcium lignosulphonate solutions (n)	Z	P	3	2G	Open	No			Yes	O	No	A	No	16.2.9
Calcium long-chain alkaryl sulphonate (C_{11}–C_{50}) (n)	Z	P	3	2G	Open	No	-	-	Yes	O	No	A	No	16.2.9
Calcium long-chain alkyl (C_5–C_{10}) phenate	Y	P	3	2G	Open	No			Yes	O	No	A	No	15.19.6
Calcium long-chain alkyl (C_{11}–C_{40}) phenate	Z	P	3	2G	Open	No			Yes	O	No	A	No	16.2.9
Calcium long-chain alkyl (C_{11}–C_{40}) phenate (n)	Y	P	2	2G	Open	No	-	-	Yes	O	No	A	No	15.19.6, 16.2.6
Calcium long-chain alkyl phenate sulphide (C_8–C_{40})	Y	P	2	2G	Open	No			Yes	O	No	A, B	No	15.19.6, 16.2.6, 16.2.9
Calcium long-chain alkyl salicylate (C_{13}+) (n)	Y	P	2	2G	Open	No			Yes	O	No	A, B	No	15.19.6, 16.2.6
Calcium nitrate/Magnesium nitrate/Potassium chloride solution (n)	Z	P	3	2G	Open	No		-	Yes	O	No	A	No	16.2.9
epsilon-Caprolactam (molten or aqueous solutions)	Z	P	3	2G	Open	No			Yes	O	No	A	No	
Carbolic oil (n)	Y	S/P	2	2G	Cont	No			Yes	C	F-T	A	No	15.12, 15.19.6, 16.2.9

a	c	d	e	f	g	h	i'	i''	i'''	j	k	l	n	o
Carbon disulphide	Y	S/P	2	1G	Cont	Pad + inert	T6	IIC	No	C	F-T	C	Yes	15.3, 15.12, 15.19
Carbon tetrachloride	Y	S/P	2	2G	Cont	No	—		NF	C	T	No	Yes	15.12, 15.17, 15.19.6
Cashew nut shell oil (untreated) (n)	Y	S	2	2G	Cont	No	—		Yes	R	T	A, B	No	15.19.6, 16.2.6, 16.2.9
Castor oil (n)	Y	S/P	2 (k)	2G	Open	No	-	-	Yes	O	No	A, B, C	No	15.19.6, 16.2.6, 16.2.9
Castor oil (containing less than 2% free fatty acids)	Y	P	2 (k)	2G	Open	No	-	-	Yes	O	No	A, B, C, D	No	15.19.6, 16.2.6
Cetyl/Eicosyl methacrylate mixture	Y	S/P	2	2G	Open	No			Yes	O	No	A, D	No	15.13, 15.19.6, 16.2.9, 16.6.1, 16.6.2
Chlorinated paraffins (C$_{10}$–C$_{13}$)	X	P	1	2G	Open	No			Yes	O	No	A	No	15.19, 16.2.6
Chlorinated paraffins (C$_{14}$–C$_{17}$) (with 50% chlorine or more, and less than 1% C$_{13}$ or shorter chains) (n)	X	P	1	2G	Open	No	-		Yes	O	No	A	No	15.19
Chloroacetic acid (80% or less)	Y	S/P	2	2G	Cont	No			NF	C	No	No	No	15.11.2, 15.11.4, 15.11.6, 15.11.7, 15.11.8, 15.12.3, 15.19, 16.2.9
Chlorobenzene	Y	S/P	2	2G	Cont	No	T1	IIA	No	R	F-T	A, B	No	15.19.6
Chloroform	Y	S/P	3	2G	Cont	No			NF	R	T	No	Yes	15.12, 15.19.6
Chlorohydrins (crude)	Y	S/P	2	2G	Cont	No		IIA	No	C	F-T	A	No	15.12, 15.19
4-Chloro-2-methylphenoxyacetic acid, dimethylamine salt solution	Y	P	2	2G	Open	No			NF	O	No	No	No	15.19.6, 16.2.9
o-Chloronitrobenzene (n)	Y	S/P	2	2G	Cont	No			Yes	C	T	A, B, D	No	15.12, 15.17, 15.18, 15.19, 16.2.6, 16.2.9
1-(4-Chlorophenyl)-4,4-dimethylpentan-3-one	Y	P	2	2G	Open	No			Yes	O	No	A, B, D	No	15.19.6, 16.2.6, 16.2.9
2- or 3-Chloropropionic acid	Z	S/P	3	2G	Open	No			Yes	O	No	A	No	15.11.2, 15.11.3, 15.11.4, 15.11.6, 15.11.7, 15.11.8, 16.2.9
Chlorosulphonic acid	Y	S/P	1	2G	Cont	No			NF	C	T	No	Yes	15.11.2, 15.11.3, 15.11.4, 15.11.5, 15.11.6, 15.11.7, 15.11.8, 15.12, 15.16.2, 15.19
m-Chlorotoluene	Y	S/P	2	2G	Cont	No			No	R	F-T	A, B	No	15.19.6
o-Chlorotoluene	Y	S/P	2	2G	Cont	No			No	R	F-T	A, B	No	15.19.6
p-Chlorotoluene	Y	S/P	2	2G	Cont	No			No	R	F-T	A, B	No	15.19.6, 16.2.9
Chlorotoluenes (mixed isomers)	Y	S/P	2	2G	Cont	No			No	R	F-T	A, B	No	15.19.6
Choline chloride solutions	Z	P	3	2G	Open	No			Yes	O	No	A	No	
Citric acid (70% or less)	Z	P	3	2G	Open	No			Yes	O	No	A	No	

a	c	d	e	f	g	h	i'	i''	i'''	j	k	l	n	o
Coal tar (n)	X	S/P	2	2G	Cont	No	T2	IIA	Yes	R	No	B, D	No	15.19.6, 16.2.6, 16.2.9
Coal tar naphtha solvent (n)	Y	S/P	2	2G	Cont	No	T3	IIA	No	R	F-T	A, D	No	15.19.6, 16.2.9
Coal tar pitch (molten) (n)	X	S/P	2	1G	Cont	No	T2	IIA	Yes	R	No	B, D	No	15.19.6, 16.2.6, 16.2.9
Cocoa butter (n)	Y	S/P	2 (k)	2G	Open	No	-	-	Yes	O	No	A, B, C	No	15.19.6, 16.2.6, 16.2.9
Coconut oil (n)	Y	S/P	2 (k)	2G	Open	No	-	-	Yes	O	No	A, B, C	No	15.19.6, 16.2.6, 16.2.9
Coconut oil (containing less than 5% free fatty acids)	Y	P	2 (k)	2G	Open	No	-	-	Yes	O	No	A, B, C, D	No	15.19.6, 16.2.6, 16.2.9
Coconut oil fatty acid (n)	Y	S/P	2	2G	Open	No	-	-	Yes	O	No	A, B, C	No	15.19.6, 16.2.6, 16.2.9
Coconut oil fatty acid methyl ester (n)	Y	P	2	2G	Open	No	-	-	Yes	O	No	A	No	15.19.6
Copper salt of long chain (C$_{17}$+) alkanoic acid (n)	Y	P	2	2G	Open	No	-	-	Yes	O	No	A	No	15.19.6, 16.2.6, 16.2.9
Corn oil (n)	Y	S/P	2 (k)	2G	Open	No	-	-	Yes	O	No	A, B, C	No	15.19.6, 16.2.6, 16.2.9
Corn oil (containing less than 10% free fatty acids)	Y	P	2 (k)	2G	Open	No	-	-	Yes	O	No	A, B, C, D	No	15.19.6, 16.2.6
Cotton seed oil (n)	Y	S/P	2 (k)	2G	Open	No	-	-	Yes	O	No	A, B, C	No	15.19.6, 16.2.6, 16.2.9
Cotton seed oil (containing less than 12% free fatty acids)	Y	P	2 (k)	2G	Open	No	-	-	Yes	O	No	A, B, C, D	No	15.19.6, 16.2.6, 16.2.9
Creosote (coal tar) (n)	X	S/P	2	2G	Cont	No	T2	IIA	Yes	R	T	A, D	No	15.12.3, 15.12.4, 15.19.6, 16.2.6, 16.2.9
Cresols (all isomers)	Y	S/P	2	2G	Open	No	T1	IIA	Yes	O	No	A, B	No	15.19.6, 16.2.9
Cresylic acid, dephenolized	Y	S/P	2	2G	Open	No			Yes	O	No	A, B	No	15.19.6
Cresylic acid, sodium salt solution (n)	Y	S/P	2	2G	Open	No			Yes	O	No	No	No	15.19.6, 16.2.9
Crotonaldehyde	Y	S/P	2	2G	Cont	No	T3	IIB	No	R	F-T	A	Yes	15.12, 15.17, 15.19.6
1,5,9-Cyclododecatriene	X	S/P	1	2G	Cont	No			Yes	R	T	A	No	15.13, 15.19, 16.6.1, 16.6.2
Cycloheptane	X	P	2	2G	Cont	No			No	R	F	A	No	15.19.6
Cyclohexane	Y	P	2	2G	Cont	No			No	R	F	A	No	15.19.6, 16.2.9
Cyclohexanol	Y	P	2	2G	Open	No			Yes	O	No	A, B	No	15.19.6, 16.2.9
Cyclohexanone	Z	S/P	3	2G	Cont	No	T2	IIA	No	R	F-T	A	No	15.19.6
Cyclohexanone, Cyclohexanol mixture	Y	S/P	3	2G	Cont	No			Yes	R	F-T	A	No	15.19.6
Cyclohexyl acetate	Y	P	3	2G	Cont	No			No	R	F	A	No	15.19.6
Cyclohexylamine	Y	S/P	3	2G	Cont	No	T3	IIA	No	R	F-T	A, C	No	15.19.6
1,3-Cyclopentadiene dimer (molten)	Y	P	2	2G	Cont	No			No	R	F	A	No	15.19.6, 16.2.6, 16.2.9
Cyclopentane	Y	P	2	2G	Cont	No			No	R	F	A	No	15.19.6

a	c	d	e	f	g	h	i'	i''	i'''	j	k	l	n	o
Cyclopentene	Y	P	2	2G	Cont	No			No	R	F	A	No	15.19.6
p-Cymene	Y	P	2	2G	Cont	No			No	R	F	A	No	15.19.6
Decahydronaphthalene	Y	P	2	2G	Cont	No			No	R	F	A, B	No	15.19.6
Decanoic acid	X	P	2	2G	Open	No			Yes	O	No	A	No	16.2.9
Decene (n)	X	P	2	2G	Cont	No			No	R	F	A	No	15.19.6
Decyl acrylate	X	S/P	1	2G	Open	No	T3	IIA	Yes	O	No	A, C, D	No	15.13, 15.19, 16.6.1, 16.6.2
Decyl alcohol (all isomers)	Y	P	2	2G	Open	No			Yes	O	No	A	No	15.19.6, 16.2.9 (e)
Decyloxytetrahydrothiophene dioxide (n)	X	S/P	2	2G	Cont	No			Yes	R	T	A	No	15.19.6, 16.2.9
Diacetone alcohol	Z	P	3	2G	Cont	No			No	R	F	A	No	
Dialkyl (C$_8$–C$_9$) diphenylamines	Z	P	3	2G	Open	No			Yes	O	No	A, B	No	
Dialkyl (C$_7$–C$_{13}$) phthalates	X	P	2	2G	Open	No			Yes	O	No	A, B	No	15.19.6, 16.2.6
Dibromomethane	Y	S/P	2	2G	Cont	No			NF	R	T	No	No	15.12.3, 15.19
Dibutylamine	Y	S/P	3	2G	Cont	No	T2	IIA	No	R	F-T	A, C, D	No	15.19.6
Dibutyl hydrogen phosphonate	Y	P	3	2G	Open	No			Yes	O	No	A	No	15.19.6, 16.2.9
2,6-Di-tert-butylphenol (n)	X	P	1	2G	Open	No	-	-	Yes	O	No	A, B, C, D	No	15.19, 16.2.9
Dibutyl phthalate	X	P	2	2G	Open	No			Yes	O	No	A	No	15.19.6
Dichlorobenzene (all isomers)	X	S/P	2	2G	Cont	No		IIA	Yes	R	T	A, B, D	No	15.19.6
3,4-Dichloro-1-butene	Y	S/P	2	2G	Cont	No	T1		No	C	F-T	A, B, C	Yes	15.12.3, 15.17, 15.19.6
1,1-Dichloroethane (n)	Z	S/P	3	2G	Cont	No	T2	IIA	No	R	F-T	A	Yes	15.19.6
Dichloroethyl ether	Y	S/P	2	2G	Cont	Dry	T2	IIA	No	R	F-T	A	No	15.19.6
1,6-Dichlorohexane (n)	Y	S/P	2	2G	Cont	No			No	R	T	A, B	No	15.19.6
2,2'-Dichloroisopropyl ether	Y	S/P	2	2G	Cont	No			Yes	R	T	A, C, D	No	15.12, 15.17, 15.19
Dichloromethane (n)	Y	S/P	3	2G	Cont	No	T1	IIA	Yes	R	T	No	No	15.19.6
2,4-Dichlorophenol	Y	S/P	2	2G	Cont	Dry			Yes	R	T	A	No	15.19.6, 16.2.6, 16.2.9
2,4-Dichlorophenoxyacetic acid, diethanolamine salt solution (n)	Y	S/P	3	2G	Open	No			NF	O	No	No	No	15.19.6, 16.2.9
2,4-Dichlorophenoxyacetic acid, dimethylamine salt solution (70% or less) (n)	Y	S/P	3	2G	Open	No			NF	O	No	No	No	15.19.6, 16.2.9
2,4-Dichlorophenoxyacetic acid, triisopropanolamine salt solution (n)	Y	S/P	3	2G	Open	No			NF	O	No	No	No	15.19.6, 16.2.6, 16.2.9
1,1-Dichloropropane	Y	S/P	2	2G	Cont	No			No	R	F-T	A, B	No	15.12, 15.19.6

a	c	d	e	f	g	h	i'	i''	i'''	j	k	l	n	o
1,2-Dichloropropane	Y	S/P	2	2G	Cont	No	T1	IIA	No	R	F-T	A, B	No	15.12, 15.19.6
1,3-Dichloropropene	X	S/P	2	2G	Cont	No	T2	IIA	No	C	F-T	A, B	Yes	15.12, 15.17, 15.18, 15.19
Dichloropropene/Dichloropropane mixtures	X	S/P	2	2G	Cont	No			No	C	F-T	A, B, D	Yes	15.12, 15.17, 15.18, 15.19
2,2-Dichloropropionic acid (n)	Y	S/P	3	2G	Cont	Dry			Yes	R	No	A	No	15.11.2, 15.11.4, 15.11.6, 15.11.7, 15.11.8, 15.19.6, 16.2.9
Diethanolamine	Y	S/P	3	2G	Open	No	T1	IIA	Yes	O	No	A	No	16.2.6, 16.2.9
Diethylamine	Y	S/P	3	2G	Cont	No	T2	IIA	No	R	F-T	A	Yes	15.12, 15.19.6
Diethylaminoethanol	Y	S/P	2	2G	Cont	No	T2	IIA	No	R	F-T	A, C	No	15.19.6
2,6-Diethylaniline (n)	Y	S/P	3	2G	Open	No			Yes	O	No	B, C, D	No	15.19.6, 16.2.9
Diethylbenzene	Y	P	2	2G	Cont	No	T2	IIA	No	R	F	A	No	15.19.6
Diethylene glycol dibutyl ether (n)	Z	S/P	3	2G	Open	No	-	-	Yes	O	No	A	No	
Diethylene glycol diethyl ether (n)	Z	P	3	2G	Open	No	-	-	Yes	O	No	A	No	
Diethylene glycol phthalate (n)	Y	P	3	2G	Open	No	-	-	Yes	O	No	A	No	15.19.6, 16.2.6
Diethylenetriamine	Y	S/P	3	2G	Open	No	T2	IIA	Yes	O	No	A	No	15.19.6
Diethylenetriaminepentaacetic acid, pentasodium salt solution (n)	Z	P	3	2G	Open	No	-	-	Yes	O	No	A	No	
Diethyl ether	Z	S/P	2	1G	Cont	Inert	T4	IIB	No	C	F-T	A	Yes	15.4, 15.14, 15.19
Di-(2-ethylhexyl) adipate	Y	P	2	2G	Open	No			Yes	O	No	A, B	No	15.19.6
Di-(2-ethylhexyl)phosphoric acid (n)	Y	S/P	2	2G	Open	No			Yes	O	No	A, D	No	15.19.6
Diethyl phthalate	Y	P	2	2G	Open	No			Yes	O	No	A	No	15.19.6
Diethyl sulphate	Y	S/P	2	2G	Cont	No			Yes	C	T	A	No	15.19.6
Diglycidyl ether of bisphenol A (n)	X	P	2	2G	Open	No			Yes	O	No	A	No	15.19.6, 16.2.6, 16.2.9
Diglycidyl ether of bisphenol F (n)	Y	P	2	2G	Open	No			Yes	O	No	A	No	15.19.6, 16.2.6
Diheptyl phthalate	Y	P	2	2G	Open	No			Yes	O	No	A, B	No	15.19.6
Di-n-hexyl adipate	X	P	1	2G	Open	No			Yes	O	No	A	No	15.19
Dihexyl phthalate	Y	P	2	2G	Open	No			Yes	O	No	A, B	No	15.19.6
Diisobutylamine	Y	S/P	2	2G	Cont	No			No	R	F-T	A, C, D	No	15.12.3, 15.19.6
Diisobutylene	Y	P	2	2G	Cont	No			No	R	F	A	No	15.19.6
Diisobutyl ketone	Y	P	3	2G	Cont	No			No	R	F	A	No	15.19.6
Diisobutyl phthalate (n)	X	P	2	2G	Open	No			Yes	O	No	A	No	15.19.6
Diisononyl adipate	Y	P	2	2G	Open	No	-		Yes	O	No	A	No	15.19.6

a	c	d	e	f	g	h	i'	i''	i'''	j	k	l	n	o
Diisooctyl phthalate	Y	P	2	2G	Open	No			Yes	O	No	A, B	No	15.19.6, 16.2.6
Diisopropanolamine	Z	S/P	3	2G	Open	No	T2	IIA	Yes	O	No	A	No	16.2.9
Diisopropylamine	Y	S/P	2	2G	Cont	No	T2	IIA	No	C	F-T	A	Yes	15.12, 15.19
Diisopropylbenzene (all isomers)	X	P	2	2G	Open	No			Yes	O	No	A	No	15.19.6
Diisopropylnaphthalene (n)	Y	P	2	2G	Open	No	-	-	Yes	O	No	A	No	15.19.6
N,N-Dimethylacetamide	Z	S/P	3	2G	Cont	No	-	-	Yes	C	T	A, C, D	No	15.12, 15.17
N,N-Dimethylacetamide solution (40% or less)	Z	S/P	3	2G	Cont	No			Yes	R	T	B	No	15.12.1, 15.17
Dimethyl adipate	X	P	2	2G	Open	No			Yes	O	No	A	No	15.19.6, 16.2.9
Dimethylamine solution (45% or less)	Y	S/P	3	2G	Cont	No	T2	IIA	No	R	F-T	A, C, D	No	15.12, 15.19.6
Dimethylamine solution (greater than 45% but not greater than 55%)	Y	S/P	2	2G	Cont	No			No	C	F-T	A, C, D	Yes	15.12, 15.17, 15.19
Dimethylamine solution (greater than 55% but not greater than 65%)	Y	S/P	2	2G	Cont	No			No	C	F-T	A, C, D	Yes	15.12, 15.14, 15.17, 15.19
N,N-Dimethylcyclohexylamine	Y	S/P	2	2G	Cont	No			No	R	F-T	A, C	No	15.12, 15.17, 15.19.6
Dimethyl disulphide	Y	S/P	2	2G	Cont	No	T2	IIA	No	R	F-T	B	No	15.12.3, 15.12.4, 15.19.6
N,N-Dimethyldodecylamine	X	S/P	1	2G	Open	No			Yes	O	No	B	No	15.19
Dimethylethanolamine	Y	S/P	3	2G	Cont	No	T3	IIA	No	R	F-T	A, D	No	15.19.6
Dimethylformamide	Y	S/P	3	2G	Cont	No	T2	IIA	No	R	F-T	A, D	No	15.19.6
Dimethyl glutarate	Y	P	3	2G	Open	No			Yes	O	No	A	No	15.19.6
Dimethyl hydrogen phosphite	Y	S/P	3	2G	Cont	No			Yes	R	T	A, D	No	15.12.1, 15.19.6
Dimethyloctanoic acid	Y	P	2	2G	Open	No			Yes	O	No	A	No	15.19.6, 16.2.6, 16.2.9
Dimethyl phthalate	Y	P	3	2G	Open	No			Yes	O	No	A	No	15.19.6, 16.2.9
Dimethylpolysiloxane	Y	P	3	2G	Open	No			Yes	O	No	A, B	No	15.19.6
2,2-Dimethylpropane-1,3-diol (molten or solution) (n)	Z	P	3	2G	Open	No	-	-	Yes	O	No	A, B	No	16.2.9
2,2-Dimethylpropane-1,3-diol (molten or solution)	Z	P	3	2G	Open	No	-	-	Yes	O	No	A, B	No	
Dimethyl succinate	Y	P	3	2G	Open	No			Yes	O	No	A	No	16.2.9
Dinitrotoluene (molten)	X	S/P	2	2G	Cont	No			Yes	C	T	A	No	15.12, 15.17, 15.19, 15.21, 16.2.6, 16.2.9, 16.6.4
Dinonyl phthalate (n)	Y	P	2	2G	Open	No	-	-	Yes	O	No	A	No	15.19.6
Dioctyl phthalate	X	P	2	2G	Open	No			Yes	O	No	A, B	No	15.19.6
1,4-Dioxane	Y	S/P	2	2G	Cont	No	T2	IIB	No	C	F-T	A	No	15.12, 15.19, 16.2.9

a	c	d	e	f	g	h	i'	i''	i'''	j	k	l	n	o
Dipentene	Y	P	3	2G	Cont	No			No	R	F	A	No	15.19.6
Diphenyl	X	P	2	2G	Open	No			Yes	O	No	B	No	15.19.6, 16.2.6, 16.2.9
Diphenylamine (molten) (n)	Y	P	2	2G	Open	No	-		Yes	O	No	B, D	No	15.19.6, 16.2.6, 16.2.9
Diphenylamine, reaction product with 2,2,4-Trimethylpentene (n)	Y	S/P	1	2G	Open	No			Yes	O	No	A	No	15.19, 16.2.6
Diphenylamines, alkylated (n)	Y	P	2	2G	Open	No			Yes	O	No	A	No	15.19.6, 16.2.6, 16.2.9
Diphenyl/Diphenyl ether mixtures	X	P	2	2G	Open	No			Yes	O	No	B	No	15.19.6, 16.2.9
Diphenyl ether	X	P	2	2G	Open	No			Yes	O	No	A	No	15.19.6, 16.2.9
Diphenyl ether/Diphenyl phenyl ether mixture	X	P	2	2G	Open	No			Yes	O	No	A	No	15.19.6, 16.2.9
Diphenylmethane diisocyanate (n)	Y	S/P	2	2G	Cont	Dry	-		Yes (a)	C	T (a)	A, B, C (b), D	No	15.12, 15.16.2, 15.17, 15.19.6, 16.2.6, 16.2.9
Diphenylolpropane–Epichlorohydrin resins	X	P	2	2G	Open	No			Yes	O	No	A	No	15.19.6, 16.2.6, 16.2.9
Di-n-propylamine	Y	S/P	2	2G	Cont	No			No	R	F-T	A	No	15.12.3, 15.19.6
Dipropylene glycol	Z	P	3	2G	Open	No			Yes	O	No	A	No	
Dithiocarbamate ester (C$_7$–C$_{35}$)	X	P	2	2G	Open	No	-		Yes	O	No	A, D	No	15.19.6, 16.2.9
Ditridecyl adipate (n)	Y	S/P	2	2G	Open	No	-		Yes	O	No	A	No	15.19.6, 16.2.6
Ditridecyl phthalate (n)	Y	S/P	2	2G	Open	No	-		Yes	O	No	A	No	15.19.6
Diundecyl phthalate	Y	P	2	2G	Open	No			Yes	O	No	A, B	No	15.19.6, 16.2.6, 16.2.9
Dodecane (all isomers)	Y	P	2	2G	Cont	No			No	R	F	A, B	No	15.19.6
tert-Dodecanethiol	X	S/P	1	2G	Cont	No	-		Yes	C	T	A, B, D	Yes	15.12, 15.17, 15.19
Dodecene (all isomers)	X	P	2	2G	Open	No			Yes	O	No	A	No	15.19.6
Dodecyl alcohol	Y	P	2	2G	Open	No			Yes	O	No	A	No	15.19.6, 16.2.9
Dodecylamine/Tetradecylamine mixture (n)	Y	S/P	2	2G	Cont	No	-		Yes	R	T	A, D	No	15.19.6, 16.2.9
Dodecylbenzene	Z	P	3	2G	Open	No			Yes	O	No	A, B	No	
Dodecyl diphenyl ether disulphonate solution (n)	X	S/P	2	2G	Open	No			NF	O	No	No	No	15.19.6, 16.2.6
Dodecyl hydroxypropyl sulphide	X	P	2	2G	Open	No			Yes	O	No	A	No	15.19.6
Dodecyl methacrylate	Z	S/P	3	2G	Open	No			Yes	O	No	A	No	15.13
Dodecyl/Octadecyl methacrylate mixture (n)	Y	S/P	3	2G	Open	No	-		Yes	O	No	A	No	15.13, 15.19.6, 16.2.6, 16.6.1, 16.6.2
Dodecyl/Octadecyl methacrylate mixture	Z	S/P	3	2G	Open	No			Yes	R	No	A, D	No	15.13, 16.6.1, 16.6.2
Dodecyl/Pentadecyl methacrylate mixture	Y	S/P	2	2G	Open	No			Yes	O	No	A, D	No	15.13, 15.19.6, 16.6.1, 16.6.2

a	c	d	e	f	g	h	i'	i''	i'''	j	k	l	n	o
Dodecylphenol	X	P	2	2G	Open	No			Yes	O	No	A	No	15.19.6, 16.2.6
Dodecylxylene	Y	P	2	2G	Open	No			Yes	O	No	A, B	No	15.19.6, 16.2.6
Drilling brines (containing zinc salts)	X	P	2	2G	Open	No			Yes	O	No	No	No	15.19.6
Drilling brines, including: calcium bromide solution, calcium chloride solution and sodium chloride solution	Z	P	3	2G	Open	No			Yes	O	No	A	No	
Epichlorohydrin	Y	S/P	2	2G	Cont	No		IIB	No	C	F-T	A	Yes	15.12, 15.17, 15.19
Ethanolamine	Y	S/P	3	2G	Open	No	T2	IIA	Yes	O	F-T	A	No	16.2.9
2-Ethoxyethyl acetate	Y	P	3	2G	Cont	No			No	R	F	A	No	15.19.6
Ethoxylated long chain (C$_{16}$+) alkyloxyalkylamine	Y	S/P	2	2G	Open	No	-		Yes	O	No	A, B	No	15.19.6, 16.2.9
Ethoxylated long chain (C$_{16}$+) alkyloxyalkylamine (n)	Z	P	3	2G	Open	No			Yes	O	No	A, B	No	
Ethyl acetate	Z	P	3	2G	Cont	No			No	R	F	A, B	No	
Ethyl acetoacetate	Z	P	3	2G	Open	No			Yes	O	No	A	No	
Ethyl acrylate	Y	S/P	2	2G	Cont	No	T2	IIB	No	R	F-T	A	Yes	15.13, 15.19.6, 16.6.1, 16.6.2
Ethylamine	Y	S/P	2	1G	Cont	No	T2	IIA	No	C	F-T	C, D	Yes	15.12, 15.14, 15.19.6
Ethylamine solutions (72% or less)	Y	S/P	2	2G	Cont	No			No	C	F-T	A, C	Yes	15.12, 15.14, 15.17, 15.19
Ethyl amyl ketone (n)	Y	P	3	2G	Cont	No			No	R	F	A	No	15.19.6
Ethylbenzene	Y	P	2	2G	Cont	No			No	R	F	A	No	15.19.6
Ethyl tert-butyl ether	Y	P	3	2G	Cont	No			No	R	F	A	No	15.19.6
Ethyl butyrate (n)	Y	P	3	2G	Cont	No			No	R	F	A	No	15.19.6
Ethylcyclohexane	Y	P	2	2G	Cont	No			No	R	F	A	No	15.19.6
N-Ethylcyclohexylamine	Y	S/P	2	2G	Cont	No			No	R	F-T	A	No	15.19.6
S-Ethyl dipropylthiocarbamate	Y	P	2	2G	Open	No			Yes	O	No	A	No	16.2.9
Ethylene chlorohydrin	Y	S/P	2	2G	Cont	No	T2	IIA	No	C	F-T	A, D	Yes	15.12, 15.17, 15.19
Ethylene cyanohydrin	Y	S/P	3	2G	Open	No		IIB	Yes	O	No	A	No	15.19.6
Ethylenediamine	Y	S/P	2	2G	Cont	No	T2	IIA	No	R	F-T	A	No	15.19.6, 16.2.9
Ethylenediaminetetraacetic acid, tetrasodium salt solution (n)	Y	S/P	3	2G	Open	No	-	-	Yes	O	No	A	No	15.19.6
Ethylene dibromide	Y	S/P	2	2G	Cont	No			NF	C	T	No	Yes	15.12, 15.19.6, 16.2.9
Ethylene dichloride	Y	S/P	2	2G	Cont	No	T2	IIA	No	R	F-T	A, B	No	15.19
Ethylene glycol	Y	P	3	2G	Open	No			Yes	O	No	A	No	15.19.6

a	c	d	e	f	g	h	i'	i''	i'''	j	k	l	n	o
Ethylene glycol acetate (n)	Y	P	3	2G	Open	No	-	-	Yes	O	No	A	No	15.19.6
Ethylene glycol butyl ether acetate	Y	P	3	2G	Open	No			Yes	O	No	A	No	15.19.6
Ethylene glycol diacetate	Y	P	3	2G	Open	No			Yes	O	No	A	No	15.19.6
Ethylene glycol methyl ether acetate (n)	Y	P	3	2G	Open	No			Yes	O	No	A	No	15.19.6
Ethylene glycol monoalkyl ethers	Y	S/P	3	2G	Cont	No			No	R	F	A	No	15.19.6, 16.2.9
Ethylene glycol phenyl ether (n)	Z	P	3	2G	Open	No	-	-	Yes	O	No	A	No	16.2.9
Ethylene glycol phenyl ether/Diethylene glycol phenyl ether mixture	Z	P	3	2G	Open	No	-	-	Yes	O	No	A	No	16.2.9
Ethylene oxide/Propylene oxide mixture with an ethylene oxide content of not more than 30% by mass	Y	S/P	2	1G	Cont	Inert	T2	IIB	No	C	F-T	A, C	No	15.8, 15.12, 15.14, 15.19
Ethylene–Vinyl acetate copolymer (emulsion) (n)	Y	P	3	2G	Open	No	-	-	Yes	O	No	A	No	15.19.6, 16.2.6, 16.2.9
Ethyl 3-ethoxypropionate	Y	P	3	2G	Cont	No			No	R	No	A	No	15.19.6
2-Ethylhexanoic acid	Y	P	3	2G	Open	No			Yes	O	No	A, B	No	15.19.6
2-Ethylhexyl acrylate	Y	S/P	3	2G	Open	No	T3	IIB	Yes	O	No	A	No	15.13, 15.19.6, 16.6.1, 16.6.2
2-Ethylhexylamine	Y	S/P	2	2G	Cont	No			No	R	F-T	A	No	15.12, 15.19.6
2-Ethyl-2-(hydroxymethyl)propane-1,3-diol (C8–C10) ester	Y	P	2	2G	Open	No			Yes	O	No	A, B	No	15.19.6, 16.2.6, 16.2.9
Ethylidenenorbornene	Y	S/P	2	2G	Cont	No			No	R	F-T	A, D	No	15.12.1, 15.19.6
Ethyl methacrylate	Y	S/P	3	2G	Cont	No	T2	IIA	No	R	F-T	A, D	No	15.13, 15.19.6, 16.6.1, 16.6.2
N-Ethylmethylallylamine	Y	S/P	2	2G	Cont	No	T2	IIB	No	C	F	A, C	Yes	15.12.3, 15.17, 15.19
Ethyl propionate (n)	Y	P	3	2G	Open	No	-	-	No	R	F	A	No	15.19.6
2-Ethyl-3-propylacrolein	Y	S/P	3	2G	Cont	No		IIA	No	R	F-T	A	No	15.19.6, 16.2.9
Ethyltoluene	Y	P	2	2G	Cont	No	-	-	No	R	F	A	No	15.19.6
Fatty acid (saturated C13+)	Y	P	2	2G	Open	No	-	-	Yes	O	No	A, B	No	15.19.6, 16.2.9
Fatty acid methyl esters (m) (n)	Y	S/P	2	2G	Cont	No	-	-	Yes	R	T	A, B, C	No	15.12.3, 15.12.4, 15.19.6, 16.2.6, 16.2.9
Fatty acids, C8–C10 (n)	Y	S/P	2	2G	Cont	No			Yes	R	T	A, B, C	No	15.12.3, 15.12.4, 15.19, 16.2.6, 16.2.9
Fatty acids, C12+ (n)	Y	S/P	2	2G	Cont	No			Yes	R	T	A, B, C	No	15.12.3, 15.12.4, 15.19.6, 16.2.6, 16.2.9
Fatty acids, C16+ (n)	Y	P	2	2G	Open	No	-	-	Yes	O	No	A, B, C	No	15.19.6, 16.2.6
Fatty acids, essentially linear (C6–C18) 2-ethylhexyl ester	Y	P	2	2G	Open	No			Yes	O	No	A, B	No	15.19.6

a	c	d	e	f	g	h	i'	i''	i'''	j	k	l	n	o
Ferric chloride solutions	Y	S/P	3	2G	Open	No			NF	O	No	No	No	15.11, 15.19.6, 16.2.9
Ferric nitrate/Nitric acid solution	Y	S/P	2	2G	Cont	No		-	NF	R	T	No	Yes	15.11, 15.19
Fish oil (n)	Y	S/P	2 (k)	2G	Open	No	-	-	Yes	O	No	A, B, C	No	15.19.6, 16.2.6, 16.2.9
Fish oil (containing less than 4% free fatty acids)	Y	P	2 (k)	2G	Open	No	-	-	Yes	O	No	A, B, C, D	No	15.19.6, 16.2.6, 16.2.9
Fluorosilicic acid (20–30%) in water solution (n)	Y	S/P	3	1G	Cont	No	-	-	NF	R	T	No	Yes	15.11, 15.19.6
Formaldehyde solutions (45% or less)	Y	S/P	3	2G	Cont	No	T2	IIB	No	R	F-T	A	Yes	15.19.6, 16.2.9
Formamide	Y	P	3	2G	Open	No	-	-	Yes	O	No	A	No	15.19.6, 16.2.9
Formic acid	Y	S/P	3	2G	Cont	No	T1	IIA	No	R	T (g)	A	Yes	15.11.2, 15.11.3, 15.11.4, 15.11.6, 15.11.7, 15.11.8, 15.19.6, 16.2.9
Furfural	Y	S/P	3	2G	Cont	No	T2	IIB	No	R	F-T	A	No	15.19.6
Furfuryl alcohol	Y	P	3	2G	Open	No	-	-	Yes	O	No	A	No	15.19.6
Glucitol/Glycerol blend propoxylated (containing less than 10% amines) (n)	Z	S/P	3	2G	Cont	No	-	-	Yes	R	T	A, B, C	No	15.12.3, 15.12.4, 15.19.6
Glutaraldehyde solutions (50% or less)	Y	S/P	3	2G	Open	No	-		NF	O	No	No	No	15.19.6
Glycerol monooleate (n)	Y	P	2	2G	Open	No	-	-	Yes	O	No	A	No	15.19.6, 16.2.6, 16.2.9
Glycerol propoxylated (n)	Z	S/P	3	2G	Cont	No	-	-	Yes	R	T	A, B, C	No	15.12.3, 15.12.4, 15.19.6
Glycerol, propoxylated and ethoxylated (n)	Z	P	3	2G	Open	No	-	-	Yes	O	No	A, B, C	No	
Glycerol/Sucrose blend propoxylated and ethoxylated (n)	Z	P	3	2G	Open	No	-	-	Yes	O	No	A, B, C	No	
Glyceryl triacetate	Z	P	3	2G	Open	No			Yes	O	No	A, B	No	
Glycidyl ester of C₁₀ trialkylacetic acid	Y	P	2	2G	Open	No			Yes	O	No	A	No	15.19.6
Glycine, sodium salt solution	Z	P	3	2G	Open	No			Yes	O	No	A	No	
Glycolic acid solution (70% or less)	Z	S/P	3	2G	Open	No	-		NF	O	No	No	No	15.19.6, 16.2.9
Glyoxal solution (40% or less)	Y	P	3	2G	Open	No	-	-	Yes	O	No	A	No	15.19.6, 16.2.9
Glyoxylic acid solution (50% or less) (n)	Y	S/P	3	2G	Open	No	-	-	Yes	O	No	A, C, D	No	15.11.2, 15.11.3, 15.11.4, 15.11.6, 15.11.7, 15.11.8, 15.19.6, 16.2.9, 16.6.1, 16.6.2, 16.6.3
Glyphosate solution (not containing surfactant)	Y	P	2	2G	Open	No			Yes	O	No	A	No	15.19.6, 16.2.9
Groundnut oil (n)	Y	P	2 (k)	2G	Open	No	-	-	Yes	O	No	A, B, C	No	15.19.6, 16.2.6, 16.2.9
Groundnut oil (containing less than 4% free fatty acids)	Y	P	2 (k)	2G	Open	No	-	-	Yes	O	No	A, B, C, D	No	15.19.6, 16.2.6, 16.2.9

a	c	d	e	f	g	h	i'	i''	i'''	j	k	l	n	o
Heptane (all isomers)	X	P	2	2G	Cont	No			No	R	F	A	No	15.19.6, 16.2.9
n-Heptanoic acid	Z	P	3	2G	Open	No			Yes	O	No	A, B	No	
Heptanol (all isomers) (d)	Y	P	3	2G	Cont	No			No	R	F	A	No	15.19.6
Heptene (all isomers)	Y	P	3	2G	Cont	No			No	R	F	A	No	15.19.6
Heptyl acetate	Y	P	2	2G	Open	No			Yes	O	No	A	No	15.19.6
1-Hexadecylnaphthalene/1,4-Bis(hexadecyl)naphthalene mixture	Y	P	2	2G	Open	No			Yes	O	No	A, B	No	15.19.6, 16.2.6
Hexamethylenediamine adipate (50% in water)	Z	P	3	2G	Open	No			Yes	O	No	A	No	
Hexamethylenediamine (molten)	Y	S/P	2	2G	Cont	No			Yes	C	T	C	Yes	15.12, 15.17, 15.18, 15.19.6, 16.2.9
Hexamethylenediamine solution	Y	S/P	3	2G	Cont	No			Yes	R	T	A	No	15.19.6
Hexamethylene diisocyanate	Y	S/P	2	1G	Cont	Dry	T1	IIB	Yes	C	T	A, C (b), D	Yes	15.12, 15.17, 15.16.2, 15.18, 15.19
Hexamethylene glycol	Z	P	3	2G	Open	No			Yes	O	No	A	No	
Hexamethyleneimine	Y	S/P	2	2G	Cont	No			No	R	F-T	A, C	No	15.19.6
Hexane (all isomers)	Y	P	2	2G	Cont	No			No	R	F	A	No	15.19.6
1,6-Hexanediol, distillation overheads (n)	Y	P	3	2G	Open	No	-		Yes	O	No	A	No	15.12.3, 15.12.4, 15.19.6, 16.2.9
Hexanoic acid	Y	P	3	2G	Open	No			Yes	O	No	A, B	No	15.19.6
Hexanol	Y	P	3	2G	Open	No			Yes	O	No	A, B	No	15.19.6
Hexene (all isomers)	Y	P	3	2G	Cont	No			No	R	F	A	No	15.19.6
Hexyl acetate	Y	P	2	2G	Cont	No			No	R	F	A	No	15.19.6
Hydrochloric acid	Z	S/P	3	1G	Cont	No			NF	R	T	No	Yes	15.11
Hydrogen peroxide solutions (over 60% but not over 70% by mass)	Y	S/P	2	2G	Cont	No			NF	C	No	No	No	15.5.1, 15.19.6
Hydrogen peroxide solutions (over 8% but not over 60% by mass) (n)	Y	S/P	3	2G	Cont	No			NF	C	No	No	No	15.5.2, 15.18, 15.19.6
2-Hydroxyethyl acrylate	Y	S/P	2	2G	Cont	No			Yes	C	T	A	No	15.12, 15.13, 15.19.6, 16.6.1, 16.6.2
N-(Hydroxyethyl)ethylenediaminetriacetic acid, trisodium salt solution	Y	P	3	2G	Open	No			Yes	O	No	A	No	15.19.6
2-Hydroxy-4-(methylthio)butanoic acid	Z	P	3	2G	Open	No	-		Yes	O	No	A	No	
Illipe oil (n)	Y	P	2 (k)	2G	Open	No			Yes	O	No	A, B, C	No	15.19.6, 16.2.6, 16.2.9
Isoamyl alcohol	Z	P	3	2G	Cont	No			No	R	F	A, B	No	

a	c	d	e	f	g	h	i'	i''	i'''	j	k	l	n	o
Iso- and cyclo-alkanes (C$_{10}$–C$_{11}$) (n)	Y	P	3	2G	Cont	No	-		No	R	F	A	No	15.19.6
Iso- and cyclo-alkanes (C$_{10}$–C$_{11}$)	Z	P	3	2G	Cont	No			No	R	F	A	No	
Iso- and cyclo-alkanes (C$_{12}$+)	Z	P	3	2G	Cont	No			No	R	F	A	No	
Iso- and cyclo-alkanes (C$_{12}$+) (n)	Y	P	3	2G	Cont	No	-		No	R	F	A	No	
Isobutyl alcohol	Z	P	3	2G	Cont	No			No	R	F	A, B	No	
Isobutyl formate	Z	P	3	2G	Cont	No			No	R	F	A, B	No	
Isobutyl methacrylate	Z	S/P	3	2G	Cont	No		IIA	No	C	F-T	B, D	Yes	15.12, 15.13, 15.17, 15.19, 16.6.1, 16.6.2
Isophorone	Y	S/P	3	2G	Cont	No			Yes	R	No	A	No	15.19.6
Isophoronediamine	Y	S/P	3	2G	Cont	No			Yes	R	T	A	No	16.2.9
Isophorone diisocyanate	X	S/P	2	2G	Cont	Dry			Yes	C	T	A, B, D	No	15.12, 15.16.2, 15.17, 15.19.6
Isoprene	Y	S/P	3	2G	Cont	No	T3	IIB	No	R	F	B	No	15.13, 15.14, 15.19.6, 16.6.1, 16.6.2
Isopropanolamine	Y	S/P	3	2G	Open	No	T2	IIA	Yes	O	F-T	A	No	15.19.6, 16.2.6, 16.2.9
Isopropyl acetate	Z	P	3	2G	Cont	No			No	R	F	A, B	No	
Isopropylamine	Y	S/P	2	2G	Cont	No	T2	IIA	No	C	F-T	C, D	Yes	15.12, 15.14, 15.19
Isopropylamine (70% or less) solution (n)	Y	S/P	2	2G	Cont	No			No	C	F-T	C, D	Yes	15.12, 15.19.6, 16.2.9
Isopropylcyclohexane	Y	P	2	2G	Cont	No			No	R	F	A	No	15.19.6, 16.2.9
Isopropyl ether	Y	S/P	3	2G	Cont	Inert			No	R	F	A	No	15.4.6, 15.13.3, 15.19.6
Lactic acid	Z	P	3	2G	Open	No			No	O	No	A	No	
Lactonitrile solution (80% or less)	Y	S/P	2	1G	Cont	No			Yes	C	T	A, C, D	Yes	15.12, 15.13, 15.17, 15.18, 15.19, 16.6.1, 16.6.2, 16.6.3
Lard (n)	Y	S/P	2 (k)	2G	Open	No			Yes	O	No	A, B, C	No	15.19.6, 16.2.6, 16.2.9
Lard (containing less than 1% free fatty acids)	Y	P	2 (k)	2G	Open	No			Yes	O	No	A, B, C, D	No	15.19.6, 16.2.6, 16.2.9
Latex, ammonia (1% or less)-inhibited (n)	Y	S/P	3	2G	Open	No			Yes	O	No	A	No	15.19.6, 16.2.6, 16.2.9
Latex: Carboxylated styrene–Butadiene copolymer; Styrene–Butadiene rubber (n)	Z	P	3	2G	Open	No			Yes	O	No·	A	No	16.2.9
Lauric acid	X	P	2	2G	Open	No			Yes	O	No	A	No	15.19.6, 16.2.6, 16.2.9
Ligninsulphonic acid, sodium salt solution (n)	Z	P	3	2G	Open	No			Yes	O	No	A	No	16.2.9
Linseed oil (n)	Y	S/P	2 (k)	2G	Open	No			Yes	O	No	A, B, C	No	15.19.6, 16.2.6, 16.2.9
Linseed oil (containing less than 2% free fatty acids)	Y	P	2 (k)	2G	Open	No			Yes	O	No	A, B, C, D	No	15.19.6, 16.2.6

a	c	d	e	f	g	h	i'	i''	i'''	j	k	l	n	o
Liquid chemical wastes	X	S/P	2	2G	Cont	No			No	C	F-T	A	Yes	15.12, 15.19.6, 20.5.1
Long-chain alkaryl polyether (C$_{11}$–C$_{20}$)	Y	P	2	2G	Open	No			Yes	O	No	A, B	No	15.19.6, 16.2.6, 16.2.9
Long-chain alkaryl sulphonic acid (C$_{16}$–C$_{60}$) (n)	Y	P	2	2G	Open	No	-	-	Yes	O	No	A	No	15.19.6, 16.2.9
Long-chain alkylphenate/Phenol sulphide mixture (n)	Y	P	2	2G	Open	No	-	-	Yes	O	No	A	No	15.19.6, 16.2.6, 16.2.9
L-Lysine solution (60% or less)	Z	P	3	2G	Open	No			Yes	O	No	A	No	
Magnesium chloride solution	Z	P	3	2G	Open	No			Yes	O	No	A	No	
Magnesium long-chain alkaryl sulphonate (C$_{11}$–C$_{50}$) (n)	Y	P	2	2G	Open	No	-	-	Yes	O	No	A	No	15.19.6, 16.2.6, 16.2.9
Magnesium long-chain alkyl salicylate (C$_{11}$+) (n)	Y	P	2	2G	Open	No			Yes	O	No	A, B	No	15.19.6, 16.2.6, 16.2.9
Maleic anhydride	Y	S/P	3	2G	Cont	No			Yes	R	No	A, C (f)	No	16.2.9
Mango kernel oil (n)	Y	P	2 (k)	2G	Open	No	-	-	Yes	O	No	A, B, C	No	15.19.6, 16.2.6, 16.2.9
Mercaptobenzothiazol, sodium salt solution	X	S/P	2	2G	Open	No			NF	O	No	No	No	15.19.6, 16.2.9
Mesityl oxide	Z	S/P	3	2G	Cont	No	T2	IIB	No	R	F-T	A	No	15.19.6
Metam sodium solution	X	S/P	1	2G	Open	No			NF	O	No	No	No	15.19, 16.2.9
Methacrylic acid–Alkoxypoly(alkylene oxide) methacrylate copolymer, sodium salt aqueous solution (45% or less) (n)	Z	S/P	3	2G	Open	No	-	-	NF	O	No	A, C	No	16.2.9
Methacrylic acid	Y	S/P	3	2G	Cont	No			Yes	R	T	A	No	15.13, 15.19.6, 16.2.9, 16.6.1
Methacrylic resin in ethylene dichloride	Y	S/P	2	2G	Cont	No	T2	IIA	No	R	F-T	A, B	No	15.19, 16.2.9
Methacrylonitrile	Y	S/P	2	2G	Cont	No			No	C	F-T	A	Yes	15.12, 15.13, 15.17, 15.19
3-Methoxy-1-butanol	Z	P	3	2G	Cont	No			No	R	F	A	No	
3-Methoxybutyl acetate	Y	P	3	2G	Open	No			Yes	O	No	A, B	No	15.19.6
N-(2-Methoxy-1-methylethyl)-2-ethyl-6-methylchloroacetanilide	X	P	1	2G	Open	No			Yes	O	No	A	No	15.19, 16.2.6
Methyl acetate	Z	P	3	2G	Cont	No			No	R	F	A	No	
Methyl acetoacetate	Z	P	3	2G	Open	No			Yes	O	No	A	No	
Methyl acrylate	Y	S/P	2	2G	Cont	No	T1	IIB	No	R	F-T	A	Yes	15.13, 15.19.6, 16.6.1, 16.6.2
Methyl alcohol	Y	P	3	2G	Cont	No			No	R	F	A	No	15.19.6
Methylamine solutions (42% or less)	Y	S/P	2	2G	Cont	No			No	C	F-T	A, C, D	Yes	15.12, 15.17, 15.19
Methylamyl acetate	Y	P	2	2G	Cont	No			No	R	F	A	No	15.19.6
Methylamyl alcohol	Z	P	3	2G	Cont	No			No	R	F	A	No	15.19.6

a	c	d	e	f	g	h	i'	i''	i'''	j	k	l	n	o
Methyl amyl ketone	Z	P	3	2G	Cont	No			No	R	F	A	No	15.19.6
Methylbutenol	Y	P	3	2G	Cont	No			No	R	F	A	No	15.19.6, 16.2.9
Methyl *tert*-butyl ether	Z	P	3	2G	Cont	No			No	R	F	A, B	No	
Methyl butyl ketone	Y	P	3	2G	Cont	No			No	R	F	A, B	No	15.19.6
Methylbutynol	Z	P	3	2G	Cont	No			No	R	F	A	No	
Methyl butyrate	Y	P	3	2G	Cont	No			No	R	F	A	No	15.19.6
Methylcyclohexane	Y	P	2	2G	Cont	No			No	R	F	A	No	15.19.6
Methylcyclopentadiene dimer	Y	P	2	2G	Cont	No			No	R	F	B	No	15.19.6
Methylcyclopentadienyl manganese tricarbonyl	X	S/P	1	1G	Cont	No	-		Yes	C	T	A, B, C, D	Yes	15.12, 15.18, 15.19, 16.2.9
Methyl diethanolamine	Y	S/P	3	2G	Open	No			Yes	O	No	A	No	15.19.6, 16.2.6
2-Methyl-6-ethylaniline	Y	S/P	3	2G	Open	No			Yes	O	No	A, D	No	15.19.6
Methyl ethyl ketone	Z	P	3	2G	Cont	No			No	R	F	A	No	
2-Methyl-5-ethylpyridine	Y	S/P	3	2G	Open	No		IIA	Yes	O	No	A, D	No	15.19.6
Methyl formate	Z	S/P	2	2G	Cont	No			No	R	F-T	A	Yes	15.12, 15.14, 15.19
2-Methyl-2-hydroxy-3-butyne	Z	S/P	3	2G	Cont	No		IIA	No	R	F-T	A, B, D	No	15.19.6, 16.2.9
Methyl isobutyl ketone	Z	P	3	2G	Cont	No			No	R	F	A, B	No	
Methyl methacrylate	Y	S/P	2	2G	Cont	No	T2	IIA	No	R	F-T	A	No	15.13, 15.19.6, 16.6.1, 16.6.2
3-Methyl-3-methoxybutanol	Z	P	3	2G	Open	No			Yes	O	No	A	No	
Methylnaphthalene (molten)	X	S/P	2	2G	Cont	No			Yes	R	No	A, D	No	15.19.6
2-Methyl-1,3-propanediol (n)	Z	P	3	2G	Open	No	-		Yes	O	No	A	No	
2-Methylpyridine	Z	S/P	2	2G	Cont	No			No	C	F	A	No	15.12.3, 15.19.6
3-Methylpyridine	Z	S/P	2	2G	Cont	No			No	C	F	A, C	No	15.12.3, 15.19
4-Methylpyridine	Z	S/P	2	2G	Cont	No			No	C	F-T	A	No	15.12.3, 15.19, 16.2.9
N-Methyl-2-pyrrolidone	Y	P	3	2G	Open	No			Yes	O	No	A	No	15.19.6
Methyl salicylate	Y	P	3	2G	Open	No			Yes	O	No	A	No	15.19.6
alpha-Methylstyrene	Y	S/P	2	2G	Cont	No	T1	IIB	No	R	F-T	A, D (j)	No	15.13, 15.19.6, 16.6.1, 16.6.2
3-(Methylthio)propionaldehyde	Y	S/P	2	2G	Cont	No	T3	IIA	Yes	C	T	B, C	Yes	15.12, 15.17, 15.19
3'-(Methylthio)propionaldehyde (n)	Y	S/P	2	2G	Cont	No	T3	IIA	No	C	F-T	B, C	Yes	15.12, 15.17, 15.19
Molybdenum polysulfide long chain alkyl dithiocarbamide complex (n)	Y	S/P	2	2G	Cont	No	-	-	Yes	C	T	A, B, C	Yes	15.12, 15.17, 15.19, 16.2.6, 16.2.9

a	c	d	e	f	g	h	i'	i''	i'''	j	k	l	n	o
Morpholine	Y	S/P	3	2G	Cont	No	T2	IIA	No	R	F	A	No	15.19.6
Motor fuel anti-knock compounds (containing lead alkyls)	X	S/P	1	1G	Cont	No	T4	IIA	No	C	F-T	A, C	Yes	15.6, 15.12, 15.18, 15.19
Myrcene (n)	X	P	2	2G	Cont	No	-	-	No	R	F	A	No	15.19.6, 16.2.9
Naphthalene (molten)	X	S/P	2	2G	Cont	No	T1	IIA	Yes	R	No	A, D	No	15.19.6, 16.2.9
Naphthalenesulphonic acid–Formaldehyde copolymer, sodium salt solution (n)	Z	P	3	2G	Open	No	-	-	Yes	O	No	A	No	16.2.9
Neodecanoic acid	Y	P	2	2G	Open	No			Yes	O	No	A	No	15.19.6
Nitrating acid (mixture of sulphuric and nitric acids)	Y	S/P	2	2G	Cont	No			NF	C	T	No	Yes	15.11, 15.16.2, 15.17, 15.19
Nitric acid (70% and over)	Y	S/P	2	2G	Cont	No			NF	C	T	No	Yes	15.11, 15.19
Nitric acid (less than 70%)	Y	S/P	2	2G	Cont	No			NF	R	T	No	Yes	15.11, 15.19
Nitrilotriacetic acid, trisodium salt solution	Y	P	3	2G	Open	No			Yes	O	No	A	No	15.19.6
Nitrobenzene	Y	S/P	2	2G	Cont	No	T1	IIA	Yes	C	T	A, D	No	15.12, 15.17, 15.18, 15.19, 16.2.9
Nitroethane	Y	S/P	3	2G	Cont	No		IIB	No	R	F-T	A (f)	No	15.19.6, 16.6.1, 16.6.2, 16.6.4
Nitroethane (80%)/Nitropropane (20%)	Y	S/P	3	2G	Cont	No		IIB	No	R	F-T	A (f)	No	15.19.6, 16.6.1, 16.6.2, 16.6.3
Nitroethane, 1-Nitropropane (each 15% or more) mixture (n)	Y	S/P	3	2G	Cont	No	-	-	No	R	F	A	No	15.19.6, 16.2.6, 16.6.1, 16.6.2, 16.6.3
o-Nitrophenol (molten)	Y	S/P	2	2G	Cont	No			Yes	C	T	A, D	No	15.12, 15.19.6, 16.2.6, 16.2.9
1- or 2-Nitropropane	Y	S/P	3	2G	Cont	No	T2	IIB	No	R	F-T	A	No	15.19.6
Nitropropane (60%)/Nitroethane (40%) mixture	Y	S/P	3	2G	Cont	No			No	R	F-T	A (f)	No	15.19.6
o- or p-Nitrotoluenes (n)	Y	S/P	2	2G	Cont	No		IIB	Yes	C	T	A, B	No	15.12, 15.17, 15.19.6
Nonane (all isomers)	X	P	2	2G	Cont	No			No	R	F	B, C	No	15.19.6
Nonanoic acid (all isomers)	Y	P	3	2G	Open	No			Yes	O	No	A, B	No	15.19.6, 16.2.9
Non-edible industrial grade palm oil	Y	S/P	2	2G	Cont	No	-	-	Yes	R	No	A, B, C	No	15.12.3, 15.12.4, 15.19.6, 16.2.6, 16.2.9
Nonene (all isomers)	Y	P	2	2G	Cont	No			No	R	F	A	No	15.19.6
Nonyl alcohol (all isomers)	Y	P	2	2G	Open	No			Yes	O	No	A	No	15.19.6
Nonyl methacrylate monomer	Y	P	2	2G	Open	No			Yes	O	No	A, B	No	15.19.6, 16.2.9
Nonylphenol	X	P	1	2G	Open	No			Yes	O	No	A	No	15.19, 16.2.6, 16.2.9
Nonylphenol poly(4+)ethoxylate (n)	Y	P	2	2G	Open	No	-	-	Yes	O	No	A	No	15.19.6, 16.2.6
Noxious liquid, NF, (1) n.o.s. (trade name . . ., contains . . .) ST1, Cat. X	X	P	1	2G	Open	No	-	-	Yes	O	No	A	No	15.19, 16.2.6

a	c	d	e	f	g	h	i'	i''	i'''	j	k	l	n	o
Noxious liquid, F, (2) n.o.s. (trade name . . . , contains . . .) ST1, Cat. X	X	P	1	2G	Cont	No	T3	IIA	No	R	F	A	No	15.19, 16.2.6
Noxious liquid, NF, (3) n.o.s. (trade name . . ., contains . . .) ST2, Cat. X	X	P	2	2G	Open	No	-		Yes	O	No	A	No	15.19, 16.2.6
Noxious liquid, F, (4) n.o.s. (trade name . . ., contains . . .) ST2, Cat. X	X	P	2	2G	Cont	No	T3	IIA	No	R	F	A	No	15.19, 16.2.6
Noxious liquid, NF, (5) n.o.s. (trade name . . ., contains . . .) ST2, Cat. Y	Y	P	2	2G	Open	No	-		Yes	O	No	A	No	15.19, 16.2.6, 16.2.9 (l)
Noxious liquid, F, (6) n.o.s. (trade name . . ., contains . . .) ST2, Cat. Y	Y	P	2	2G	Cont	No	T3	IIA	No	R	F	A	No	15.19, 16.2.6, 16.2.9 (l)
Noxious liquid, NF, (7) n.o.s. (trade name . . ., contains . . .) ST3, Cat. Y	Y	P	3	2G	Open	No	-	-	Yes	O	No	A	No	15.19, 16.2.6, 16.2.9 (l)
Noxious liquid, F, (8) n.o.s. (trade name . . ., contains . . .) ST3, Cat. Y	Y	P	3	2G	Cont	No	T3	IIA	No	R	F	A	No	15.19, 16.2.6, 16.2.9 (l)
Noxious liquid, NF, (9) n.o.s. (trade name . . ., contains . . .) ST3, Cat. Z	Z	P	3	2G	Open	No	-		Yes	O	No	A	No	
Noxious liquid, F, (10) n.o.s. (trade name . . ., contains . . .) ST3, Cat. Z	Z	P	3	2G	Cont	No	T3	IIA	No	R	F	A	No	
Octane (all isomers) (n)	X	P	2	2G	Cont	No			No	R	F	A	No	15.19.6
Octanoic acid (all isomers) (n)	Y	P	3	2G	Open	No	-	-	Yes	O	No	A	No	15.19.6
Octanoic acid (all isomers)	Z	P	3	2G	Open	No			Yes	O	No	A, B	No	
Octanol (all isomers)	Y	P	2	2G	Open	No			Yes	O	No	A	No	
Octene (all isomers)	Y	P	2	2G	Cont	No			No	R	F	A	No	15.19.6
n-Octyl acetate (n)	Y	P	3	2G	Open	No			Yes	O	No	A	No	15.19.6, 16.2.9
Octyl aldehydes (n)	Y	P	2	2G	Cont	No			No	R	F	A	No	15.19.6, 16.2.9
Octyl aldehydes	Y	P	3	2G	Cont	No			No	R	F	A	No	15.19.6, 16.2.9
Octyl decyl adipate (n)	Y	P	2	2G	Open	No			Yes	O	No	A	No	15.19.6, 16.2.9
Olefin–Alkyl ester copolymer (molecular weight 2000+)	Y	P	2	2G	Open	No			Yes	O	No	A, B	No	15.19.6, 16.2.6, 16.2.9
Olefin mixtures (C5–C7) (n)	Y	P	3	2G	Cont	No			No	R	F	A	No	15.19.6
Olefin mixtures (C5–C15) (n)	X	P	2	2G	Cont	No			No	R	F	A	No	15.19.6
Olefins (C13+, all isomers)	Y	P	2	2G	Open	No			Yes	O	No	A, B	No	15.19.6, 16.2.9
alpha-Olefins (C6–C18) mixtures (n)	X	P	2	2G	Cont	No			No	R	F	A	No	15.19.6, 16.2.9
Oleic acid	Y	P	2	2G	Open	No			Yes	O	No	A, B	No	15.19.6, 16.2.9

a	c	d	e	f	g	h	i'	i''	i'''	j	k	l	n	o
Oleum	Y	S/P	2	2G	Cont	No			NF	C	T	No	Yes	15.11.2 to 15.11.8, 15.12.1, 15.16.2, 15.17, 15.19, 16.2.6
Oleylamine (n)	X	S/P	2	2G	Cont	No			Yes	R	T	A	No	15.19.6, 16.2.9
Olive oil (n)	Y	S/P	2 (k)	2G	Open	No	-	-	Yes	O	No	A, B, C	No	15.19.6, 16.2.6, 16.2.9
Olive oil (containing less than 3.3% free fatty acids)	Y	P	2 (k)	2G	Open	No	-	-	Yes	O	No	A, B, C, D	No	15.19.6, 16.2.6, 16.2.9
Oxygenated aliphatic hydrocarbon mixture (n)	Z	S/P	3	2G	Open	No	-	-	Yes	O	No	A, B, C	No	
Palm acid oil (n)	Y	S/P	2	2G	Open	No	-	-	Yes	O	No	A, B, C	No	15.19.6, 16.2.6, 16.2.9
Palm fatty acid distillate (n)	Y	S/P	2	2G	Open	No	-	-	Yes	O	No	A, B, C	No	15.19.6, 16.2.6, 16.2.9
Palm kernel acid oil (n)	Y	S/P	2	2G	Open	No	-	-	Yes	O	No	A, B, C	No	15.19.6, 16.2.6, 16.2.9
Palm kernel oil (n)	Y	S/P	2 (k)	2G	Open	No	-	-	Yes	O	No	A, B, C	No	15.19.6, 16.2.6, 16.2.9
Palm kernel oil (containing less than 5% free fatty acids)	Y	P	2 (k)	2G	Open	No	T3	IIB	Yes	O	No	A, B	No	15.19.6, 16.2.6, 16.2.9
Palm kernel olein (n)	Y	P	2 (k)	2G	Open	No	-	-	Yes	O	No	A, B, C	No	15.19.6, 16.2.6, 16.2.9
Palm kernel stearin (n)	Y	P	2 (k)	2G	Open	No	-	-	Yes	O	No	A, B, C	No	15.19.6, 16.2.6, 16.2.9
Palm mid fraction (n)	Y	P	2 (k)	2G	Open	No	-	-	Yes	O	No	A, B, C	No	15.19.6, 16.2.6, 16.2.9
Palm oil (n)	Y	S/P	2 (k)	2G	Open	No	-	-	Yes	O	No	A, B, C	No	15.19.6, 16.2.6, 16.2.9
Palm oil (containing less than 5% free fatty acids)	Y	P	2 (k)	2G	Open	No	-	-	Yes	O	No	A, B, C, D	No	15.19.6, 16.2.6, 16.2.9
Palm oil fatty acid methyl ester (n)	Y	P	2	2G	Open	No	-	-	Yes	O	No	A	No	15.19.6, 16.2.9
Palm olein (n)	Y	P	2 (k)	2G	Open	No	-	-	Yes	O	No	A, B, C	No	15.19.6, 16.2.6, 16.2.9
Palm olein (containing less than 5% free fatty acids)	Y	P	2 (k)	2G	Open	No	-	-	Yes	O	No	A, B, C, D	No	15.19.6, 16.2.6, 16.2.9
Palm stearin (n)	Y	P	2 (k)	2G	Open	No	-	-	Yes	O	No	A, B, C	No	15.19.6, 16.2.6, 16.2.9
Palm stearin (containing less than 5% free fatty acids)	Y	P	2 (k)	2G	Open	No	-	-	Yes	O	No	A, B, C, D	No	15.19.6, 16.2.6, 16.2.9
Paraffin wax	Y	P	2	2G	Open	No			Yes	O	No	A, B	No	15.19.6, 16.2.6, 16.2.9
Paraldehyde	Z	S/P	3	2G	Cont	No	T3	IIB	No	R	F	A	No	15.19.6, 16.2.9
Paraldehyde–Ammonia reaction product	Y	S/P	2	2G	Cont	No			No	C	F-T	A	No	15.12.3, 15.19
Pentachloroethane	Y	S/P	2	2G	Cont	No			NF	R	T	No	No	15.12, 15.17, 15.19.6
1,3-Pentadiene (n)	Y	S/P	3	2G	Cont	No			No	R	F-T	A, B	No	15.13, 15.19.6, 16.6.1, 16.6.2, 16.6.3
1,3-Pentadiene	Y	P	3	2G	Cont	No			No	R	F-T	A, B	No	15.13, 15.19.6, 16.6.1, 16.6.2, 16.6.3

a	c	d	e	f	g	h	i'	i''	i'''	j	k	l	n	o
Pentaethylenehexamine	X	S/P	2	2G	Open	No			Yes	O	No	B	Yes	15.19
Pentane (all isomers)	Y	P	3	2G	Cont	No			No	R	F	A	No	15.14, 15.19.6
Pentanoic acid	Y	P	3	2G	Open	No			Yes	O	No	A, B	No	15.19.6
n-Pentanoic acid (64%)/2-Methylbutyric acid (36%) mixture	Y	S/P	2	2G	Open	No	T2		Yes	C	No	A, D	No	15.11.2, 15.11.3, 15.11.4, 15.11.6, 15.11.7, 15.11.8, 15.12.3, 15.19
Pentene (all isomers)	Y	P	3	2G	Cont	No			No	R	F	A	No	15.14, 15.19.6
n-Pentyl propionate	Y	P	3	2G	Cont	No			No	R	F	A	No	15.19.6
Perchloroethylene	Y	S/P	2	2G	Cont	No			NF	R	T	No	No	15.12.1, 15.12.2, 15.19.6
Petrolatum (n)	Y	P	2	2G	Open	No	-		Yes	O	No	A	No	15.19.6, 16.2.6, 16.2.9
Petrolatum	Z	P	3	2G	Open	No	-		Yes	O	No	A, B	No	16.2.6, 16.2.9
Phenol	Y	S/P	2	2G	Cont	No	T1	IIA	Yes	C	T	A	No	15.12, 15.19, 16.2.9
1-Phenyl-1-xylylethane	Y	P	3	2G	Open	No			Yes	O	No	A, B	No	15.19.6, 16.2.6, 16.2.9
Phosphate esters, alkyl (C$_{12}$–C$_{14}$) amine (n)	Y	P	2	2G	Cont	No	-		No	R	F	A	No	15.19.6, 16.2.6, 16.2.9
Phosphoric acid	Z	S/P	3	2G	Open	No			NF	O	No	No	No	15.11.1, 15.11.2, 15.11.3, 15.11.4, 15.11.6, 15.11.7, 15.11.8, 16.2.9
Phosphorus, yellow or white	X	S/P	1	1G	Cont	Pad + (vent or inert)			No (c)	C	No	C	Yes	15.7, 15.19, 16.2.9
Phthalic anhydride (molten)	Y	S/P	2	2G	Cont	No	T1	IIA	Yes	R	No	A, D	No	15.19.6, 16.2.6, 16.2.9
alpha-Pinene	X	P	2	2G	Cont	No			No	R	F	A	No	15.19.6
beta-Pinene	X	P	2	2G	Cont	No			No	R	F	A	No	15.19.6
Pine oil	X	P	2	2G	Open	No			Yes	O	No	A	No	15.19.6, 16.2.6, 16.2.9
Polyacrylic acid solution (40% or less) (n)	Z	S/P	3	2G	Open	No	-		Yes	O	No	A, C	No	
Polyalkyl (C$_{18}$–C$_{22}$) acrylate in xylene (n)	Y	P	2	2G	Cont	No			No	R	F	A, B	No	15.19.6, 16.2.6, 16.2.9
Polyalkyl (C$_{18}$–C$_{22}$) acrylate in xylene	Y	P	3	2G	Cont	No			No	R	F	A	No	15.19.6, 16.2.6, 16.2.9
Poly(2–8)alkylene glycol monoalkyl (C$_1$–C$_6$) ether (n)	Z	P	3	2G	Open	No	-		Yes	O	No	A	No	
Poly(2–8)alkylene glycol monoalkyl (C$_1$–C$_6$) ether acetate (n)	Y	P	2	2G	Open	No	-		Yes	O	No	A	No	15.19.6
Polyalkyl (C$_{10}$–C$_{20}$) methacrylate	Y	P	2	2G	Open	No			Yes	O	No	A, B	No	15.19.6, 16.2.6, 16.2.9
Polyalkyl (C$_{10}$–C$_{18}$) methacrylate/Ethylene–Propylene copolymer mixture	Y	P	2	2G	Open	No			Yes	O	No	A, B	No	15.19.6, 16.2.6, 16.2.9

a	c	d	e	f	g	h	i'	i''	i'''	j	k	l	n	o
Polybutene (n)	Y	P	2	2G	Open	No	-	-	Yes	O	No	A	No	15.19.6, 16.2.6
Polybutenyl succinimide (n)	Y	P	2	2G	Open	No	-	-	Yes	O	No	A	No	15.19.6, 16.2.6, 16.2.9
Poly(2+)cyclic aromatics	X	P	1	2G	Cont	No			Yes	R	No	A, D	No	15.19, 16.2.6, 16.2.9
Polyether (molecular weight 1350+) (n)	Y	P	2	2G	Open	No	-	-	Yes	O	No	A	No	15.19.6, 16.2.6
Polyethylene glycol	Z	P	3	2G	Open	No			Yes	O	No	A	No	
Polyethylene glycol dimethyl ether	Z	P	3	2G	Open	No			Yes	O	No	A	No	
Polyethylene polyamines (n)	Y	S/P	2	2G	Open	No	-		Yes	O	No	A	No	15.19.6
Polyethylene polyamines (more than 50% C_5–C_{20} paraffin oil) (n)	Y	S/P	2	2G	Open	No			Yes	O	No	A	No	15.19.6, 16.2.9
Polyferric sulphate solution	Y	S/P	3	2G	Open	No			NF	O	No	No	No	15.19.6
Poly(iminoethylene)-graft-N-poly(ethyleneoxy) solution (90% or less) (n)	Z	S/P	3	2G	Open	No	-		NF	O	No	A, C	No	16.2.9
Polyisobutenamine in aliphatic (C_{10}–C_{14}) solvent	Y	P	3	2G	Open	No	T3	IIA	Yes	O	No	A	No	15.19.6
Polyisobutenyl anhydride adduct	Z	P	3	2G	Open	No			Yes	O	No	A, B	No	
Poly(4+)isobutylene	Y	P	2	2G	Open	No			Yes	O	No	A, B	No	15.19.6, 16.2.9
Polymethylene polyphenyl isocyanate (n)	Y	S/P	2	2G	Cont	Dry			Yes (a)	C	T (a)	A	No	15.12, 15.16.2, 15.19.6, 16.2.9
Polyolefin (molecular weight 300+) (n)	Y	S/P	2	2G	Open	No	-	-	Yes	O	No	A	No	15.19.6, 16.2.6, 16.2.9
Polyolefin amide alkeneamine (C_{17}+)	Y	P	2	2G	Open	No			Yes	O	No	A, B	No	15.19.6, 16.2.6
Polyolefin amide alkeneamine borate (C_{28}–C_{250})	Y	P	2	2G	Open	No			Yes	O	No	A, B	No	15.19.6, 16.2.6, 16.2.9
Polyolefinamine (C_{28}–C_{250})	Y	P	2	2G	Open	No			Yes	O	No	A	No	15.19.6, 16.2.9
Polyolefinamine in alkyl (C_2–C_4) benzenes	Y	P	2	2G	Cont	No			No	R	F	A	No	15.19.6, 16.2.6, 16.2.9
Polyolefinamine in aromatic solvent	Y	P	2	2G	Cont	No			No	R	F	A	No	15.19.6, 16.2.6, 16.2.9
Polyolefin aminoester salts (molecular weight 2000+) (n)	Y	P	2	2G	Open	No	-	-	Yes	O	No	A	No	15.19.6, 16.2.6, 16.2.9
Polyolefin anhydride	Y	P	2	2G	Open	No			Yes	O	No	A, B	No	15.19.6, 16.2.6, 16.2.9
Polyolefin ester (C_{28}–C_{250})	Y	P	2	2G	Open	No			Yes	O	No	A, B	No	15.19.6, 16.2.6, 16.2.9
Polyolefin phenolic amine (C_{28}–C_{250})	Y	P	2	2G	Open	No			Yes	O	No	A, B	No	15.19.6, 16.2.6, 16.2.9
Polyolefin phosphorosulphide, barium derivative (C_{28}–C_{250})	Y	P	2	2G	Open	No			Yes	O	No	A, B	No	15.19.6, 16.2.6, 16.2.9
Poly(20)oxyethylene sorbitan monooleate	Y	P	2	2G	Open	No			Yes	O	No	A	No	15.19.6, 16.2.6, 16.2.9
Poly(5+)propylene (n)	Y	P	3	2G	Open	No	-	-	Yes	O	No	A	No	15.19.6, 16.2.9
Polypropylene glycol (n)	Z	S/P	3	2G	Cont	No			Yes	O	No	A, B, C	No	15.19.6

a	c	d	e	f	g	h	i'	i''	i'''	j	k	l	n	o
Polypropylene glycol	Z	P	3	2G	Cont	No			Yes	O	No	A	No	
Polysiloxane	Y	P	3	2G	Cont	No			No	R	F	A, B	No	15.19.6, 16.2.9
Potassium chloride solution (n)	Z	S/P	3	2G	Open	No	-		NF	O	No	A	No	16.2.9
Potassium hydroxide solution	Y	S/P	3	2G	Open	No			NF	O	No	No	No	15.19.6
Potassium oleate	Y	P	2	2G	Open	No			Yes	O	No	A	No	15.19.6, 16.2.6, 16.2.9
Potassium thiosulphate (50% or less)	Y	P	3	2G	Open	No			NF	O	No	No	No	15.19.6, 16.2.9
n-Propanolamine	Y	S/P	3	2G	Open	No			Yes	O	No	A, D	No	15.19.6, 16.2.9
beta-Propiolactone	Y	S/P	2	2G	Cont	No		IIA	Yes	R	T	A	No	15.19.6
Propionaldehyde	Y	S/P	3	2G	Cont	No			No	R	F-T	A	Yes	15.17, 15.19.6
Propionic acid	Y	S/P	3	2G	Cont	No	T1	IIA	No	R	F	A	Yes	15.11.2, 15.11.3, 15.11.4, 15.11.6, 15.11.7, 15.11.8, 15.19.6
Propionic anhydride	Y	S/P	3	2G	Cont	No	T2	IIA	Yes	R	T	A	No	15.19.6
Propionitrile	Y	S/P	2	1G	Cont	No	T1	IIB	No	C	F-T	A, D	Yes	15.12, 15.17, 15.18, 15.19
n-Propyl acetate	Y	P	3	2G	Cont	No			No	R	F	A, B	No	15.19.6
n-Propyl alcohol	Y	P	3	2G	Cont	No			No	R	F	A	No	15.19.6
n-Propylamine	Z	S/P	2	2G	Cont	Inert	T2	IIA	No	C	F-T	A, D	Yes	15.12, 15.19
Propylbenzene (all isomers)	Y	P	3	2G	Cont	No			No	R	F	A	No	15.19.6
Propylene glycol methyl ether acetate	Z	P	3	2G	Cont	No			No	R	F	A	No	
Propylene glycol monoalkyl ether	Z	P	3	2G	Cont	No			No	R	F	A, B	No	
Propylene glycol phenyl ether	Z	P	3	2G	Open	No			Yes	O	No	A, B	No	
Propylene oxide	Y	S/P	2	2G	Cont	Inert	T2	IIB	No	C	F-T	A, C	No	15.8, 15.12.1, 15.14, 15.19
Propylene tetramer	X	P	2	2G	Cont	No			No	R	F	A	No	15.19.6
Propylene trimer	Y	P	2	2G	Cont	No			No	R	F	A	No	15.19.6
Pyridine	Y	S/P	3	2G	Cont	No	T1	IIA	No	R	F	A	No	15.19.6
Pyrolysis gasoline (containing benzene) (n)	Y	S/P	2	2G	Cont	No	T3	IIA	No	C	F-T	A, B	No	15.12, 15.17, 15.19.6
Rapeseed oil (n)	Y	S/P	2 (k)	2G	Open	No	-	-	Yes	O	No	A, B, C	No	15.19.6, 16.2.6, 16.2.9
Rapeseed oil (low erucic acid, containing less than 4% free fatty acids)	Y	P	2 (k)	2G	Open	No	-	-	Yes	O	No	A, B, C, D	No	15.19.6, 16.2.6, 16.2.9
Rape seed oil fatty acid methyl esters (n)	Y	P	2	2G	Open	No	-	-	Yes	O	No	A	No	15.19.6
Resin oil, distilled (n)	Y	S/P	2	2G	Cont	No	T1	IIA	No	C	F-T	A, B, C	No	15.12, 15.17, 15.19.6

a	c	d	e	f	g	h	i'	i''	i'''	j	k	l	n	o
Rice bran oil (n)	Y	S/P	2 (k)	2G	Open	No	-	-	Yes	O	No	A, B, C	No	15.19.6, 16.2.6, 16.2.9
Rosin	Y	P	2	2G	Open	No			Yes	O	No	A	No	15.19.6, 16.2.6, 16.2.9
Safflower oil (n)	Y	S/P	2 (k)	2G	Open	No	-	-	Yes	O	No	A, B, C	No	15.19.6, 16.2.6, 16.2.9
Shea butter (n)	Y	S/P	2 (k)	2G	Open	No	-	-	Yes	O	No	A, B, C	No	15.19.6, 16.2.6, 16.2.9
Sodium alkyl (C_{14}–C_{17}) sulphonates (60–65% solution) (n)	Y	P	2	2G	Open	No			NF	O	No	No	No	15.19.6, 16.2.6, 16.2.9
Sodium aluminosilicate slurry	Z	P	3	2G	Open	No			Yes	O	No	A, B	No	
Sodium benzoate	Z	P	3	2G	Open	No			Yes	O	No	A	No	
Sodium borohydride (15% or less)/Sodium hydroxide solution	Y	S/P	3	2G	Open	No			NF	O	No	No	No	15.19.6, 16.2.6, 16.2.9
Sodium carbonate solution	Z	P	3	2G	Open	No			Yes	O	No	A	No	
Sodium chlorate solution (50% or less)	Z	S/P	3	2G	Open	No			NF	O	No	No	No	15.9, 16.2.9
Sodium dichromate solution (70% or less)	Y	S/P	2	2G	Open	No			NF	C	No	No	No	15.12.3, 15.19
Sodium hydrogen sulphide (6% or less)/Sodium carbonate (3% or less) solution	Z	P	3	2G	Open	No			NF	O	No	No	No	15.19.6, 16.2.9
Sodium hydrogen sulphite solution (45% or less)	Z	S/P	3	2G	Open	No			NF	O	No	No	No	16.2.9
Sodium hydrosulphide/Ammonium sulphide solution	Y	S/P	2	2G	Cont	No			No	C	F-T	A	Yes	15.12, 15.14, 15.17, 15.19, 16.6.1, 16.6.2, 16.6.3
Sodium hydrosulphide solution (45% or less)	Z	S/P	3	2G	Cont	Vent or pad (gas)			NF	R	T	No	No	15.19.6, 16.2.9
Sodium hydroxide solution	Y	S/P	3	2G	Open	No			NF	O	No	No	No	15.19.6, 16.2.6, 16.2.9
Sodium hypochlorite solution (15% or less)	Y	S/P	2	2G	Cont	No	-		NF	R	No	No	No	15.19.6
Sodium nitrite solution	Y	S/P	2	2G	Open	No			NF	O	No	No	No	15.12.3.1, 15.12.3.2, 15.19, 16.2.9
Sodium petroleum sulphonate (n)	Y	S/P	2	2G	Open	No			Yes	O	No	A	No	15.19.6, 16.2.6
Sodium poly(4+)acrylate solutions (n)	Z	P	3	2G	Open	No	-		Yes	O	No	A	No	16.2.9
Sodium silicate solution	Y	P	3	2G	Open	No			NF	O	No	No	No	15.19.6, 16.2.9
Sodium sulphide solution (15% or less)	Y	S/P	3	2G	Cont	No			NF	C	T	No	No	15.19.6, 16.2.9
Sodium sulphite solution (25% or less)	Y	P	3	2G	Open	No			NF	O	No	No	No	15.19.6, 16.2.9
Sodium thiocyanate solution (56% or less)	Y	P	3	2G	Open	No			Yes	O	No	No	No	15.19.6, 16.2.9
Soyabean oil (n)	Y	S/P	2 (k)	2G	Open	No	-		Yes	O	No	A, B, C	No	15.19.6, 16.2.6, 16.2.9
Soyabean oil (containing less than 0.5% free fatty acids)	Y	P	2 (k)	2G	Open	No	-		Yes	O	No	A, B, C, D	No	15.19.6, 16.2.6

a	c	d	e	f	g	h	i'	i''	i'''	j	k	l	n	o
Styrene monomer (n)	Y	S/P	3	2G	Cont	No	T1	IIA	No	R	F	A, B	No	15.13, 15.19.6, 16.6.1, 16.6.2
Sulphohydrocarbon (C₃–C₈₈) (n)	Y	P	2	2G	Open	No	-	-	Yes	O	No	A	No	15.19.6, 16.2.6, 16.2.9
Sulpholane	Y	P	3	2G	Open	No			Yes	O	No	A	No	15.19.6, 16.2.9
Sulphonated polyacrylate solution (o)	Z	P	3	2G	Cont	No			No	R	F	A	No	
Sulphur (molten)	Z	S	3	1G	Open	Vent or pad (gas)	T3		Yes	O	F-T	No	No	15.10, 16.2.9
Sulphuric acid	Y	S/P	3	2G	Open	No			NF	O	No	No	No	15.11, 15.16.2, 15.19.6
Sulphuric acid, spent	Y	S/P	3	2G	Open	No			NF	O	No	No	No	15.11, 15.16.2, 15.19.6
Sulphurized fat (C₁₄–C₂₀)	Z	P	3	2G	Open	No			Yes	O	No	A, B	No	
Sulphurized polyolefinamide alkene (C₂₈–C₂₅₀) amine (n)	Z	P	3	2G	Open	No	-	-	Yes	O	No	A	No	15.19.6, 16.2.6, 16.2.9
Sunflower seed oil (n)	Y	S/P	2 (k)	2G	Open	No	-	-	Yes	O	No	A, B, C	No	15.19.6, 16.2.6, 16.2.9
Sunflower seed oil (containing less than 7% free fatty acids)	Y	P	2 (k)	2G	Open	No	-	-	Yes	O	No	A, B, C, D	No	15.19.6, 16.2.6
Tall oil, crude (n)	Y	S/P	2	2G	Cont	No	-	-	Yes	C	T	A, B, C	Yes	15.12, 15.17, 15.19, 16.2.6
Tall oil, distilled (n)	Y	P	2	2G	Open	No	-	-	Yes	O	No	A, B, C	No	15.19.6, 16.2.6
Tall oil fatty acid (resin acids less than 20%) (n)	Y	S/P	2	2G	Open	No	-	-	Yes	O	No	A, B, C	No	15.19.6
Tall oil pitch (n)	Y	S/P	2	2G	Cont	No	-	-	Yes	C	T	A, B, C	Yes	15.12, 15.17, 15.19, 16.2.6, 16.2.9
Tallow (n)	Y	P	2 (k)	2G	Open	No	-	-	Yes	O	No	A, B, C	No	15.19.6, 16.2.6, 16.2.9
Tallow (containing less than 15% free fatty acids)	Y	P	2 (k)	2G	Open	No	-	-	Yes	O	No	A, B, C, D	No	15.19.6, 16.2.6, 16.2.9
Tallow fatty acid	Y	P	2	2G	Open	No	-	-	Yes	O	No	A	No	15.19.6, 16.2.6, 16.2.9
Tetrachloroethane	Y	S/P	2	2G	Cont	No			NF	R	T	No	No	15.12, 15.17, 15.19.6
Tetraethylene glycol	Z	P	3	2G	Open	No			Yes	O	No	A	No	15.19.6
Tetraethylenepentamine	Y	S/P	2	2G	Open	No			Yes	O	No	A	No	15.19.6
Tetrahydrofuran	Z	S	3	2G	Cont	No	T3	IIB	No	R	F-T	A	No	15.19.6
Tetrahydronaphthalene	Y	P	2	2G	Open	No			Yes	O	No	A	No	15.19.6
Tetramethylbenzene (all isomers)	X	P	2	2G	Open	No			Yes	O	No	A	No	15.19.6, 16.2.9
Titanium dioxide slurry	Z	P	3	2G	Open	No			Yes	O	No	A, B	No	
Toluene	Y	P	3	2G	Cont	No			No	R	F	A	No	15.19.6

a	c	d	e	f	g	h	i'	i''	i'''	j	k	l	n	o
Toluenediamine	Y	S/P	2	2G	Cont	No			Yes	C	T	A, D	Yes	15.12, 15.17, 15.19, 16.2.6, 16.2.9
Toluene diisocyanate	Y	S/P	2	2G	Cont	Dry	T1	IIA	Yes	C	F-T	A, C (b), D	Yes	15.12, 15.16.2, 15.17, 15.19, 16.2.9
o-Toluidine	Y	S/P	2	2G	Cont	No			Yes	C	T	A	No	15.12, 15.17, 15.19
Tributyl phosphate	Y	P	3	2G	Open	No			Yes	O	No	A	No	15.19.6
1,2,3-Trichlorobenzene (molten)	X	S/P	1	2G	Cont	No			Yes	C	T	A, C, D	Yes	15.12.1, 15.17, 15.19, 16.2.6, 16.2.9
1,2,4-Trichlorobenzene	X	S/P	1	2G	Cont	No			Yes	R	T	A, B	No	15.19, 16.2.9
1,1,1-Trichloroethane	Y	P	3	2G	Open	No			Yes	O	No	A	No	15.19.6
1,1,2-Trichloroethane	Y	S/P	3	2G	Cont	No			NF	R	T	No	No	15.12.1, 15.19.6
Trichloroethylene	Y	S/P	2	2G	Cont	No	T2	IIA	Yes	R	T	No	No	15.12, 15.17, 15.19.6
1,2,3-Trichloropropane	Y	S/P	2	2G	Cont	No			Yes	C	T	A, B, D	No	15.12, 15.17, 15.19
1,1,2-Trichloro-1,2,2-trifluoroethane	Y	P	2	2G	Open	No			NF	O	No	No	No	15.19.6
Tricresyl phosphate (containing 1% or more *ortho*-isomer)	Y	S/P	1	2G	Cont	No	T2	IIA	Yes	C	No	A, B	No	15.12.3, 15.19, 16.2.6
Tricresyl phosphate (containing less than 1% *ortho*-isomer) (n)	Y	S/P	2	2G	Open	No			Yes	O	No	A	No	15.19.6, 16.2.6
Tridecane	Y	P	2	2G	Open	No			Yes	O	No	A, B	No	15.19.6
Tridecanoic acid	Y	P	2	2G	Open	No			Yes	O	No	A	No	15.19.6, 16.2.6, 16.2.9
Tridecyl acetate	Y	P	3	2G	Open	No	-	-	Yes	O	No	A	No	15.19.6
Tridecyl acetate (n)	Z	P	3	2G	Open	No			Yes	O	No	A, B	No	
Triethanolamine	Z	S/P	3	2G	Open	No		IIA	Yes	O	No	A	No	16.2.9
Triethylamine	Y	S/P	2	2G	Cont	No	T2	IIA	No	R	F-T	A, C	Yes	15.12, 15.19.6
Triethylbenzene	X	P	2	2G	Open	No			Yes	O	No	A	No	15.19.6
Triethylenetetramine	Y	S/P	2	2G	Open	No	T2	IIA	Yes	O	No	A	No	15.19.6
Triethyl phosphate	Z	P	3	2G	Open	No			Yes	O	No	A	No	
Triethyl phosphite	Z	S/P	3	2G	Cont	No			No	R	F-T	A, B	No	15.12.1, 15.19.6, 16.2.9
Triisopropanolamine	Z	P	3	2G	Open	No			Yes	O	No	A	No	
Triisopropylated phenyl phosphates	X	P	2	2G	Open	No			Yes	O	No	A	No	15.19.6, 16.2.6
Trimethylacetic acid (n)	Y	S/P	2	2G	Cont	No			Yes	R	No	A	No	15.11.2, 15.11.3, 15.11.4, 15.11.5, 15.11.6, 15.11.7, 15.11.8, 15.19.6, 16.2.6, 16.2.9

a	c	d	e	f	g	h	i'	i''	i'''	j	k	l	n	o
Trimethylacetic acid	Y	S/P	3	2G	Cont	No			Yes	R	No	A	No	15.11.2, 15.11.3, 15.11.4, 15.11.5, 15.11.6, 15.11.7, 15.11.8, 15.19.6, 16.2.6, 16.2.9
Trimethylamine solution (30% or less)	Z	S/P	2	2G	Cont	No			No	C	F-T	A, C	Yes	15.12, 15.14, 15.19, 16.2.9
Trimethylbenzene (all isomers)	X	P	2	2G	Cont	No			No	R	F	A	No	15.19.6
Trimethylolpropane propoxylated (n)	Z	S/P	3	2G	Open	No	-		Yes	O	No	A, B, C	No	
2,2,4-Trimethyl-1,3-pentanediol diisobutyrate	Z	P	3	2G	Open	No			Yes	O	No	A, B	No	
2,2,4-Trimethyl-1,3-pentanediol-1-isobutyrate	Y	P	2	2G	Open	No			Yes	O	No	A	No	15.19.6
1,3,5-Trioxane	Y	S/P	3	2G	Cont	No			No	R	F	A, D	No	15.19.6, 16.2.9
Tripropylene glycol	Z	P	3	2G	Open	No			Yes	O	No	A	No	
Trixylyl phosphate	X	P	2	2G	Open	No			Yes	O	No	A	No	15.19.6, 16.2.6
Tung oil (n)	Y	S/P	2 (k)	2G	Open	No	-	-	Yes	O	No	A, B, C	No	15.19.6, 16.2.6, 16.2.9
Tung oil (containing less than 2.5% free fatty acids)	Y	P	2 (k)	2G	Open	No	-	-	Yes	O	No	A, B, C, D	No	15.19.6, 16.2.6, 16.2.9
Turpentine	X	P	2	2G	Cont	No			No	R	F	A	No	15.19.6
Undecanoic acid	Y	P	2	2G	Open	No			Yes	O	No	A	No	16.2.6, 16.2.9
1-Undecene	X	P	2	2G	Open	No			Yes	O	No	A	No	15.19.6
Undecyl alcohol	X	P	2	2G	Open	No			Yes	O	No	A	No	15.19.6, 16.2.9
Urea/Ammonium nitrate solution	Z	P	3	2G	Open	No			Yes	O	No	A	No	
Urea/Ammonium nitrate solution (containing aqua ammonia)	Z	S/P	3	2G	Cont	No	T2	IIA	NF	R	T	A	No	16.2.9
Urea/Ammonium nitrate solution (containing less than 1% free ammonia) (n)	Z	S/P	3	2G	Cont	No			NF	R	T	A	No	16.2.9
Urea/Ammonium phosphate solution	Y	P	2	2G	Open	No			Yes	O	No	A	No	15.19.6
Urea solution	Z	P	3	2G	Open	No			Yes	O	No	A	No	
Valeraldehyde (all isomers)	Y	S/P	3	2G	Cont	Inert	T3	IIB	No	R	F-T	A	No	15.4.6, 15.19.6
Vegetable acid oils (m) (n)	Y	S/P	2	2G	Open	No	-	-	Yes	O	No	A, B, C	No	15.19.6, 16.2.6, 16.2.9
Vegetable fatty acid distillates (m) (n)	Y	S/P	2	2G	Open	No	-	-	Yes	O	No	A, B, C	No	15.19.6, 16.2.6, 16.2.9
Vegetable protein solution (hydrolysed) (o)	Z	P	3	2G	Open	No			Yes	O	No	A	No	
Vinyl acetate	Y	S/P	3	2G	Cont	No	T2	IIA	No	R	F	A	No	15.13, 15.19.6, 16.6.1, 16.6.2
Vinyl ethyl ether	Z	S/P	2	1G	Cont	Inert	T3	IIB	No	C	F-T	A	Yes	15.4, 15.13, 15.14, 15.19, 16.6.1, 16.6.2

a	c	d	e	f	g	h	i'	i''	i'''	j	k	l	n	o
Vinylidene chloride	Y	S/P	2	2G	Cont	Inert	T2	IIA	No	R	F-T	B	Yes	15.13, 15.14, 15.19.6, 16.6.1, 16.6.2
Vinyl neodecanoate	Y	S/P	2	2G	Open	No			Yes	O	No	A, B	No	15.13, 15.19.6, 16.6.1, 16.6.2
Vinyltoluene	Y	S/P	2	2G	Cont	No		IIA	No	R	F	A, B	No	15.13, 15.19.6, 16.6.1, 16.6.2
Waxes (n)	Y	P	2	2G	Open	No	-	-	Yes	O	No	A, B	No	15.19.6, 16.2.6, 16.2.9
Waxes	Z	P	3	2G	Open	No			Yes	O	No	A, B	No	16.2.6, 16.2.9
White spirit, low (15–20%) aromatic (n)	Y	P	2	2G	Cont	No			No	R	F	A	No	15.19.6, 16.2.9
Xylenes	Y	P	2	2G	Cont	No			No	R	F	A	No	15.19.6, 16.2.9 (h)
Xylenes/Ethylbenzene (10% or more) mixture (n)	Y	P	2	2G	Cont	No	-	-	No	R	F	A	No	15.19.6
Xylenol (n)	Y	S/P	2	2G	Open	No		IIA	Yes	O	No	A, B	No	15.19.6, 16.2.9
Xylenol	Y	S/P	3	2G	Open	No		IIA	Yes	O	No	A, B	No	15.19.6, 16.2.9
Zinc alkaryl dithiophosphate (C$_7$–C$_{16}$)	Y	P	2	2G	Open	No			Yes	O	No	A, B	No	15.19.6, 16.2.6, 16.2.9
Zinc alkenyl carboxamide	Y	P	2	2G	Open	No			Yes	O	No	A, B	No	15.19.6, 16.2.6
Zinc alkyl dithiophosphate (C$_3$–C$_{14}$)	Y	P	2	2G	Open	No			Yes	O	No	A, B	No	15.19.6, 16.2.6

a   If the product to be carried contains flammable solvents such that the flashpoint does not exceed 60°C, then special electrical systems and a flammable-vapour detector shall be provided.

b   Although water is suitable for extinguishing open-air fires involving chemicals to which this footnote applies, water shall not be allowed to contaminate closed tanks containing these chemicals because of the risk of hazardous gas generation.

c   Phosphorus, yellow or white is carried above its autoignition temperature and therefore flashpoint is not appropriate. Electrical equipment requirements may be similar to those for substances with a flashpoint above 60°C.

d   Requirements are based on those isomers having a flashpoint of 60°C, or less; some isomers have a flashpoint greater than 60°C, and therefore the requirements based on flammability would not apply to such isomers.

e   Applies to *n*-decyl alcohol only.

f   Dry chemical shall not be used as fire-extinguishing media.

g   Confined spaces shall be tested for both formic acid vapours and carbon monoxide gas, a decomposition product.

h   Applies to *p*-xylene only.

i   For mixtures containing no other components with safety hazards and where the pollution category is Y or less.

j   Only certain alcohol-resistant foams are effective.

k   Requirements for Ship Type identified in *column e* might be subject to regulation 4.1.3 of Annex II of MARPOL 73/78.

l   Applicable when the melting point is equal to or greater than 0°C.

m   From vegetable oils specified in the IBC Code.

n   Pending official adoption and entry into force which is expected to be 1 January 2009. Products marked with this footnote appear in List 1 of the MEPC.2 Circular. Where these are double entries, those marked with this footnote take precedence.

o   Refer to the entry in chapter 18.

Chapter 18

List of products to which the Code does not apply

18.1   The following are products which have been reviewed for their safety and pollution hazards and determined not to present hazards to such an extent as to warrant application of the Code.

18.2   Although the products listed in this chapter fall outside the scope of the Code, the attention of Administrations is drawn to the fact that some safety precautions may be needed for their safe transportation. Accordingly, Administrations shall prescribe appropriate safety requirements.

18.3   Some liquid substances are identified as falling into Pollution Category Z and, therefore, subject to certain requirements of Annex II of MARPOL 73/78.

18.4   Liquid mixtures which are assessed or provisionally assessed under regulation 6.3 of MARPOL Annex II as falling into Pollution Category Z or OS, and which do not present safety hazards, may be carried under the appropriate entry in this chapter for ''Noxious or Non-Noxious Liquid Substances, not otherwise specified (n.o.s.)''.

EXPLANATORY NOTES

Product name	The product name shall be used in the shipping document for any cargo offered for bulk shipments. Any additional name may be included in brackets after the product name. In some cases, the product names are not identical with the names given in previous issues of the Code.
Pollution Category	The letter Z means the Pollution Category assigned to each product under Annex II of MARPOL 73/78. OS means the product was evaluated and found to fall outside Categories X, Y, or Z.

Product name	Pollution category
Acetone	Z
Alcoholic beverages, n.o.s.	Z
Apple juice	OS
n-Butyl alcohol	Z
sec-Butyl alcohol	Z
Calcium nitrate solutions (50% or less) (a)	Z
Clay slurry	OS
Coal slurry	OS
Diethylene glycol	Z
Ethyl alcohol	Z
Ethylene carbonate	Z
Glucose solution	OS
Glycerine	Z
Glycerol monooleate (b)	Z

Product name	Pollution category
Hexamethylenetetramine solutions	Z
Hexylene glycol	Z
Hydrogenated starch hydrolysate (a)	OS
Isopropyl alcohol	Z
Kaolin slurry	OS
Lecithin (a)	OS
Magnesium hydroxide slurry	Z
Maltitol solution (a)	OS
N-Methylglucamine solution (70% or less)	Z
Methyl propyl ketone	Z
Molasses	OS
Noxious liquid, (11) n.o.s. (trade name ..., contains ...) Cat. Z	Z
Non noxious liquid, (12) n.o.s. (trade name ..., contains ...) Cat. OS	OS
Polyaluminium chloride solution	Z
Polyglycerin, sodium salt solution (containing less than 3% sodium hydroxide) (a)	Z
Potassium formate solutions	Z
Propylene carbonate	Z
Propylene glycol	Z
Sodium acetate solutions	Z
Sodium sulphate solutions	Z
Sorbitol solution (a)	OS
Sulphonated polyacrylate solution (a)	Z
Tetraethyl silicate monomer/oligomer (20% in ethanol)	Z
Triethylene glycol	Z
Vegetable protein solution (hydrolysed) (a)	OS
Water	OS

a Pending official adoption and entry into force, which is expected to be 1 January 2009. Products marked with this footnote appear in List 1 of the MEPC.2 Circular.

b Refer to the entry in chapter 17.

Chapter 19

Index of Products Carried in Bulk

19.1 The first column of the Index of Products Carried in Bulk (hereafter referred to as "the Index") provides the so-called Index Name. Where the Index Name is in capital and in bold, the Index Name is identical to the Product Name in either chapter 17 or chapter 18. The second column listing the relevant Product Name is therefore empty. Where the Index Name is in non-bold lower case it reflects a synonym for which the Product Name in either chapter 17 or chapter 18 is given in the second column. The relevant chapter of the IBC Code is reflected in the third column. The fourth column gives the UN Numbers of products which were available up to February 2001.*

19.2 The Index has been developed for information purposes only. None of the Index Names indicated in non-bold lower case in the first column shall be used as Product Name on the shipping document.

19.3 Prefixes forming an integral part of the name are shown in ordinary (roman) type and are taken into account in determining the alphabetical order of entries. These include such prefixes as:

Mono Di Tri Tetra Penta Iso Bis Neo Ortho Cyclo

19.4 Prefixes that are disregarded for purposes of alphabetical order are in italics and include the following:

n-	(normal-)
sec-	(secondary-)
tert-	(tertiary-)
o-	(*ortho*-)
m-	(*meta*-)
p-	(*para*-)
N-	
O-	
S-	
sym-	(symmetrical)
uns-	(unsymmetrical)
dl-	
D-	
L-	
cis-	
trans-	
(E)-	
(Z)-	
alpha-	(α-)
beta-	(β-)
gamma-	(γ-)
epsilon-	(ϵ-)
omega-	(ω-)

---

* The reason for this decision is given in paragraph 7.10 of BLG 6/16.

Index Name	Product Name	Chapter	UN Number
Abietic anhydride	ROSIN	17	
Acedimethylamide	*N,N*-DIMETHYLACETAMIDE	17	
Acetaldehyde cyanohydrin	LACTONITRILE SOLUTION (80% OR LESS)	17	
Acetaldehyde trimer	PARALDEHYDE	17	
ACETIC ACID		17	
Acetic acid anhydride	ACETIC ANHYDRIDE	17	
Acetic acid, ethenyl ester	VINYL ACETATE	17	
Acetic acid, methyl ester	METHYL ACETATE	17	
Acetic acid, vinyl ester	VINYL ACETATE	17	
ACETIC ANHYDRIDE		17	1715
Acetic ester	ETHYL ACETATE	17	
Acetic ether	ETHYL ACETATE	17	
Acetic oxide	ACETIC ANHYDRIDE	17	
Acetoacetic acid, methyl ester	METHYL ACETOACETATE	17	
Acetoacetic ester	ETHYL ACETOACETATE	17	
ACETOCHLOR		17	
ACETONE		18	
ACETONE CYANOHYDRIN		17	1541
ACETONITRILE		17	1648
ACETONITRILE (LOW PURITY GRADE)		17	
Acetyl anhydride	ACETIC ANHYDRIDE	17	
Acetylene tetrachloride	TETRACHLOROETHANE	17	
Acetyl ether	ACETIC ANHYDRIDE	17	
Acetyl oxide	ACETIC ANHYDRIDE	17	
ACID OIL MIXTURE FROM SOYABEAN, CORN (MAIZE) AND SUNFLOWER OIL REFINING		17	
Acintene	*beta*-PINENE	17	
Acroleic acid	ACRYLIC ACID	17	
ACRYLAMIDE SOLUTION (50% OR LESS)		17	2074
ACRYLIC ACID		17	2218
Acrylic acid, 2-hydroxyethyl ester	2-HYDROXYETHYL ACRYLATE	17	
Acrylic amide solution, 50% or less	ACRYLAMIDE SOLUTION (50% OR LESS)	17	
Acrylic resin monomer	METHYL METHACRYLATE	17	
ACRYLONITRILE		17	1093
ACRYLONITRILE–STYRENE COPOLYMER DISPERSION IN POLYETHER POLYOL		17	
Adipic acid, bis(2-ethylhexyl) ester	DI-(2-ETHYLHEXYL) ADIPATE	17	
ADIPONITRILE		17	2205
ALACHLOR TECHNICAL (90% OR MORE)		17	
Alcohol	ETHYL ALCOHOL	18	
Alcohol, C_7	HEPTANOL (ALL ISOMERS)	17	
Alcohol, C_8	OCTANOL (ALL ISOMERS)	17	
Alcohol, C_9	NONYL ALCOHOL (ALL ISOMERS)	17	
Alcohol, C_{10}	DECYL ALCOHOL (ALL ISOMERS)	17	
Alcohol, C_{11}	UNDECYL ALCOHOL	17	

Index Name	Product Name	Chapter	UN Number
Alcohol, C_{12}	DODECYL ALCOHOL	17	
ALCOHOLIC BEVERAGES, N.O.S.		18	
ALCOHOL (C_9–C_{11}) POLY(2.5–9)ETHOXYLATE		17	
ALCOHOL (C_{12}–C_{16}) POLY(1–6)ETHOXYLATES		17	
ALCOHOL (C_{12}–C_{16}) POLY(7–19)ETHOXYLATES		17	
ALCOHOL (C_{12}–C_{16}) POLY(20+)ETHOXYLATES		17	
ALCOHOL (C_6–C_{17}) (SECONDARY) POLY(3–6)ETHOXYLATES		17	
ALCOHOL (C_6–C_{17}) (SECONDARY) POLY(7–12)ETHOXYLATES		17	
ALCOHOLS (C_{13}+)		17	
Alcohols, C_{13}–C_{15}	ALCOHOLS (C_{13}+)	17	
ALCOHOLS (C_8–C_{11}), PRIMARY, LINEAR AND ESSENTIALLY LINEAR		17	
ALCOHOLS (C_{12}–C_{13}), PRIMARY, LINEAR AND ESSENTIALLY LINEAR		17	
ALCOHOLS (C_{14}–C_{18}), PRIMARY, LINEAR AND ESSENTIALLY LINEAR		17	
Aldehyde collidine	2-METHYL-5-ETHYLPYRIDINE	17	
Aldehydine	2-METHYL-5-ETHYLPYRIDINE	17	
ALKANES (C_6–C_9)		17	
n-ALKANES (C_{10}+)		17	
Alkane(C_{10}–C_{18})sulfonic acid, phenyl ester	ALKYL SULPHONIC ACID ESTER OF PHENOL	17	
ALKARYL POLYETHERS (C_9–C_{20})		17	
ALKENYL (C_{11}+) AMIDE		17	
ALKENYL (C_{16}–C_{20}) SUCCINIC ANHYDRIDE		17	
ALKYL ACRYLATE-VINYLPYRIDINE COPOLYMER IN TOLUENE		17	
ALKYLARYL PHOSPHATE MIXTURES (MORE THAN 40% DIPHENYL TOLYL PHOSPHATE, LESS THAN 0.02% ortho-ISOMERS)		17	
ALKYLATED (C_4–C_9) HINDERED PHENOLS		17	
ALKYLBENZENE, ALKYLINDANE, ALKYLINDENE MIXTURE (EACH C_{12}–C_{17})		17	
ALKYL BENZENE DISTILLATION BOTTOMS		17	
ALKYLBENZENE MIXTURES (CONTAINING AT LEAST 50% OF TOLUENE)		17	
ALKYL (C_3–C_4) BENZENES		17	
ALKYL (C_5–C_8) BENZENES		17	
ALKYL(C_9+)BENZENES		17	
ALKYL (C_{11}–C_{17}) BENZENE SULPHONIC ACID		17	2584, 2586
ALKYLBENZENE SULPHONIC ACID, SODIUM SALT SOLUTION		17	
ALKYL (C_{12}+) DIMETHYLAMINE		17	2735
ALKYL DITHIOCARBAMATE (C_{19}–C_{35})		17	
ALKYLDITHIOTHIADIAZOLE (C_6–C_{24})		17	
ALKYL ESTER COPOLYMER (C_4–C_{20})		17	
ALKYL (C_8–C_{10})/(C_{12}–C_{14}):(40% OR LESS/60% OR MORE) POLYGLUCOSIDE SOLUTION (55% OR LESS)		17	

Index Name	Product Name	Chapter	UN Number
ALKYL (C_8–C_{10})/(C_{12}–C_{14}):(50%/50%) POLYGLUCOSIDE SOLUTION (55% OR LESS)		17	
ALKYL (C_8–C_{10})/(C_{12}–C_{14}):(60% OR MORE/40% OR LESS) POLYGLUCOSIDE SOLUTION (55% OR LESS)		17	
ALKYL (C_7–C_9) NITRATES		17	
2,2′-[3-(Alkyl(C_{16}–C_{18})oxy)propylimino]diethanol	ETHOXYLATED LONG CHAIN (C_{16}+) ALKYLOXYALKYLAMINE	17	
ALKYL(C_7–C_{11})PHENOL POLY(4–12)ETHOXYLATE		17	
ALKYL (C_8–C_{40}) PHENOL SULPHIDE		17	
ALKYL (C_8–C_9) PHENYLAMINE IN AROMATIC SOLVENTS		17	1993
ALKYL (C_9–C_{15}) PHENYL PROPOXYLATE		17	
ALKYL (C_8–C_{10}) POLYGLUCOSIDE SOLUTION (65% OR LESS)		17	
ALKYL (C_{12}–C_{14}) POLYGLUCOSIDE SOLUTION (55% OR LESS)		17	
ALKYL(C_{10}–C_{20}, SATURATED AND UNSATURATED) PHOSPHITE		17	
ALKYL SULPHONIC ACID ESTER OF PHENOL		17	
3-Alkyl(C_{16}–C_{18})oxy-$N,N′$-bis(2-hydroxyethyl)propan-1-amine	ETHOXYLATED LONG CHAIN (C_{16}+) ALKYLOXYALKYLAMINE	17	
ALLYL ALCOHOL		17	1098
ALLYL CHLORIDE		17	1100
Aluminium silicate hydroxide	KAOLIN SLURRY	18	
ALUMINIUM SULPHATE SOLUTION		17	
Aminoacetic acid, sodium salt solution	GLYCINE, SODIUM SALT SOLUTION	17	
1-Amino-3-aminomethyl-3,5,5-trimethylcyclohexane	ISOPHORONEDIAMINE	17	
Aminobenzene	ANILINE	17	
1-Aminobutane	BUTYLAMINE (ALL ISOMERS)	17	
2-Aminobutane	BUTYLAMINE (ALL ISOMERS)	17	
Aminocyclohexane	CYCLOHEXYLAMINE	17	
Aminoethane	ETHYLAMINE	17	
Aminoethane solutions, 72% or less	ETHYLAMINE SOLUTIONS (72% OR LESS)	17	
2-Aminoethanol	ETHANOLAMINE	17	
2-(2-AMINOETHOXY)ETHANOL		17	3055
2-(2-Aminoethylamino)ethanol	AMINOETHYLETHANOLAMINE	17	
AMINOETHYLDIETHANOLAMINE/ AMINOETHYLETHANOLAMINE SOLUTION		17	
AMINOETHYLETHANOLAMINE		17	
N-(2-Aminoethyl)ethylenediamine	DIETHYLENETRIAMINE	17	
1-(2-Aminoethyl)piperazine	N-AMINOETHYLPIPERAZINE	17	
N-AMINOETHYLPIPERAZINE		17	2815
2-Aminoisobutane	BUTYLAMINE (ALL ISOMERS)	17	
Aminomethane	METHYLAMINE SOLUTIONS (42% OR LESS)	17	
Aminomethane solutions, 42% or less	METHYLAMINE SOLUTIONS (42% OR LESS)	17	
1-Amino-2-methylbenzene	o-TOLUIDINE	17	
2-Amino-1-methylbenzene	o-TOLUIDINE	17	
2-AMINO-2-METHYL-1-PROPANOL		17	

Index Name	Product Name	Chapter	UN Number
3-Aminomethyl-3,5,5-trimethylcyclohexylamine	ISOPHORONEDIAMINE	17	
Aminophen	ANILINE	17	
1-Aminopropane	*n*-PROPYLAMINE	17	
2-Aminopropane	ISOPROPYLAMINE	17	
2-Aminopropane (70% or less) solution	ISOPROPYLAMINE (70% OR LESS) SOLUTION	17	
1-Amino-2-propanol	ISOPROPANOLAMINE	17	
1-Aminopropan-2-ol	ISOPROPANOLAMINE	17	
3-Aminopropan-1-ol	*n*-PROPANOLAMINE	17	
2-Aminotoluene	*o*-TOLUIDINE	17	
o-Aminotoluene	*o*-TOLUIDINE	17	
5-Amino-1,3,3-trimethylcyclohexylmethylamine	ISOPHORONEDIAMINE	17	
AMMONIA AQUEOUS (28% OR LESS)		17	2672
Ammonia water, 28% or less	AMMONIA AQUEOUS (28% OR LESS)	17	
AMMONIUM HYDROGEN PHOSPHATE SOLUTION		17	
Ammonium hydroxide, 28% or less	AMMONIA AQUEOUS (28% OR LESS)	17	
AMMONIUM LIGNOSULPHONATE SOLUTIONS		17	
AMMONIUM NITRATE SOLUTION (93% OR LESS)		17	
AMMONIUM POLYPHOSPHATE SOLUTION		17	
AMMONIUM SULPHATE SOLUTION		17	
AMMONIUM SULPHIDE SOLUTION (45% OR LESS)		17	2683
AMMONIUM THIOSULPHATE SOLUTION (60% OR LESS)		17	
AMYL ACETATE (ALL ISOMERS)		17	1104
Amyl acetate, commercial	AMYL ACETATE (ALL ISOMERS)	17	
n-Amyl acetate	AMYL ACETATE (ALL ISOMERS)	17	
sec-Amyl acetate	AMYL ACETATE (ALL ISOMERS)	17	
Amylacetic ester	AMYL ACETATE (ALL ISOMERS)	17	
Amyl alcohol	*n*-AMYL ALCOHOL	17	
n-AMYL ALCOHOL		17	
sec-AMYL ALCOHOL		17	
tert-AMYL ALCOHOL		17	
AMYL ALCOHOL, PRIMARY		17	
Amyl aldehyde	VALERALDEHYDE (ALL ISOMERS)	17	
Amyl carbinol	HEXANOL	17	
alpha-n-Amylene	PENTENE (ALL ISOMERS)	17	
Amylene hydrate	*tert*-AMYL ALCOHOL	17	
tert-Amylenes	PENTENE (ALL ISOMERS)	17	
Amyl ethyl ketone	ETHYL AMYL KETONE	17	
Amyl hydrate	*n*-AMYL ALCOHOL	17	
Amyl hydride	PENTANE (ALL ISOMERS)	17	
tert-AMYL METHYL ETHER		17	1993
n-Amyl methyl ketone	METHYL AMYL KETONE	17	
n-Amyl propionate	*n*-PENTYL PROPIONATE	17	
Anaesthetic ether	DIETHYL ETHER	17	
ANILINE		17	1547

Index Name	Product Name	Chapter	UN Number
Aniline oil	ANILINE	17	
Anilinobenzene	DIPHENYLAMINE (MOLTEN)	17	
Anthracene oil (coal tar fraction)	COAL TAR	17	
Ant oil, artificial	FURFURAL	17	
APPLE JUICE		18	
Aqua fortis	NITRIC ACID (70% AND OVER)	17	
Argilla	KAOLIN SLURRY	18	
ARYL POLYOLEFINS (C_{11}–C_{50})		17	
AVIATION ALKYLATES (C_8 PARAFFINS AND ISO-PARAFFINS BPT 95–120°C)		17	
Azacycloheptane	HEXAMETHYLENEIMINE	17	
3-Azapentane-1,5-diamine	DIETHYLENETRIAMINE	17	
Azepane	HEXAMETHYLENEIMINE	17	
Azotic acid	NITRIC ACID (70% AND OVER)	17	
Banana oil	AMYL ACETATE (ALL ISOMERS)	17	
BARIUM LONG CHAIN (C_{11}–C_{50}) ALKARYL SULPHONATE		17	2810
Basic calcium alkyl salicylate in approximately 30% mineral oil	CALCIUM LONG-CHAIN ALKYL SALICYLATE (C_{13}+)	17	
Battery acid	SULPHURIC ACID	17	
Behenyl alcohol	ALCOHOLS (C_{13}+)	17	
Benzenamine	2-METHYL-5-ETHYLPYRIDINE	17	
1,2-Benzenedicarboxylic acid, diethyl ester	DIETHYL PHTHALATE	17	
1,2-Benzenedicarboxylic acid, diundecyl ester	DIUNDECYL PHTHALATE	17	
BENZENE AND MIXTURES HAVING 10% BENZENE OR MORE		17	1114
BENZENESULPHONYL CHLORIDE		17	2225
BENZENETRICARBOXYLIC ACID, TRIOCTYL ESTER		17	
Benzenol	PHENOL	17	
Benzol	BENZENE AND MIXTURES HAVING 10% BENZENE OR MORE	17	
Benzole	BENZENE AND MIXTURES HAVING 10% BENZENE OR MORE	17	
Benzophenol	PHENOL	17	
Benzothiazole-2-thiol (, sodium salt)	MERCAPTOBENZOTHIAZOL, SODIUM SALT SOLUTION	17	
2-Benzothiazolethiol (, sodium salt)	MERCAPTOBENZOTHIAZOL, SODIUM SALT SOLUTION	17	
(2-Benzothiazolylthio) sodium solution	MERCAPTOBENZOTHIAZOL, SODIUM SALT SOLUTION	17	
BENZYL ACETATE		17	
BENZYL ALCOHOL		17	
Benzyl butyl phthalate	BUTYL BENZYL PHTHALATE	17	
BENZYL CHLORIDE		17	1738
Betaprone	beta-PROPIOLACTONE	17	
Betula oil	METHYL SALICYLATE	17	
Biformyl	GLYOXAL SOLUTION (40% OR LESS)	17	
Bihexyl	DODECANE (ALL ISOMERS)	17	

Index Name	Product Name	Chapter	UN Number
Biphenyl	DIPHENYL	17	
2,5-Bis(alkyl(C$_7$+)thio)-1,3,4-thiadiazole	ALKYLDITHIOTHIADIAZOLE (C$_6$–C$_{24}$)	17	
Bis(2-aminoethyl)amine	DIETHYLENETRIAMINE	17	
N,N'-Bis(2-aminoethyl)ethane-1,2-diamine	TRIETHYLENETETRAMINE	17	
N,N'-Bis(2-aminoethyl)ethylenediamine	TRIETHYLENETETRAMINE	17	
N,N-Bis(2-(bis(carboxymethyl)amino)ethyl)glycine, pentasodium salt	DIETHYLENETRIAMINEPENTAACETIC ACID, PENTASODIUM SALT SOLUTION	17	
Bis(2-butoxyethyl) ether	DIETHYLENE GLYCOL DIBUTYL ETHER	17	
N,N-Bis(carboxymethyl)glycine trisodium salt	NITRILOTRIACETIC ACID, TRISODIUM SALT SOLUTION	17	
Bis(chloroethyl) ether	DICHLOROETHYL ETHER	17	
Bis(2-chloroethyl) ether	DICHLOROETHYL ETHER	17	
Bis(2-chloroisopropyl) ether	2,2'-DICHLOROISOPROPYL ETHER	17	
Bis(2-chloro-1-methylethyl) ether	2,2'-DICHLOROISOPROPYL ETHER	17	
1,1-Bis[4-(2,3-epoxypropoxy)phenyl]ethane	DIGLYCIDYL ETHER OF BISPHENOL A	17	
Bis[2-(2,3-epoxypropoxy)phenyl]methane	DIGLYCIDYL ETHER OF BISPHENOL F	17	
Bis(2-ethoxyethyl) ether	DIETHYLENE GLYCOL DIETHYL ETHER	17	
Bis(2-ethylhexyl) adipate	DI-(2-ETHYLHEXYL) ADIPATE	17	
Bis(2-ethylhexyl) hydrogen phosphate	DI-(2-ETHYLHEXYL)PHOSPHORIC ACID	17	
Bis(2-ethylhexyl) phthalate	DIOCTYL PHTHALATE	17	
Bis(2-hydroxyethyl)amine	DIETHANOLAMINE	17	
Bis(2-hydroxyethyl)ammonium 2,4-dichlorophenoxyacetate	2,4-DICHLOROPHENOXYACETIC ACID, DIETHANOLAMINE SALT SOLUTION	17	
Bis(2-hydroxyethyl) ether	DIETHYLENE GLYCOL	18	
Bis(2-hydroxypropyl)amine	DIISOPROPANOLAMINE	17	
Bis(methylcyclopentadiene)	METHYLCYCLOPENTADIENE DIMER	17	
Bis(6-methylheptyl) phthalate	DIOCTYL PHTHALATE	17	
Blackstrap molasses	MOLASSES	18	
Bolus alba	KAOLIN SLURRY	18	
BRAKE FLUID BASE MIX: POLY(2–8)ALKYLENE (C$_2$–C$_3$) GLYCOLS/POLYALKYLENE (C$_2$–C$_{10}$) GLYCOLS MONOALKYL (C$_1$–C$_4$) ETHERS AND THEIR BORATE ESTERS		17	
Bran oil	FURFURAL	17	
Brimstone	SULPHUR (MOLTEN)	17	
BROMOCHLOROMETHANE		17	
Butaldehyde	BUTYRALDEHYDE (ALL ISOMERS)	17	
Butanal	BUTYRALDEHYDE (ALL ISOMERS)	17	
n-Butanal	BUTYRALDEHYDE (ALL ISOMERS)	17	
Butane-1,3-diol	BUTYLENE GLYCOL	17	
1,3-Butanediol	BUTYLENE GLYCOL	17	
Butane-1,4-diol	BUTYLENE GLYCOL	17	
1,4-Butanediol	BUTYLENE GLYCOL	17	
Butane-2,3-diol	BUTYLENE GLYCOL	17	
2,3-Butanediol	BUTYLENE GLYCOL	17	
Butanoic acid	BUTYRIC ACID	17	
Butanol	*n*-BUTYL ALCOHOL	18	

Index Name	Product Name	Chapter	UN Number
Butanol-1	*n*-BUTYL ALCOHOL	18	
Butan-1-ol	*n*-BUTYL ALCOHOL	18	
1-Butanol	*n*-BUTYL ALCOHOL	18	
Butan-2-ol	*sec*-BUTYL ALCOHOL	18	
2-Butanol	*sec*-BUTYL ALCOHOL	18	
n-Butanol	*n*-BUTYL ALCOHOL	18	
sec-Butanol	*sec*-BUTYL ALCOHOL	18	
tert-Butanol	*tert*-BUTYL ALCOHOL	17	
Butanol acetate	BUTYL ACETATE (ALL ISOMERS)	17	
2-Butanol acetate	BUTYL ACETATE (ALL ISOMERS)	17	
1,4-Butanolide	*gamma*-BUTYROLACTONE	17	
Butan-4-olide	*gamma*-BUTYROLACTONE	17	
Butan-2-one	METHYL ETHYL KETONE	17	
2-Butanone	METHYL ETHYL KETONE	17	
(*E*)-But-2-enal	CROTONALDEHYDE	17	
2-Butenal	CROTONALDEHYDE	17	
Butene dimer	OCTENE (ALL ISOMERS)	17	
cis-Butenedioic anhydride	MALEIC ANHYDRIDE	17	
BUTENE OLIGOMER		17	
1-Butoxybutane	*n*-BUTYL ETHER	17	
2-Butoxyethanol	ETHYLENE GLYCOL MONOALKYL ETHERS	17	
2-*tert*-Butoxyethanol	ETHYLENE GLYCOL MONOALKYL ETHERS	17	
2-(2-Butoxyethoxy)ethanol	POLY(2–8)ALKYLENE GLYCOL MONOALKYL (C_1–C_6) ETHER	17	
2-(2-Butoxyethoxy)ethyl acetate	POLY(2–8)ALKYLENE GLYCOL MONOALKYL (C_1–C_6) ETHER ACETATE	17	
2-Butoxyethyl acetate	ETHYLENE GLYCOL BUTYL ETHER ACETATE	17	
1-Butoxypropan-2-ol	PROPYLENE GLYCOL MONOALKYL ETHER	17	
Butyl acetate	BUTYL ACETATE (ALL ISOMERS)	17	
BUTYL ACETATE (ALL ISOMERS)		17	1123
n-Butyl acetate	BUTYL ACETATE (ALL ISOMERS)	17	
sec-Butyl acetate	BUTYL ACETATE (ALL ISOMERS)	17	
tert-Butyl acetate	BUTYL ACETATE (ALL ISOMERS)	17	
BUTYL ACRYLATE (ALL ISOMERS)		17	2348
n-Butyl acrylate	BUTYL ACRYLATE (ALL ISOMERS)	17	
Butyl alcohol	*n*-BUTYL ALCOHOL	18	
n-BUTYL ALCOHOL		18	
sec-BUTYL ALCOHOL		18	
tert-BUTYL ALCOHOL		17	
n-Butyl aldehyde	BUTYRALDEHYDE (ALL ISOMERS)	17	
BUTYLAMINE (ALL ISOMERS)		17	1125, 1214
n-Butylamine	BUTYLAMINE (ALL ISOMERS)	17	
sec-Butylamine	BUTYLAMINE (ALL ISOMERS)	17	
tert-Butylamine	BUTYLAMINE (ALL ISOMERS)	17	
BUTYLBENZENE (ALL ISOMERS)		17	2709

Index Name	Product Name	Chapter	UN Number
tert-Butylbenzene	BUTYLBENZENE (ALL ISOMERS)	17	
BUTYL BENZYL PHTHALATE		17	
Butyl butanoate	BUTYL BUTYRATE (ALL ISOMERS)	17	
BUTYL BUTYRATE (ALL ISOMERS)		17	
n-Butyl butyrate	BUTYL BUTYRATE (ALL ISOMERS)	17	
n-Butylcarbinol	*n*-AMYL ALCOHOL	17	
Butyl carbitol	POLY(2–8)ALKYLENE GLYCOL MONOALKYL (C_1–C_6) ETHER	17	
Butyl carbitol acetate	POLY(2–8)ALKYLENE GLYCOL MONOALKYL (C_1–C_6) ETHER ACETATE	17	
Butyl cellosolve	ETHYLENE GLYCOL MONOALKYL ETHERS	17	
Butyl cellosolve acetate	ETHYLENE GLYCOL BUTYL ETHER ACETATE	17	
BUTYL/DECYL/CETYL/EICOSYL METHACRYLATE MIXTURE		17	
Butyl/decyl/hexadecyl/icosyl methacrylate mixture	BUTYL/DECYL/CETYL/EICOSYL METHACRYLATE MIXTURE	17	
Butyl diglycol acetate	POLY(2–8)ALKYLENE GLYCOL MONOALKYL (C_1–C_6) ETHER ACETATE	17	
BUTYLENE GLYCOL		17	
alpha-Butylene glycol	BUTYLENE GLYCOL	17	
beta-Butylene glycol	BUTYLENE GLYCOL	17	
Butylene glycol momomethyl ether	3-METHOXY-1-BUTANOL	17	
Butylene glycol monomethyl ether acetate	3-METHOXYBUTYL ACETATE	17	
Butylene oxide	TETRAHYDROFURAN	17	
1,2-BUTYLENE OXIDE		17	3022
Butyl ester	BUTYL ACETATE (ALL ISOMERS)	17	
Butyl ethanoate	BUTYL ACETATE (ALL ISOMERS)	17	
Butyl ether	*n*-BUTYL ETHER	17	
n-BUTYL ETHER		17	1149
Butylethylacetic acid	OCTANOIC ACID (ALL ISOMERS)	17	
Butylethylene	HEXENE (ALL ISOMERS)	17	
tert-Butyl ethyl ether	ETHYL *tert*-BUTYL ETHER	17	
Butylic ether	*n*-BUTYL ETHER	17	
BUTYL METHACRYLATE		17	
tert-Butyl methyl ether	METHYL *tert*-BUTYL ETHER	17	
Butyl methyl ketone	METHYL BUTYL KETONE	17	
Butyl phthalate	DIBUTYL PHTHALATE	17	
n-BUTYL PROPIONATE		17	1914
BUTYRALDEHYDE (ALL ISOMERS)		17	1129
n-Butyraldehyde	BUTYRALDEHYDE (ALL ISOMERS)	17	
BUTYRIC ACID		17	2820
n-Butyric acid	BUTYRIC ACID	17	
Butyric alcohol	*n*-BUTYL ALCOHOL	18	
Butyric aldehyde	BUTYRALDEHYDE (ALL ISOMERS)	17	
gamma-BUTYROLACTONE		17	
Cajeputene	DIPENTENE	17	

Index Name	Product Name	Chapter	UN Number
Calcium alkyl(long chain) salicylate (overbased) in mineral oil (LOA)	CALCIUM LONG-CHAIN ALKYL SALICYLATE (C_{13}+)	17	
Calcium alkyl salicylate	CALCIUM LONG-CHAIN ALKYL SALICYLATE (C_{13}+)	17	
Calcium bis(O-alkylsalicylate)	CALCIUM LONG-CHAIN ALKYL SALICYLATE (C_{13}+)	17	
Calcium bromide/Zinc bromide solution	DRILLING BRINES (CONTAINING ZINC SALTS)	17	
CALCIUM CARBONATE SLURRY		17	
CALCIUM HYDROXIDE SLURRY		17	
CALCIUM HYPOCHLORITE SOLUTION (15% OR LESS)		17	
CALCIUM HYPOCHLORITE SOLUTION (MORE THAN 15%)		17	
CALCIUM LIGNOSULPHONATE SOLUTIONS		17	
CALCIUM LONG-CHAIN ALKARYL SULPHONATE (C_{11}–C_{50})		17	
CALCIUM LONG-CHAIN ALKYL(C_5–C_{10}) PHENATE		17	
CALCIUM LONG-CHAIN ALKYL(C_{11}–C_{40}) PHENATE		17	
CALCIUM LONG-CHAIN ALKYL PHENATE SULPHIDE (C_8–C_{40})		17	
CALCIUM LONG-CHAIN ALKYL SALICYLATE (C_{13}+)		17	
CALCIUM NITRATE/MAGNESIUM NITRATE/ POTASSIUM CHLORIDE SOLUTION		17	
CALCIUM NITRATE SOLUTIONS (50% OR LESS)		18	1454
Cane molasses	MOLASSES	18	
Capric acid	DECANOIC ACID	17	
Caproic acid	HEXANOIC ACID	17	
alpha-Caproic acid	OCTANOIC ACID (ALL ISOMERS)	17	
Caprolactam	epsilon-CAPROLACTAM (MOLTEN OR AQUEOUS SOLUTIONS)	17	
epsilon-CAPROLACTAM (MOLTEN OR AQUEOUS SOLUTIONS)		17	
Caproyl alcohol	HEXANOL	17	
Capryl alcohol	OCTANOL (ALL ISOMERS)	17	
Caprylic acid	OCTANOIC ACID (ALL ISOMERS)	17	
Caprylyl acetate	n-OCTYL ACETATE	17	
Carbamide	UREA SOLUTION	17	
Carbinol	METHYL ALCOHOL	17	
Carbitol acetate	POLY(2–8)ALKYLENE GLYCOL MONOALKYL (C_1–C_6) ETHER ACETATE	17	
Carbitol solvent	POLY(2–8)ALKYLENE GLYCOL MONOALKYL (C_1–C_6) ETHER	17	
Carbolic acid	PHENOL	17	
CARBOLIC OIL		17	
Carbon bisulphide	CARBON DISULPHIDE	17	
CARBON DISULPHIDE		17	1131
CARBON TETRACHLORIDE		17	1846
Carbonyldiamide	UREA SOLUTION	17	
Carbonyldiamine	UREA SOLUTION	17	
1,3-Carbonyl dioxypropane	PROPYLENE CARBONATE	18	

Index Name	Product Name	Chapter	UN Number
Carboxyethyliminobis(ethylenenitrilo)tetraacetic acid, pentasodium salt	DIETHYLENETRIAMINEPENTAACETIC ACID, PENTASODIUM SALT SOLUTION	17	
CASHEW NUT SHELL OIL (UNTREATED)		17	
CASTOR OIL		17	
Caustic potash solution	POTASSIUM HYDROXIDE SOLUTION	17	
Caustic soda	SODIUM HYDROXIDE SOLUTION	17	
Caustic soda solution	SODIUM HYDROXIDE SOLUTION	17	
Cellosolve acetate	2-ETHOXYETHYL ACETATE	17	
Cellosolve solvent	ETHYLENE GLYCOL MONOALKYL ETHERS	17	
CETYL/EICOSYL METHACRYLATE MIXTURE		17	
Cetyl/Stearyl alcohol	ALCOHOLS (C$_{13}$+)	17	
China clay	KAOLIN SLURRY	18	
CHLORINATED PARAFFINS (C$_{10}$–C$_{13}$)		17	
CHLORINATED PARAFFINS (C$_{14}$–C$_{17}$) (WITH 50% CHLORINE OR MORE, AND LESS THAN 1% C$_{13}$ OR SHORTER CHAINS)		17	
CHLOROACETIC ACID (80% OR LESS)		17	1750
alpha-Chloroallyl chloride	1,3-DICHLOROPROPENE	17	
Chloroallylene	ALLYL CHLORIDE	17	
CHLOROBENZENE		17	1134
Chlorobenzol	CHLOROBENZENE	17	
Chlorobromomethane	BROMOCHLOROMETHANE	17	
1-Chloro-2-(*beta*-chloroethoxy)ethane	DICHLOROETHYL ETHER	17	
1-Chloro-2,3-epoxypropane	EPICHLOROHYDRIN	17	
Chloroethanol-2	ETHYLENE CHLOROHYDRIN	17	
2-Chloroethanol	ETHYLENE CHLOROHYDRIN	17	
2-Chloro-*N*-ethoxymethyl-6'-ethylacet-*o*-toluidide	ACETOCHLOR	17	
2-Chloro-*N*-(ethoxymethyl)-*N*-(2-ethyl-6-methylphenyl)acetamide	ACETOCHLOR	17	
2-Chloroethyl alcohol	ETHYLENE CHLOROHYDRIN	17	
beta-Chloroethyl alcohol	ETHYLENE CHLOROHYDRIN	17	
Chloroethyl ether	DICHLOROETHYL ETHER	17	
2-Chloro-6'-ethyl-*N*-(2-methoxy-1-methylethyl)acet-*o*-toluidide	*N*-(2-METHOXY-1-METHYLETHYL)-2-ETHYL-6-METHYLCHLOROACETANILIDE	17	
2-Chloro-*N*-(2-ethyl-6-methylphenyl)-*N*-(2-methoxy-1-methylethyl)acetamide	*N*-(2-METHOXY-1-METHYLETHYL)-2-ETHYL-6-METHYLCHLOROACETANILIDE	17	
CHLOROFORM		17	1888
CHLOROHYDRINS (CRUDE)		17	
m-Chloromethylbenzene	*m*-CHLOROTOLUENE	17	
o-Chloromethylbenzene	*o*-CHLOROTOLUENE	17	
p-Chloromethylbenzene	*p*-CHLOROTOLUENE	17	
Chloromethylethylene oxide	EPICHLOROHYDRIN	17	
(2-Chloro-1-methylethyl) ether	2,2'-DICHLOROISOPROPYL ETHER	17	
2-Chloro-1-methylethyl ether	2,2'-DICHLOROISOPROPYL ETHER	17	
Chloromethyloxirane	EPICHLOROHYDRIN	17	
4-CHLORO-2-METHYLPHENOXYACETIC ACID, DIMETHYLAMINE SALT SOLUTION		17	

Index Name	Product Name	Chapter	UN Number
1-Chloro-2-nitrobenzene	o-CHLORONITROBENZENE	17	
o-CHLORONITROBENZENE		17	1578
1-(4-CHLOROPHENYL)-4,4-DIMETHYLPENTAN-3-ONE		17	
2- or 3-Chloropropanoic acid	2- OR 3-CHLOROPROPIONIC ACID	17	
3-Chloropropene	ALLYL CHLORIDE	17	
2- OR 3-CHLOROPROPIONIC ACID		17	2511
alpha- or beta-Chloropropionic acid	2- OR 3-CHLOROPROPIONIC ACID	17	
3-Chloropropylene	ALLYL CHLORIDE	17	
alpha-Chloropropylene	ALLYL CHLORIDE	17	
Chloropropylene oxide	EPICHLOROHYDRIN	17	
CHLOROSULPHONIC ACID		17	1754
Chlorosulphuric acid	CHLOROSULPHONIC ACID	17	
3-Chlorotoluene	m-CHLOROTOLUENE	17	
4-Chlorotoluene	p-CHLOROTOLUENE	17	
alpha-Chlorotoluene	BENZYL CHLORIDE	17	
m-CHLOROTOLUENE		17	2238
o-CHLOROTOLUENE		17	2238
p-CHLOROTOLUENE		17	2238
CHLOROTOLUENES (MIXED ISOMERS)		17	2238
CHOLINE CHLORIDE SOLUTIONS		17	
Cinene	DIPENTENE	17	
Cinnamene	STYRENE MONOMER	17	
Cinnamol	STYRENE MONOMER	17	
CITRIC ACID (70% OR LESS)		17	
CLAY SLURRY		18	
Cleaning solvents	WHITE SPIRIT, LOW (15–20%) AROMATIC	17	
COAL SLURRY		18	
COAL TAR		17	
Coal tar distillate	COAL TAR NAPHTHA SOLVENT	17	
COAL TAR NAPHTHA SOLVENT		17	
COAL TAR PITCH (MOLTEN)		17	
COCOA BUTTER		17	
COCONUT OIL		17	
COCONUT OIL FATTY ACID		17	
COCONUT OIL FATTY ACID METHYL ESTER		17	
Colamine	ETHANOLAMINE	17	
Cologne spirits	ETHYL ALCOHOL	18	
Colonial spirit	METHYL ALCOHOL	17	
Colophony	ROSIN	17	
Columbian spirit	METHYL ALCOHOL	17	
Columbian spirits	METHYL ALCOHOL	17	
COPPER SALT OF LONG CHAIN (C$_{17}$+) ALKANOIC ACID		17	
CORN OIL		17	
COTTON SEED OIL		17	

Index Name	Product Name	Chapter	UN Number
CREOSOTE (COAL TAR)		17	
Creosote salts	NAPHTHALENE (MOLTEN)	17	
CRESOLS (ALL ISOMERS)		17	2076
CRESYLIC ACID, DEPHENOLIZED		17	
Cresylic acids	CRESOLS (ALL ISOMERS)	17	
CRESYLIC ACID, SODIUM SALT SOLUTION		17	
Cresylols	CRESOLS (ALL ISOMERS)	17	
CROTONALDEHYDE		17	1143
Crotonic aldehyde	CROTONALDEHYDE	17	
Cumene	PROPYLBENZENE (ALL ISOMERS)	17	
Cumol	PROPYLBENZENE (ALL ISOMERS)	17	
Cyanoethylene	ACRYLONITRILE	17	
2-Cyano-2-propanol	ACETONE CYANOHYDRIN	17	
2-Cyanopropan-2-ol	ACETONE CYANOHYDRIN	17	
2-Cyanopropene-1	METHACRYLONITRILE	17	
Cyclic propylene carbonate	PROPYLENE CARBONATE	18	
1,5,9-CYCLODODECATRIENE		17	
CYCLOHEPTANE		17	2241
Cyclohexamethylenimine	HEXAMETHYLENEIMINE	17	
CYCLOHEXANE		17	1145
CYCLOHEXANOL		17	
CYCLOHEXANONE		17	1915
CYCLOHEXANONE, CYCLOHEXANOL MIXTURE		17	
Cyclohexatriene	BENZENE AND MIXTURES HAVING 10% BENZENE OR MORE	17	
CYCLOHEXYL ACETATE		17	2243
CYCLOHEXYLAMINE		17	2357
Cyclohexyldimethylamine	*N,N*-DIMETHYLCYCLOHEXYLAMINE	17	
Cyclohexyl(ethyl)amine	*N*-ETHYLCYCLOHEXYLAMINE	17	
Cyclohexyl ketone	CYCLOHEXANONE	17	
Cyclohexylmethane	METHYLCYCLOHEXANE	17	
1,3-CYCLOPENTADIENE DIMER (MOLTEN)		17	
CYCLOPENTANE		17	1146
CYCLOPENTENE		17	2246
Cyclotetramethylene oxide	TETRAHYDROFURAN	17	
p-CYMENE		17	2046
Cymol	*p*-CYMENE	17	
Dalapon (ISO)	2,2-DICHLOROPROPIONIC ACID	17	
2,4-D-diolamine	2,4-DICHLOROPHENOXYACETIC ACID, DIETHANOLAMINE SALT SOLUTION	17	
'D-D Soil fumigant'	DICHLOROPROPENE/DICHLOROPROPANE MIXTURES	17	
Deanol	DIMETHYLETHANOLAMINE	17	
DECAHYDRONAPHTHALENE		17	
DECANOIC ACID		17	
Decan-1-ol	DECYL ALCOHOL (ALL ISOMERS)	17	

Index Name	Product Name	Chapter	UN Number
n-Decanol	DECYL ALCOHOL (ALL ISOMERS)	17	
Decatoic acid	DECANOIC ACID	17	
DECENE		17	
Decoic acid	DECANOIC ACID	17	
DECYL ACRYLATE		17	
Decyl alcohol	DECYL ALCOHOL (ALL ISOMERS)	17	
DECYL ALCOHOL (ALL ISOMERS)		17	
Decylbenzene	ALKYL(C$_9$+)BENZENES	17	
Decylic acid	DECANOIC ACID	17	
Decyl octyl adipate	OCTYL DECYL ADIPATE	17	
DECYLOXYTETRAHYDROTHIOPHENE DIOXIDE		17	
1-Deoxy-1-methylamino-*D*-glucitol	*N*-METHYLGLUCAMINE SOLUTION (70% OR LESS)	18	
Detergent alkylate	ALKYL(C$_9$+)BENZENES	17	
Diacetic ester	ETHYL ACETOACETATE	17	
Diacetone	DIACETONE ALCOHOL	17	
DIACETONE ALCOHOL		17	
Di[alkyl/alkenyl(C$_{10}$–C$_{20}$)] hydrogen phosphite	ALKYL(C$_{10}$–C$_{20}$, SATURATED AND UNSATURATED) PHOSPHITE	17	
DIALKYL (C$_8$–C$_9$) DIPHENYLAMINES		17	
DIALKYL (C$_7$–C$_{13}$) PHTHALATES		17	
1,2-Diaminoethane	ETHYLENEDIAMINE	17	
1,6-Diaminohexane	HEXAMETHYLENEDIAMINE (MOLTEN)	17	
1,6-Diaminohexane solutions	HEXAMETHYLENEDIAMINE SOLUTION	17	
2,6-Diaminohexanioc acid	*L*-LYSINE SOLUTION (60% OR LESS)	17	
Diaminotoluene	TOLUENEDIAMINE	17	
2,4-Diaminotoluene	TOLUENEDIAMINE	17	
2,6-Diaminotoluene	TOLUENEDIAMINE	17	
4,6-Diamino-3,5,5-trimethylcyclohex-2-enone	ISOPHORONEDIAMINE	17	
3,6-Diazaoctane-1,8-diamine	TRIETHYLENETETRAMINE	17	
1,2-Dibromoethane	ETHYLENE DIBROMIDE	17	
DIBROMOMETHANE		17	
DIBUTYLAMINE		17	
Dibutylbenzene-1,2-dicarboxylate	DIBUTYL PHTHALATE	17	
Dibutyl carbinol	NONYL ALCOHOL (ALL ISOMERS)	17	
Dibutylcarbitol	DIETHYLENE GLYCOL DIBUTYL ETHER	17	
Dibutyl ether	*n*-BUTYL ETHER	17	
n-Dibutyl ether	*n*-BUTYL ETHER	17	
2,2'-Dibutylethyl ether	DIETHYLENE GLYCOL DIBUTYL ETHER	17	
Dibutyl hydrogen phosphite	DIBUTYL HYDROGEN PHOSPHONATE	17	
DIBUTYL HYDROGEN PHOSPHONATE		17	
2,6-DI-*tert*-BUTYLPHENOL		17	
Dibutyl phosphonate	DIBUTYL HYDROGEN PHOSPHONATE	17	
DIBUTYL PHTHALATE		17	
Dibutyl *ortho*-phthalate	DIBUTYL PHTHALATE	17	
DICHLOROBENZENE (ALL ISOMERS)		17	

Index Name	Product Name	Chapter	UN Number
1,2-Dichlorobenzene	DICHLOROBENZENE (ALL ISOMERS)	17	
m-Dichlorobenzene	DICHLOROBENZENE (ALL ISOMERS)	17	
o-Dichlorobenzene	DICHLOROBENZENE (ALL ISOMERS)	17	
3,4-DICHLORO-1-BUTENE		17	
3,4-Dichlorobut-1-ene	3,4-DICHLORO-1-BUTENE	17	
2,2′-Dichlorodiethyl ether	DICHLOROETHYL ETHER	17	
Dichlorodiisopropyl ether	2,2′-DICHLOROISOPROPYL ETHER	17	
1,1-DICHLOROETHANE		17	2362
1,2-Dichloroethane	ETHYLENE DICHLORIDE	17	
sym-Dichloroethane	ETHYLENE DICHLORIDE	17	
1,1-Dichloroethene	VINYLIDENE CHLORIDE	17	
Dichloroether	DICHLOROETHYL ETHER	17	
1,1-Dichloroethylene	VINYLIDENE CHLORIDE	17	
DICHLOROETHYL ETHER		17	1916
2,2′-Dichloroethyl ether	DICHLOROETHYL ETHER	17	
sym-Dichloroethyl ether	DICHLOROETHYL ETHER	17	
Dichloroethyl oxide	DICHLOROETHYL ETHER	17	
1,6-DICHLOROHEXANE		17	
2,2′-DICHLOROISOPROPYL ETHER		17	2490
DICHLOROMETHANE		17	1593
2,4-DICHLOROPHENOL		17	2021
2,4-DICHLOROPHENOXYACETIC ACID, DIETHANOLAMINE SALT SOLUTION		17	
2,4-DICHLOROPHENOXYACETIC ACID, DIMETHYLAMINE SALT SOLUTION (70% OR LESS)		17	
2,4-DICHLOROPHENOXYACETIC ACID, TRIISOPROPANOLAMINE SALT SOLUTION		17	
1,1-DICHLOROPROPANE		17	
1,2-DICHLOROPROPANE		17	1279
Dichloropropane/Dichloropropene mixtures	DICHLOROPROPENE/DICHLOROPROPANE MIXTURES	17	
2,2-Dichloropropanoic acid	2,2-DICHLOROPROPIONIC ACID	17	
1,3-DICHLOROPROPENE		17	2047
DICHLOROPROPENE/DICHLOROPROPANE MIXTURES		17	
2,2-DICHLOROPROPIONIC ACID		17	
Dichloropropylene	1,3-DICHLOROPROPENE	17	
1,4-Dicyanobutane	ADIPONITRILE	17	
Dicyclopentadiene	1,3-CYCLOPENTADIENE DIMER (MOLTEN)	17	
Didecyl phthalate	DIALKYL (C$_7$–C$_{13}$) PHTHALATES	17	
Didodecyl phthalate	DIALKYL (C$_7$–C$_{13}$) PHTHALATES	17	
DIETHANOLAMINE		17	
DIETHYLAMINE		17	1154
DIETHYLAMINOETHANOL		17	2686
2-Diethylaminoethanol	DIETHYLAMINOETHANOL	17	
2,6-DIETHYLANILINE		17	

Index Name	Product Name	Chapter	UN Number
DIETHYLBENZENE		17	2049
Diethylcarbitol	DIETHYLENE GLYCOL DIETHYL ETHER	17	
Diethyl 'carbitol'	DIETHYLENE GLYCOL DIETHYL ETHER	17	
1,4-Diethylene dioxide	1,4-DIOXANE	17	
Diethylene ether	1,4-DIOXANE	17	
DIETHYLENE GLYCOL		18	
Diethylene glycol butyl ether	POLY(2–8)ALKYLENE GLYCOL MONOALKYL (C_1–C_6) ETHER	17	
Diethylene glycol butyl ether acetate	POLY(2–8)ALKYLENE GLYCOL MONOALKYL (C_1–C_6) ETHER ACETATE	17	
DIETHYLENE GLYCOL DIBUTYL ETHER		17	
DIETHYLENE GLYCOL DIETHYL ETHER		17	
Diethylene glycol ethyl ether	POLY(2–8)ALKYLENE GLYCOL MONOALKYL (C_1–C_6) ETHER	17	
Diethylene glycol ethyl ether acetate	POLY(2–8)ALKYLENE GLYCOL MONOALKYL (C_1–C_6) ETHER ACETATE	17	
Diethylene glycol methyl ether	POLY(2–8)ALKYLENE GLYCOL MONOALKYL (C_1–C_6) ETHER	17	
Diethylene glycol methyl ether acetate	POLY(2–8)ALKYLENE GLYCOL MONOALKYL (C_1–C_6) ETHER ACETATE	17	
Diethylene glycol monobutyl ether	POLY(2–8)ALKYLENE GLYCOL MONOALKYL (C_1–C_6) ETHER	17	
Diethylene glycol monobutyl ether acetate	POLY(2–8)ALKYLENE GLYCOL MONOALKYL (C_1–C_6) ETHER ACETATE	17	
Diethylene glycol monoethyl ether	POLY(2–8)ALKYLENE GLYCOL MONOALKYL (C_1–C_6) ETHER	17	
Diethylene glycol monoethyl ether acetate	POLY(2–8)ALKYLENE GLYCOL MONOALKYL (C_1–C_6) ETHER ACETATE	17	
Diethylene glycol monomethyl ether	POLY(2–8)ALKYLENE GLYCOL MONOALKYL (C_1–C_6) ETHER	17	
Diethylene glycol monomethyl ether acetate	POLY(2–8)ALKYLENE GLYCOL MONOALKYL (C_1–C_6) ETHER ACETATE	17	
DIETHYLENE GLYCOL PHTHALATE		17	
Diethylene oxide	1,4-DIOXANE	17	
DIETHYLENETRIAMINE		17	2079
DIETHYLENETRIAMINEPENTAACETIC ACID, PENTASODIUM SALT SOLUTION		17	
N,N-Diethylethanamine	TRIETHYLAMINE	17	
Diethylethanolamine	DIETHYLAMINOETHANOL	17	
N,N-Diethylethanolamine	DIETHYLAMINOETHANOL	17	
DIETHYL ETHER		17	1155
N,N-Diethylethylamine	TRIETHYLAMINE	17	
DI-(2-ETHYLHEXYL) ADIPATE		17	
DI-(2-ETHYLHEXYL)PHOSPHORIC ACID		17	1902
Diethyl oxide	DIETHYL ETHER	17	
DIETHYL PHTHALATE		17	
DIETHYL SULPHATE		17	1594
Diformyl	GLYOXAL SOLUTION (40% OR LESS)	17	
DIGLYCIDYL ETHER OF BISPHENOL A		17	
DIGLYCIDYL ETHER OF BISPHENOL F		17	

Index Name	Product Name	Chapter	UN Number
Diglycol	DIETHYLENE GLYCOL	18	
Diglycolamine	2-(2-AMINOETHOXY)ETHANOL	17	
Diglycol phthalate	DIETHYLENE GLYCOL PHTHALATE	17	
DIHEPTYL PHTHALATE		17	
Dihexyl	DODECANE (ALL ISOMERS)	17	
DI-*n*-HEXYL ADIPATE		17	
DIHEXYL PHTHALATE		17	
1,3-Dihydroisobenzofuran-1,3-dione	PHTHALIC ANHYDRIDE (MOLTEN)	17	
2,3-Dihydroxybutane	BUTYLENE GLYCOL	17	
2,2′-Dihydroxydiethylamine	DIETHANOLAMINE	17	
Di-(2-hydroxyethyl)amine	DIETHANOLAMINE	17	
Dihydroxyethyl ether	DIETHYLENE GLYCOL	18	
Dihydroxyhexane	HEXAMETHYLENE GLYCOL	17	
1,2-Dihydroxypropane	PROPYLENE GLYCOL	18	
Diisobutene	DIISOBUTYLENE	17	
DIISOBUTYLAMINE		17	2361
Diisobutylcarbinol	NONYL ALCOHOL (ALL ISOMERS)	17	
DIISOBUTYLENE		17	2050
alpha-Diisobutylene	DIISOBUTYLENE	17	
beta-Diisobutylene	DIISOBUTYLENE	17	
DIISOBUTYL KETONE		17	
DIISOBUTYL PHTHALATE		17	
2,4-Diisocyanato-1-methylbenzene	TOLUENE DIISOCYANATE	17	
2,4-Diisocyanatotoluene	TOLUENE DIISOCYANATE	17	
Diisodecyl phthalate	DIALKYL (C$_7$–C$_{13}$) PHTHALATES	17	
DIISONONYL ADIPATE		17	
Diisononyl phthalate	DIALKYL (C$_7$–C$_{13}$) PHTHALATES	17	
DIISOOCTYL PHTHALATE		17	
DIISOPROPANOLAMINE		17	
Diisopropylacetone	DIISOBUTYL KETONE	17	
DIISOPROPYLAMINE		17	1158
DIISOPROPYLBENZENE (ALL ISOMERS)		17	
Diisopropyl ether	ISOPROPYL ETHER	17	
DIISOPROPYLNAPHTHALENE		17	3082
Diisopropyl oxide	ISOPROPYL ETHER	17	
N,N-DIMETHYLACETAMIDE		17	
Dimethylacetamide acetate	*N,N*-DIMETHYLACETAMIDE	17	
N,N-DIMETHYLACETAMIDE SOLUTION (40% OR LESS)		17	
Dimethylacetylene carbinol	2-METHYL-2-HYDROXY-3-BUTYNE	17	
DIMETHYL ADIPATE		17	
DIMETHYLAMINE SOLUTION (45% OR LESS)		17	1160
DIMETHYLAMINE SOLUTION (GREATER THAN 45% BUT NOT GREATER THAN 55%)		17	1160
DIMETHYLAMINE SOLUTION (GREATER THAN 55% BUT NOT GREATER THAN 65%)		17	1160

Index Name	Product Name	Chapter	UN Number
Dimethylaminoethanol	DIMETHYLETHANOLAMINE	17	
2-Dimethylaminoethanol	DIMETHYLETHANOLAMINE	17	
Dimethylbenzenes	XYLENES	17	
1,3-Dimethylbutanol	METHYLAMYL ALCOHOL	17	
1,3-Dimethylbutan-1-ol	METHYLAMYL ALCOHOL	17	
1,3-Dimethylbutyl acetate	METHYLAMYL ACETATE	17	
Dimethylcarbinol	ISOPROPYL ALCOHOL	18	
N,N-DIMETHYLCYCLOHEXYLAMINE		17	2264
DIMETHYL DISULPHIDE		17	2381
N,N-Dimethyldodecanamine	ALKYL (C$_{12}$+) DIMETHYLAMINE	17	
N,N-Dimethyldodecan-1-amine	N,N-DIMETHYLDODECYLAMINE	17	
N,N-DIMETHYLDODECYLAMINE		17	
1,1-Dimethylethanol	tert-BUTYL ALCOHOL	17	
DIMETHYLETHANOLAMINE		17	2051
1,1-Dimethylethyl alcohol	tert-BUTYL ALCOHOL	17	
Dimethyl ethyl carbinol	tert-AMYL ALCOHOL	17	
sym-Dimethylethylene glycol	BUTYLENE GLYCOL	17	
1,1-Dimethylethyl methyl ether	METHYL tert-BUTYL ETHER	17	
Dimethyl formaldehyde	ACETONE	18	
DIMETHYLFORMAMIDE		17	2265
DIMETHYL GLUTARATE		17	
2,6-Dimethyl-4-heptanone	DIISOBUTYL KETONE	17	
2,6-Dimethylheptan-4-one	DIISOBUTYL KETONE	17	
N,N-Dimethylhexanamine	ALKYL (C$_{12}$+) DIMETHYLAMINE	17	
DIMETHYL HYDROGEN PHOSPHITE		17	
Dimethylhydroxybenzenes	XYLENOL	17	
1,1'-Dimethyl-2,2'-iminodiethanol	DIISOPROPANOLAMINE	17	
Dimethyl ketal	ACETONE	18	
Dimethyl ketone	ACETONE	18	
Dimethyllaurylamine	N,N-DIMETHYLDODECYLAMINE	17	
N,N-Dimethylmethanamine	TRIMETHYLAMINE SOLUTION (30% OR LESS)	17	
N,N-Dimethylmethylamine	TRIMETHYLAMINE SOLUTION (30% OR LESS)	17	
6,6-Dimethyl-2-methylenebicyclo[3.1.1]heptane	beta-PINENE	17	
DIMETHYLOCTANOIC ACID		17	
2,2-Dimethyloctanoic acid	NEODECANOIC ACID	17	
2,3-Dimethylphenol	XYLENOL	17	
2,4-Dimethylphenol	XYLENOL	17	
2,5-Dimethylphenol	XYLENOL	17	
2,6-Dimethylphenol	XYLENOL	17	
3,4-Dimethylphenol	XYLENOL	17	
3,5-Dimethylphenol	XYLENOL	17	
Dimethylphenols	XYLENOL	17	
Dimethylphenyl phosphate (3:1)	TRIXYLYL PHOSPHATE	17	
DIMETHYL PHTHALATE		17	

Index Name	Product Name	Chapter	UN Number
DIMETHYLPOLYSILOXANE		17	
2,2-Dimethylpropane	PENTANE (ALL ISOMERS)	17	
2,2-DIMETHYLPROPANE-1,3-DIOL (MOLTEN OR SOLUTION)		17	
2,2-Dimethylpropanoic acid	TRIMETHYLACETIC ACID	17	
1,1-Dimethylpropargyl alcohol	2-METHYL-2-HYDROXY-3-BUTYNE	17	
2,2-Dimethylpropionic acid	TRIMETHYLACETIC ACID	17	
1,1-Dimethylpropynol	2-METHYL-2-HYDROXY-3-BUTYNE	17	
DIMETHYL SUCCINATE		17	
N,N-Dimethyltetradecanamine	ALKYL (C$_{12}$+) DIMETHYLAMINE	17	
Dimethyltetradecylamine	ALKYL (C$_{12}$+) DIMETHYLAMINE	17	
3,9-Dimethyltricyclo[5.2.1.0^{2,6}]deca-3,8-diene	METHYLCYCLOPENTADIENE DIMER	17	
Dimethyltrimethylene glycol	2,2-DIMETHYLPROPANE-1,3-DIOL (MOLTEN OR SOLUTION)	17	
DINITROTOLUENE (MOLTEN)		17	1600
Dinonyl phthalate	DIALKYL (C$_7$–C$_{13}$) PHTHALATES	17	
DINONYL PHTHALATE		17	
3,6-Dioxaoctane-1,8-diol	TRIETHYLENE GLYCOL	18	
Dioctyl adipate	DI-(2-ETHYLHEXYL) ADIPATE	17	
Dioctyl hydrogen phosphate	DI-(2-ETHYLHEXYL)PHOSPHORIC ACID	17	
Dioctyl phosphoric acid	DI-(2-ETHYLHEXYL)PHOSPHORIC ACID	17	
DIOCTYL PHTHALATE		17	
1,4-Dioxan	1,4-DIOXANE	17	
1,4-DIOXANE		17	1165
Dioxolanone	PROPYLENE CARBONATE	18	
1,3-Dioxolan-2-one	ETHYLENE CARBONATE	18	
Dioxolone-2	ETHYLENE CARBONATE	18	
1,1-Dioxothiolan	SULPHOLANE	17	
Dioxyethylene ether	1,4-DIOXANE	17	
DIPENTENE		17	2052
DIPHENYL		17	
DIPHENYLAMINE (MOLTEN)		17	
DIPHENYLAMINE, REACTION PRODUCT WITH 2,2,4-TRIMETHYLPENTENE		17	
DIPHENYLAMINES, ALKYLATED		17	
DIPHENYL/DIPHENYL ETHER MIXTURES		17	
Diphenyl/diphenyl oxide mixtures	DIPHENYL/DIPHENYL ETHER MIXTURES	17	
Diphenyl dodecyl ether disulphonate solution	DODECYL DIPHENYL ETHER DISULPHONATE SOLUTION	17	
Diphenyl dodecyl oxide disulphonate solution	DODECYL DIPHENYL ETHER DISULPHONATE SOLUTION	17	
DIPHENYL ETHER		17	
DIPHENYL ETHER/DIPHENYL PHENYL ETHER MIXTURE		17	
DIPHENYLMETHANE DIISOCYANATE		17	2489
DIPHENYLOLPROPANE–EPICHLOROHYDRIN RESINS		17	
Diphenyl oxide	DIPHENYL ETHER	17	

Index Name	Product Name	Chapter	UN Number
Diphenyl oxide/diphenyl phenyl ether mixture	DIPHENYL ETHER/DIPHENYL PHENYL ETHER MIXTURE	17	
Dipropylamine	DI-*n*-PROPYLAMINE	17	
DI-*n*-PROPYLAMINE		17	2383
n-Dipropylamine	DI-*n*-PROPYLAMINE	17	
DIPROPYLENE GLYCOL		17	
Dipropylene glycol methyl ether	POLY(2–8)ALKYLENE GLYCOL MONOALKYL (C$_1$–C$_6$) ETHER	17	
Dipropylene glycol monomethyl ether	POLY(2–8)ALKYLENE GLYCOL MONOALKYL (C$_1$–C$_6$) ETHER	17	
Disodium carbonate	SODIUM CARBONATE SOLUTION	17	
Distillates (Petroleum), Steam Cracked, C$_8$–C$_{12}$ Fraction	RESIN OIL, DISTILLED	17	
DITHIOCARBAMATE ESTER (C$_7$–C$_{35}$)		17	
DITRIDECYL ADIPATE		17	
DITRIDECYL PHTHALATE		17	
DIUNDECYL PHTHALATE		17	
Docosan-1-ol	ALCOHOLS (C$_{13}$+)	17	
1-Docosanol	ALCOHOLS (C$_{13}$+)	17	
DODECANE (ALL ISOMERS)		17	
tert-DODECANETHIOL		17	
Dodecanoic acid	LAURIC ACID	17	
Dodecan-1-ol	DODECYL ALCOHOL	17	
1-Dodecanol	DODECYL ALCOHOL	17	
n-Dodecanol	DODECYL ALCOHOL	17	
DODECENE (ALL ISOMERS)		17	
Dodecyl, Tetradecyl, Hexadecyl-dimethylamine mixture	ALKYL (C$_{12}$+) DIMETHYLAMINE	17	
DODECYL ALCOHOL		17	
n-Dodecyl alcohol	DODECYL ALCOHOL	17	
DODECYLAMINE/TETRADECYLAMINE MIXTURE		17	
DODECYLBENZENE		17	
Dodecylbenzenesulphonic acid (contains 1.5% sulphuric acid)	ALKYL (C$_{11}$–C$_{17}$) BENZENE SULPHONIC ACID	17	
Dodecyldimethylamine	ALKYL (C$_{12}$+) DIMETHYLAMINE	17	
DODECYL DIPHENYL ETHER DISULPHONATE SOLUTION		17	
Dodecyl diphenyl oxide disulphonate solution	DODECYL DIPHENYL ETHER DISULPHONATE SOLUTION	17	
Dodecylene	DODECENE (ALL ISOMERS)	17	
DODECYL HYDROXYPROPYL SULPHIDE		17	
Dodecylic acid	LAURIC ACID	17	
tert-Dodecyl mercaptan	*tert*-DODECANETHIOL	17	
DODECYL METHACRYLATE		17	
Dodecyl 2-methyl-2-propenoate	DODECYL METHACRYLATE	17	
Dodecyl 2-methylprop-2-enoate	DODECYL METHACRYLATE	17	
DODECYL/OCTADECYL METHACRYLATE MIXTURE		17	
DODECYL/PENTADECYL METHACRYLATE MIXTURE		17	
DODECYLPHENOL		17	

Index Name	Product Name	Chapter	UN Number
2-Dodecylthio-1-methylethanol	DODECYL HYDROXYPROPYL SULPHIDE	17	
1-Dodecylthiopropan-2-ol	DODECYL HYDROXYPROPYL SULPHIDE	17	
DODECYLXYLENE		17	
Drilling brine: potassium chloride solution	POTASSIUM CHLORIDE SOLUTION	17	
DRILLING BRINES (CONTAINING ZINC SALTS)		17	
DRILLING BRINES, INCLUDING: CALCIUM BROMIDE SOLUTION, CALCIUM CHLORIDE SOLUTION AND SODIUM CHLORIDE SOLUTION		17	
2,4-D-tris(2-hydroxy-2-methylethyl)ammonium	2,4-DICHLOROPHENOXYACETIC ACID, TRIISOPROPANOLAMINE SALT SOLUTION	17	
Dutch liquid	ETHYLENE DICHLORIDE	17	
Dutch oil	ETHYLENE DICHLORIDE	17	
Enanthic acid	*n*-HEPTANOIC ACID	17	
Enanthyl alcohol	HEPTANOL (ALL ISOMERS)	17	
Enanthylic acid	*n*-HEPTANOIC ACID	17	
Engravers' acid	NITRIC ACID (70% AND OVER)	17	
EPICHLOROHYDRIN		17	2023
1,2-Epoxybutane	1,2-BUTYLENE OXIDE	17	
1,4-Epoxybutane	TETRAHYDROFURAN	17	
1,2-Epoxypropane	PROPYLENE OXIDE	17	
2,3-Epoxy propyl ester of mixed trialkyl acetic acids	GLYCIDYL ESTER OF C_{10} TRIALKYLACETIC ACID	17	
2,3-Epoxypropyl neodecanoate	GLYCIDYL ESTER OF C_{10} TRIALKYLACETIC ACID	17	
alpha-2,3-Epoxypropyl-*omega*-{*alpha*-[4-(2,3-epoxypropoxy)phenyl]-*p*-tolyloxy}poly[oxy-*p*-phenylenemethylene-*p*-phenyleneoxy(2-hydroxytrimethylene)]	DIGLYCIDYL ETHER OF BISPHENOL F	17	
alpha-2,3-Epoxypropyl-*omega*-{*alpha*-[4-(2,3-epoxypropyl)phenyl]-*alpha*,*alpha*-dimethyl-*p*-tolyloxy}poly[oxy-*p*-phenyleneisopropylidene-*p*-phenylenoxy(2-hydroxytrimethylene)]	DIGLYCIDYL ETHER OF BISPHENOL A	17	
EPTC	*S*-ETHYL DIPROPYLTHIOCARBAMATE	17	
Essence of Mirbane	NITROBENZENE	17	
Essence of Myrbane	NITROBENZENE	17	
Ethanamine solutions, 72% or less	ETHYLAMINE SOLUTIONS (72% OR LESS)	17	
Ethanecarbonitrile	PROPIONITRILE	17	
Ethanedial	GLYOXAL SOLUTION (40% OR LESS)	17	
1,2-Ethanediol	ETHYLENE GLYCOL	17	
Ethanoic acid	ACETIC ACID	17	
Ethanoic anhydride	ACETIC ANHYDRIDE	17	
Ethanol	ETHYL ALCOHOL	18	
ETHANOLAMINE		17	2491
Ethenyl acetate	VINYL ACETATE	17	
Ethenyl ethanoate	VINYL ACETATE	17	
Ether	DIETHYL ETHER	17	
Ethinyl trichloride	TRICHLOROETHYLENE	17	
2-Ethoxyethanol	ETHYLENE GLYCOL MONOALKYL ETHERS	17	
2-(2-Ethoxyethoxy)ethanol	POLY(2–8)ALKYLENE GLYCOL MONOALKYL (C_1–C_6) ETHER	17	

Index Name	Product Name	Chapter	UN Number
2-(2-Ethoxyethoxy)ethyl acetate	POLY(2–8)ALKYLENE GLYCOL MONOALKYL (C$_1$–C$_6$) ETHER ACETATE	17	
2-ETHOXYETHYL ACETATE		17	1172
ETHOXYLATED LONG CHAIN (C$_{16}$+) ALKYLOXYALKYLAMINE		17	
2-Ethoxy-2-methylpropane	ETHYL tert-BUTYL ETHER	17	
1-Ethoxypropan-2-ol	PROPYLENE GLYCOL MONOALKYL ETHER	17	
ETHYL ACETATE		17	
ETHYL ACETOACETATE		17	
Ethyl acetone	METHYL PROPYL KETONE	18	
ETHYL ACRYLATE		17	1917
ETHYL ALCOHOL		18	
ETHYLAMINE		17	1036
ETHYLAMINE SOLUTIONS (72% OR LESS)		17	2270
Ethylaminocyclohexane	N-ETHYLCYCLOHEXYLAMINE	17	
ETHYL AMYL KETONE		17	2271
ETHYLBENZENE		17	1175
Ethyl benzol	ETHYLBENZENE	17	
Ethyl butanoate	ETHYL BUTYRATE	17	
ETHYL tert-BUTYL ETHER		17	1993
ETHYL BUTYRATE		17	1180
2-Ethylcaproic acid	2-ETHYLHEXANOIC ACID	17	
Ethyl carbinol	n-PROPYL ALCOHOL	17	
Ethyl cyanide	PROPIONITRILE	17	
ETHYLCYCLOHEXANE		17	
Ethyl(cyclohexyl)amine	N-ETHYLCYCLOHEXYLAMINE	17	
N-ETHYLCYCLOHEXYLAMINE		17	
Ethyldimethylmethane	PENTANE (ALL ISOMERS)	17	
S-Ethyl dipropylcarbamothioate	S-ETHYL DIPROPYLTHIOCARBAMATE	17	
S-Ethyl dipropyldithiocarbamate	S-ETHYL DIPROPYLTHIOCARBAMATE	17	
S-ETHYL DIPROPYLTHIOCARBAMATE		17	
Ethylene alcohol	ETHYLENE GLYCOL	17	
Ethylene bisiminodiacetic acid tetrasodium salt solution	ETHYLENEDIAMINETETRAACETIC ACID, TETRASODIUM SALT SOLUTION	17	
Ethylene bromide	ETHYLENE DIBROMIDE	17	
ETHYLENE CARBONATE		18	
Ethylenecarboxylic acid	ACRYLIC ACID	17	
Ethylene chloride	ETHYLENE DICHLORIDE	17	
ETHYLENE CHLOROHYDRIN		17	1135
ETHYLENE CYANOHYDRIN		17	
Ethylene diacetate	ETHYLENE GLYCOL DIACETATE	17	
ETHYLENEDIAMINE		17	1604
ETHYLENEDIAMINETETRAACETIC ACID, TETRASODIUM SALT SOLUTION		17	
ETHYLENE DIBROMIDE		17	1605
ETHYLENE DICHLORIDE		17	1184

Index Name	Product Name	Chapter	UN Number
2,2′-Ethylenedi-iminodi(ethylamine)	TRIETHYLENETETRAMINE	17	
Ethylenedinitrilotetraacetic acid tetrasodium salt solution	ETHYLENEDIAMINETETRAACETIC ACID, TETRASODIUM SALT SOLUTION	17	
2,2′-Ethylenedioxydiethanol	TRIETHYLENE GLYCOL	18	
ETHYLENE GLYCOL		17	
ETHYLENE GLYCOL ACETATE		17	
Ethylene glycol acrylate	2-HYDROXYETHYL ACRYLATE	17	
Ethylene glycol butyl ether	ETHYLENE GLYCOL MONOALKYL ETHERS	17	
ETHYLENE GLYCOL BUTYL ETHER ACETATE		17	
Ethylene glycol *tert*-butyl ether	ETHYLENE GLYCOL MONOALKYL ETHERS	17	
ETHYLENE GLYCOL DIACETATE		17	
Ethylene glycol ethyl ether	ETHYLENE GLYCOL MONOALKYL ETHERS	17	
Ethylene glycol ethyl ether acetate	2-ETHOXYETHYL ACETATE	17	
Ethylene glycol isopropyl ether	ETHYLENE GLYCOL MONOALKYL ETHERS	17	
Ethylene glycol methyl ether	ETHYLENE GLYCOL MONOALKYL ETHERS	17	
ETHYLENE GLYCOL METHYL ETHER ACETATE		17	
ETHYLENE GLYCOL MONOALKYL ETHERS		17	
Ethylene glycol monobutyl ether	ETHYLENE GLYCOL MONOALKYL ETHERS	17	
Ethylene glycol mono-*tert*-butyl ether	ETHYLENE GLYCOL MONOALKYL ETHERS	17	
Ethylene glycol monoethyl ether	ETHYLENE GLYCOL MONOALKYL ETHERS	17	
Ethylene glycol monoethyl ether acetate	2-ETHOXYETHYL ACETATE	17	
Ethylene glycol monomethyl ether	ETHYLENE GLYCOL MONOALKYL ETHERS	17	
Ethylene glycol monomethyl ether acetate	ETHYLENE GLYCOL METHYL ETHER ACETATE	17	
Ethylene glycol monophenyl ether	ETHYLENE GLYCOL PHENYL ETHER	17	
ETHYLENE GLYCOL PHENYL ETHER		17	
ETHYLENE GLYCOL PHENYL ETHER/DIETHYLENE GLYCOL PHENYL ETHER MIXTURE		17	
ETHYLENE OXIDE/PROPYLENE OXIDE MIXTURE WITH AN ETHYLENE OXIDE CONTENT OF NOT MORE THAN 30% BY MASS		17	2983
Ethylene tetrachloride	PERCHLOROETHYLENE	17	
Ethylene trichloride	TRICHLOROETHYLENE	17	
ETHYLENE–VINYL ACETATE COPOLYMER (EMULSION)		17	
Ethyl ethanoate	ETHYL ACETATE	17	
Ethyl ether	DIETHYL ETHER	17	
ETHYL 3-ETHOXYPROPIONATE		17	
Ethyl fluid	MOTOR FUEL ANTI-KNOCK COMPOUNDS (CONTAINING LEAD ALKYLS)	17	
Ethylformic acid	PROPIONIC ACID	17	
Ethyl glycol	ETHYLENE GLYCOL MONOALKYL ETHERS	17	
2-Ethylhexaldehyde	OCTYL ALDEHYDES	17	
2-Ethylhexanal	OCTYL ALDEHYDES	17	
2-ETHYLHEXANOIC ACID		17	
2-Ethylhexanol	OCTANOL (ALL ISOMERS)	17	
2-Ethylhexenal	2-ETHYL-3-PROPYLACROLEIN	17	
2-Ethylhex-2-enal	2-ETHYL-3-PROPYLACROLEIN	17	

Index Name	Product Name	Chapter	UN Number
2-Ethylhexoic acid	OCTANOIC ACID (ALL ISOMERS)	17	
2-ETHYLHEXYL ACRYLATE		17	
2-Ethylhexyl alcohol	OCTANOL (ALL ISOMERS)	17	
2-ETHYLHEXYLAMINE		17	2276
2-ETHYL-2-(HYDROXYMETHYL)PROPANE-1,3-DIOL (C_8–C_{10}) ESTER		17	
Ethylic acid	ACETIC ACID	17	
5-Ethylidenebicyclo(2,2,1)hept-2-ene	ETHYLIDENENORBORNENE	17	
Ethylidene chloride	1,1-DICHLOROETHANE	17	
Ethylidene dichloride	1,1-DICHLOROETHANE	17	
ETHYLIDENENORBORNENE		17	
ETHYL METHACRYLATE		17	2277
N-ETHYLMETHYLALLYLAMINE		17	
N-Ethyl-2-methylallylamine	N-ETHYLMETHYLALLYLAMINE	17	
2-Ethyl-6-methylaniline	2-METHYL-6-ETHYLANILINE	17	
2-Ethyl-6-methylbenzenamine	2-METHYL-6-ETHYLANILINE	17	
Ethyl methyl ketone	METHYL ETHYL KETONE	17	
5-Ethyl-2-methylpyridine	2-METHYL-5-ETHYLPYRIDINE	17	
Ethyl oxide	DIETHYL ETHER	17	
Ethyl phosphate	TRIETHYL PHOSPHATE	17	
Ethyl phthalate	DIETHYL PHTHALATE	17	
5-Ethyl-2-picoline	2-METHYL-5-ETHYLPYRIDINE	17	
3-Ethylpropan-1-ol	PROPYLENE GLYCOL MONOALKYL ETHER	17	
Ethyl propenoate	ETHYL ACRYLATE	17	
ETHYL PROPIONATE		17	
2-ETHYL-3-PROPYLACROLEIN		17	
Ethyl sulphate	DIETHYL SULPHATE	17	
ETHYLTOLUENE		17	
5-Ethyl-o-toluidine	2-METHYL-5-ETHYLPYRIDINE	17	
6-Ethyl-2-toluidine	2-METHYL-6-ETHYLANILINE	17	
6-Ethyl-o-toluidine	2-METHYL-6-ETHYLANILINE	17	
Ethyl vinyl ether	VINYL ETHYL ETHER	17	
Ethynyldimethylcarbinol	2-METHYL-2-HYDROXY-3-BUTYNE	17	
FATTY ACID (SATURATED C_{13}+)		17	
FATTY ACID METHYL ESTERS		17	
FATTY ACIDS, C_8–C_{10}		17	
FATTY ACIDS, C_{12}+		17	
FATTY ACIDS, C_{16}+		17	
FATTY ACIDS, ESSENTIALLY LINEAR (C_6–C_{18}) 2-ETHYLHEXYL ESTER		17	
Feeding corn molasses	MOLASSES	18	
Fermentation alcohol	ETHYL ALCOHOL	18	
FERRIC CHLORIDE SOLUTIONS		17	2582
FERRIC NITRATE/NITRIC ACID SOLUTION		17	
FISH OIL		17	

Index Name	Product Name	Chapter	UN Number
FLUOROSILICIC ACID (20–30%) IN WATER SOLUTION		17	1778
FORMALDEHYDE SOLUTIONS (45% OR LESS)		17	1198, 2209
Formaldehyde trimer	1,3,5-TRIOXANE	17	
Formalin	FORMALDEHYDE SOLUTIONS (45% OR LESS)	17	
FORMAMIDE		17	
Formdimethylamide	DIMETHYLFORMAMIDE	17	
FORMIC ACID		17	1779
Formic aldehyde	FORMALDEHYDE SOLUTIONS (45% OR LESS)	17	
Formylformic acid	GLYOXYLIC ACID SOLUTION (50% OR LESS)	17	
Fural	FURFURAL	17	
2-Furaldehyde	FURFURAL	17	
Furan-2,5-dione	MALEIC ANHYDRIDE	17	
2,5-Furandione	MALEIC ANHYDRIDE	17	
FURFURAL		17	1199
2-Furfuraldehyde	FURFURAL	17	
FURFURYL ALCOHOL		17	2874
Furylcarbinol	FURFURYL ALCOHOL	17	
Fused poly(2+)cyclic aromatic hydrocarbons	POLY(2+)CYCLIC AROMATICS	17	
Gaultheria oil	METHYL SALICYLATE	17	
Glacial acetic acid	ACETIC ACID	17	
D-Glucitol	SORBITOL SOLUTION	18	
GLUCITOL/GLYCEROL BLEND PROPOXYLATED (CONTAINING LESS THAN 10% AMINES)		17	
Glucitol solution	SORBITOL SOLUTION	18	
D-Glucopyranoside C_8–C_{14} alkyl	ALKYL (C_8–C_{10})/(C_{12}–C_{14}):(40% OR LESS/60% OR MORE) POLYGLUCOSIDE SOLUTION (55% OR LESS)	17	
D-Glucopyranoside C_8–C_{14} alkyl	ALKYL (C_8–C_{10})/(C_{12}–C_{14}):(60% OR MORE/40% OR LESS) POLYGLUCOSIDE SOLUTION (55% OR LESS)	17	
GLUCOSE SOLUTION		18	
GLUTARALDEHYDE SOLUTIONS (50% OR LESS)		17	
Glycerin	GLYCERINE	18	
GLYCERINE		18	
Glycerin triacetate	GLYCERYL TRIACETATE	17	
Glyceritol	GLYCERINE	18	
Glycerol	GLYCERINE	18	
GLYCEROL MONOOLEATE		17	
Glycerol oleate	GLYCEROL MONOOLEATE	17	
Glycerol 1-oleate	GLYCEROL MONOOLEATE	17	
GLYCEROL PROPOXYLATED		17	
GLYCEROL, PROPOXYLATED AND ETHOXYLATED		17	
GLYCEROL/SUCROSE BLEND PROPOXYLATED AND ETHOXYLATED		17	
Glycerol triacetate	GLYCERYL TRIACETATE	17	
GLYCERYL TRIACETATE		17	
GLYCIDYL ESTER OF C_{10} TRIALKYLACETIC ACID		17	
Glycidyl neodecanoate	GLYCIDYL ESTER OF C_{10} TRIALKYLACETIC ACID	17	

Index Name	Product Name	Chapter	UN Number
Glycine soda solution	GLYCINE, SODIUM SALT SOLUTION	17	
GLYCINE, SODIUM SALT SOLUTION		17	
Glycol	ETHYLENE GLYCOL	17	
Glycol carbonate	ETHYLENE CARBONATE	18	
Glycol chlorohydrin	ETHYLENE CHLOROHYDRIN	17	
Glycol dichloride	ETHYLENE DICHLORIDE	17	
GLYCOLIC ACID SOLUTION (70% OR LESS)		17	3265
Glycol monobutyl ether	ETHYLENE GLYCOL MONOALKYL ETHERS	17	
Glycols, polyethylene mono(p-nonylphenyl) ether	ALKARYL POLYETHERS (C_9–C_{20})	17	
Glycyl alcohol	GLYCERINE	18	
Glyoxaldehyde	GLYOXAL SOLUTION (40% OR LESS)	17	
Glyoxalic acid	GLYOXYLIC ACID SOLUTION (50% OR LESS)	17	
GLYOXAL SOLUTION (40% OR LESS)		17	
GLYOXYLIC ACID SOLUTION (50% OR LESS)		17	1760
Glyphosate	GLYPHOSATE SOLUTION (NOT CONTAINING SURFACTANT)	17	
Glyphosate-mono(isopropylammonium)	GLYPHOSATE SOLUTION (NOT CONTAINING SURFACTANT)	17	
GLYPHOSATE SOLUTION (NOT CONTAINING SURFACTANT)		17	
Grain alcohol	ETHYL ALCOHOL	18	
GROUNDNUT OIL		17	
Hemimellitine	TRIMETHYLBENZENE (ALL ISOMERS)	17	
Hendecanoic acid	UNDECANOIC ACID	17	
1-Hendecanol	UNDECYL ALCOHOL	17	
Heptamethylene	CYCLOHEPTANE	17	
HEPTANE (ALL ISOMERS)		17	1206
1-Heptanecarboxylic acid	OCTANOIC ACID (ALL ISOMERS)	17	
3-Heptanecarboxylic acid	OCTANOIC ACID (ALL ISOMERS)	17	
Heptanoic acid	n-HEPTANOIC ACID	17	
n-HEPTANOIC ACID		17	
HEPTANOL (ALL ISOMERS)		17	
Heptan-2-one	METHYL AMYL KETONE	17	
2-Heptanone	METHYL AMYL KETONE	17	
Heptan-2-one	METHYL AMYL KETONE	17	
HEPTENE (ALL ISOMERS)		17	
Heptoic acid	n-HEPTANOIC ACID	17	
HEPTYL ACETATE		17	
Heptyl alcohol, all isomers	HEPTANOL (ALL ISOMERS)	17	
Heptylcarbinol	OCTANOL (ALL ISOMERS)	17	
Heptylene, mixed isomers	HEPTENE (ALL ISOMERS)	17	
Heptylic acid	n-HEPTANOIC ACID	17	
n-Heptylic acid	n-HEPTANOIC ACID	17	
1-Hexadecene	OLEFINS (C_{13}+, ALL ISOMERS)	17	
Hexadecyl and icosyl methacrylate mixture	CETYL/EICOSYL METHACRYLATE MIXTURE	17	

Index Name	Product Name	Chapter	UN Number
1-HEXADECYLNAPHTHALENE/1,4-BIS(HEXADECYL)NAPHTHALENE MIXTURE		17	
Hexadecylnaphthalene/dihexadecylnaphthalene mixture	1-HEXADECYLNAPHTHALENE/1,4-BIS(HEXADECYL)NAPHTHALENE MIXTURE	17	
Hexadecyl/octadecyl alcohol	ALCOHOLS (C$_{13}$+)	17	
Hexadecyl, octadecyl and icosyl methacrylates, mixtures	CETYL/EICOSYL METHACRYLATE MIXTURE	17	
Hexaethylene glycol	POLYETHYLENE GLYCOL	17	
Hexahydroaniline	CYCLOHEXYLAMINE	17	
Hexahydrobenzene	CYCLOHEXANE	17	
Hexahydro-1*H*-azepine	HEXAMETHYLENEIMINE	17	
Hexahydro-1-*H*-azepine	HEXAMETHYLENEIMINE	17	
Hexahydrophenol	CYCLOHEXANOL	17	
Hexahydrotoluene	METHYLCYCLOHEXANE	17	
Hexamethylene	CYCLOHEXANE	17	
HEXAMETHYLENEDIAMINE ADIPATE (50% IN WATER)		17	
HEXAMETHYLENEDIAMINE (MOLTEN)		17	
HEXAMETHYLENEDIAMINE SOLUTION		17	1783
1,6-Hexamethylenediamine solution	HEXAMETHYLENEDIAMINE SOLUTION	17	
Hexamethylenediammonium adipate solution (50% solution)	HEXAMETHYLENEDIAMINE ADIPATE (50% IN WATER)	17	
HEXAMETHYLENE DIISOCYANATE		17	2281
Hexamethylene-1,6-diisocyanate	HEXAMETHYLENE DIISOCYANATE	17	
HEXAMETHYLENE GLYCOL		17	
HEXAMETHYLENEIMINE		17	2493
HEXAMETHYLENETETRAMINE SOLUTIONS		18	
Hexamine	HEXAMETHYLENETETRAMINE SOLUTIONS	18	
Hexanaphthene	CYCLOHEXANE	17	
HEXANE (ALL ISOMERS)		17	1208
1,6-Hexanediamine	HEXAMETHYLENEDIAMINE (MOLTEN)	17	
1,6-Hexanediamine hexanedioate (1:1)	HEXAMETHYLENEDIAMINE ADIPATE (50% IN WATER)	17	
Hexane-1,6-diamine solutions	HEXAMETHYLENEDIAMINE SOLUTION	17	
1,6-Hexanediamine solutions	HEXAMETHYLENEDIAMINE SOLUTION	17	
Hexanedioic acid, bis(2-ethylhexyl) ester	DI-(2-ETHYLHEXYL) ADIPATE	17	
Hexane-1,6-diol	HEXAMETHYLENE GLYCOL	17	
1,6-Hexanediol	HEXAMETHYLENE GLYCOL	17	
1,6-HEXANEDIOL, DISTILLATION OVERHEADS		17	1987
n-Hexane	HEXANE (ALL ISOMERS)	17	
HEXANOIC ACID		17	
HEXANOL		17	2282
Hexan-1-ol	HEXANOL	17	
Hexan-6-olide	*epsilon*-CAPROLACTAM (MOLTEN OR AQUEOUS SOLUTIONS)	17	
Hexan-2-one	METHYL BUTYL KETONE	17	
2-Hexanone	METHYL BUTYL KETONE	17	
HEXENE (ALL ISOMERS)		17	2370
Hexene-1	HEXENE (ALL ISOMERS)	17	

Index Name	Product Name	Chapter	UN Number
Hex-1-ene	HEXENE (ALL ISOMERS)	17	
2-Hexene	HEXENE (ALL ISOMERS)	17	
Hexone	METHYL ISOBUTYL KETONE	17	
HEXYL ACETATE		17	1233
sec-Hexyl acetate	METHYLAMYL ACETATE	17	
Hexyl alcohol	HEXANOL	17	
Hexyldimethylamine	ALKYL (C_{12}+) DIMETHYLAMINE	17	
Hexylene	HEXENE (ALL ISOMERS)	17	
HEXYLENE GLYCOL		18	
Hexyl ethanoate	HEXYL ACETATE	17	
Homopiperidine	HEXAMETHYLENEIMINE	17	
HYDROCHLORIC ACID		17	1789
Hydrofuran	TETRAHYDROFURAN	17	
Hydrogenated glucose syrup	MALTITOL SOLUTION	18	
Hydrogenated maltose syrup	MALTITOL SOLUTION	18	
Hydrogenated oligosaccharide	HYDROGENATED STARCH HYDROLYSATE	18	
HYDROGENATED STARCH HYDROLYSATE		18	
Hydrogencarboxylic acid	FORMIC ACID	17	
Hydrogen chloride, aqueous	HYDROCHLORIC ACID	17	
HYDROGEN PEROXIDE SOLUTIONS (OVER 60% BUT NOT OVER 70% BY MASS)		17	2015
HYDROGEN PEROXIDE SOLUTIONS (OVER 8% BUT NOT OVER 60% BY MASS)		17	2014, 2984
Hydrogen sulphate	SULPHURIC ACID	17	
alpha-Hydro-omega-hydroxypoly[oxy(methyl-1,2-ethanediyl)]	POLYPROPYLENE GLYCOL	17	
Hydroxyacetic acid	GLYCOLIC ACID SOLUTION (70% OR LESS)	17	
Hydroxybenzene	PHENOL	17	
4-Hydroxybutanoic acid lactone	gamma-BUTYROLACTONE	17	
4-Hydroxybutyric acid lactone	gamma-BUTYROLACTONE	17	
gamma-Hydroxybutyric acid lactone	gamma-BUTYROLACTONE	17	
Hydroxydimethylbenzenes	XYLENOL	17	
Hydroxyethanoic acid	GLYCOLIC ACID SOLUTION (70% OR LESS)	17	
2-Hydroxyethyl acetate	ETHYLENE GLYCOL ACETATE	17	
2-HYDROXYETHYL ACRYLATE		17	
beta-Hydroxyethyl acrylate	2-HYDROXYETHYL ACRYLATE	17	
2-Hydroxyethylamine	ETHANOLAMINE	17	
N-beta-Hydroxyethylethylenediamine	AMINOETHYLETHANOLAMINE	17	
N-(HYDROXYETHYL)ETHYLENEDIAMINETRIACETIC ACID, TRISODIUM SALT SOLUTION		17	
beta-Hydroxyethyl phenyl ether	ETHYLENE GLYCOL PHENYL ETHER	17	
2-Hydroxyethyl propenoate	2-HYDROXYETHYL ACRYLATE	17	
2-Hydroxyethyl 2-propenoate	2-HYDROXYETHYL ACRYLATE	17	
alpha-Hydroxyisobutyronitrile	ACETONE CYANOHYDRIN	17	
4-Hydroxy-2-keto-4-methylpentane	DIACETONE ALCOHOL	17	
4-Hydroxy-4-methylpentanone-2	DIACETONE ALCOHOL	17	

Index Name	Product Name	Chapter	UN Number
4-Hydroxy-4-methylpentan-2-one	DIACETONE ALCOHOL	17	
2-(Hydroxymethyl)propane	ISOBUTYL ALCOHOL	17	
2-Hydroxy-2-methylpropiononitrile	ACETONE CYANOHYDRIN	17	
2-HYDROXY-4-(METHYLTHIO)BUTANOIC ACID		17	
2-Hydroxy-4-methylthiobutyric acid	2-HYDROXY-4-(METHYLTHIO)BUTANOIC ACID	17	
2-Hydroxynitrobenzene (molten)	*o*-NITROPHENOL (MOLTEN)	17	
1-Hydroxy-2-phenoxyethane	ETHYLENE GLYCOL PHENYL ETHER	17	
2-Hydroxypropanoic acid	LACTIC ACID	17	
2-Hydroxypropionic acid	LACTIC ACID	17	
alpha-Hydroxypropionic acid	LACTIC ACID	17	
3-Hydroxypropionic acid, lactone	*beta*-PROPIOLACTONE	17	
2-Hydroxypropionitrile	LACTONITRILE SOLUTION (80% OR LESS)	17	
alpha-Hydroxypropionitrile	LACTONITRILE SOLUTION (80% OR LESS)	17	
beta-Hydroxypropionitrile	ETHYLENE CYANOHYDRIN	17	
2-Hydroxypropiononitrile	LACTONITRILE SOLUTION (80% OR LESS)	17	
3-Hydroxypropiononitrile	ETHYLENE CYANOHYDRIN	17	
2-[2-(2-Hydroxypropoxy)propoxy]propan-1-ol	TRIPROPYLENE GLYCOL	17	
2-Hydroxypropylamine	ISOPROPANOLAMINE	17	
3-Hydroxypropylamine	*n*-PROPANOLAMINE	17	
alpha-Hydroxytoluene	BENZYL ALCOHOL	17	
3-Hydroxy-2,2,4-trimethylpentyl isobutyrate	2,2,4-TRIMETHYL-1,3-PENTANEDIOL-1-ISOBUTYRATE	17	
ILLIPE OIL		17	
2,2′-[Iminobis(ethyleneimino)]diethylamine	TETRAETHYLENEPENTAMINE	17	
2,2′-Iminodi(ethylamine)	DIETHYLENETRIAMINE	17	
2,2′-Iminodiethanol	DIETHANOLAMINE	17	
1,1′-Iminodipropan-2-ol	DIISOPROPANOLAMINE	17	
Iron(III) chloride solutions	FERRIC CHLORIDE SOLUTIONS	17	
Iron(III) nitrate/nitric acid solution	FERRIC NITRATE/NITRIC ACID SOLUTION	17	
Isoacetophenone	ISOPHORONE	17	
Isoamyl acetate	AMYL ACETATE (ALL ISOMERS)	17	
ISOAMYL ALCOHOL		17	
ISO- AND CYCLO-ALKANES (C$_{10}$–C$_{11}$)		17	
ISO- AND CYCLO-ALKANES (C$_{12}$+)		17	
Isobutaldehyde	BUTYRALDEHYDE (ALL ISOMERS)	17	
Isobutanal	BUTYRALDEHYDE (ALL ISOMERS)	17	
Isobutanol	ISOBUTYL ALCOHOL	17	
Isobutanolamine	2-AMINO-2-METHYL-1-PROPANOL	17	
Isobutyl acetate	BUTYL ACETATE (ALL ISOMERS)	17	
Isobutyl acrylate	BUTYL ACRYLATE (ALL ISOMERS)	17	
ISOBUTYL ALCOHOL		17	1212
Isobutyl aldehyde	BUTYRALDEHYDE (ALL ISOMERS)	17	
Isobutylamine	BUTYLAMINE (ALL ISOMERS)	17	
Isobutylcarbinol	ISOAMYL ALCOHOL	17	
ISOBUTYL FORMATE		17	2393

Index Name	Product Name	Chapter	UN Number
Isobutyl ketone	DIISOBUTYL KETONE	17	
Iso-butyl ketone	DIISOBUTYL KETONE	17	
ISOBUTYL METHACRYLATE		17	
Isobutylmethylcarbinol	METHYLAMYL ALCOHOL	17	
Isobutyl methyl ketone	METHYL ISOBUTYL KETONE	17	
Isobutylmethylmethanol	METHYLAMYL ALCOHOL	17	
Isobutyraldehyde	BUTYRALDEHYDE (ALL ISOMERS)	17	
Isobutyric aldehyde	BUTYRALDEHYDE (ALL ISOMERS)	17	
alpha-Isocyanatobenzyl-omega-isocyanatophenylpoly[(phenyl isocyanate)-alt-formaldehyde]	POLYMETHYLENE POLYPHENYL ISOCYANATE	17	
1-Isocyanato-3-isocyanatomethyl-trimethylcyclohexane	ISOPHORONE DIISOCYANATE	17	
3-Isocyanatomethyl-3,5,5-trimethylcyclohexyl isocyanate	ISOPHORONE DIISOCYANATE	17	
Isodecanol	DECYL ALCOHOL (ALL ISOMERS)	17	
Isodecyl alcohol	DECYL ALCOHOL (ALL ISOMERS)	17	
Isododecane	DODECANE (ALL ISOMERS)	17	
Isodurene	TETRAMETHYLBENZENE (ALL ISOMERS)	17	
Isononanoic acid	NONANOIC ACID (ALL ISOMERS)	17	
Isononanol	NONYL ALCOHOL (ALL ISOMERS)	17	
Isooctane	OCTANE (ALL ISOMERS)	17	
Isooctanol	OCTANOL (ALL ISOMERS)	17	
Isopentane	PENTANE (ALL ISOMERS)	17	
Isopentanol	AMYL ALCOHOL, PRIMARY	17	
Isopentanol	ISOAMYL ALCOHOL	17	
Isopentene	PENTENE (ALL ISOMERS)	17	
Isopentyl acetate	AMYL ACETATE (ALL ISOMERS)	17	
Isopentyl alcohol	ISOAMYL ALCOHOL	17	
ISOPHORONE		17	
ISOPHORONEDIAMINE		17	2289
ISOPHORONE DIISOCYANATE	.	17	2290
ISOPRENE		17	1218
Isopropanol	ISOPROPYL ALCOHOL	18	
ISOPROPANOLAMINE		17	
Isopropenylbenzene	alpha-METHYLSTYRENE	17	
2-Isopropoxyethanol	ETHYLENE GLYCOL MONOALKYL ETHERS	17	
2-Isopropoxypropane	ISOPROPYL ETHER	17	
ISOPROPYL ACETATE		17	1220
Isopropylacetone	METHYL ISOBUTYL KETONE	17	
ISOPROPYL ALCOHOL		18	
ISOPROPYLAMINE		17	1221
ISOPROPYLAMINE (70% OR LESS) SOLUTION		17	
Isopropylammonium N-(phosphonomethyl)glycine	GLYPHOSATE SOLUTION (NOT CONTAINING SURFACTANT)	17	
Isopropyl carbinol	ISOBUTYL ALCOHOL	17	
Isopropylcarbinol	ISOBUTYL ALCOHOL	17	
ISOPROPYLCYCLOHEXANE		17	

Index Name	Product Name	Chapter	UN Number
1-Isopropyl-3,3-dimethyltrimethylene diisobutyrate	2,2,4-TRIMETHYL-1,3-PENTANEDIOL DIISOBUTYRATE	17	
ISOPROPYL ETHER		17	1159
Isopropylideneacetone	MESITYL OXIDE	17	
Isopropyl oxide	ISOPROPYL ETHER	17	
Isopropyltoluene	p-CYMENE	17	
4-Isopropyltoluene	p-CYMENE	17	
4-Isopropyltoluol	p-CYMENE	17	
Isovaleral	VALERALDEHYDE (ALL ISOMERS)	17	
Isovaleraldehyde	VALERALDEHYDE (ALL ISOMERS)	17	
Isovaleric aldehyde	VALERALDEHYDE (ALL ISOMERS)	17	
Isovalerone	DIISOBUTYL KETONE	17	
Kaolin clay slurry	KAOLIN SLURRY	18	
Kaolinite slurry	KAOLIN SLURRY	18	
KAOLIN SLURRY		18	
Ketohexamethylene	CYCLOHEXANONE	17	
Ketone propane	ACETONE	18	
Ketopropane	ACETONE	18	
LACTIC ACID		17	
dl-Lactic acid	LACTIC ACID	17	
LACTONITRILE SOLUTION (80% OR LESS)		17	
LARD		17	
LATEX, AMMONIA (1% OR LESS)-INHIBITED		17	
LATEX: CARBOXYLATED STYRENE–BUTADIENE COPOLYMER; STYRENE–BUTADIENE RUBBER		17	
LAURIC ACID		17	
Lauryl alcohol	DODECYL ALCOHOL	17	
Lauryl mercaptan	tert-DODECANETHIOL	17	
Lauryl methacrylate	DODECYL METHACRYLATE	17	
Lead alkyls, n.o.s.	MOTOR FUEL ANTI-KNOCK COMPOUNDS (CONTAINING LEAD ALKYLS)	17	
Lead tetraethyl	MOTOR FUEL ANTI-KNOCK COMPOUNDS (CONTAINING LEAD ALKYLS)	17	
Lead tetramethyl	MOTOR FUEL ANTI-KNOCK COMPOUNDS (CONTAINING LEAD ALKYLS)	17	
LECITHIN		18	
LIGNINSULPHONIC ACID, SODIUM SALT SOLUTION		17	3806
Limonene	DIPENTENE	17	
Linear alkylbenzene (LAB) bottoms	ALKYL BENZENE DISTILLATION BOTTOMS	17	
LINSEED OIL		17	
LIQUID CHEMICAL WASTES		17	
LONG-CHAIN ALKARYL POLYETHER (C_{11}–C_{20})		17	
LONG-CHAIN ALKARYL SULPHONIC ACID (C_{16}–C_{60})		17	
LONG-CHAIN ALKYLPHENATE/PHENOL SULPHIDE MIXTURE		17	
Lye	SODIUM HYDROXIDE SOLUTION	17	
Lye, potash	POTASSIUM HYDROXIDE SOLUTION	17	

Index Name	Product Name	Chapter	UN Number
Lye, soda	SODIUM HYDROXIDE SOLUTION	17	
Lye solution	SODIUM HYDROXIDE SOLUTION	17	
L-LYSINE SOLUTION (60% OR LESS)		17	
Magnesia hydrate	MAGNESIUM HYDROXIDE SLURRY	18	
MAGNESIUM CHLORIDE SOLUTION		17	
MAGNESIUM HYDROXIDE SLURRY		18	
MAGNESIUM LONG-CHAIN ALKARYL SULPHONATE (C_{11}–C_{50})		17	
MAGNESIUM LONG-CHAIN ALKYL SALICYLATE (C_{11}+)		17	
MALEIC ANHYDRIDE		17	2215
Maltitol	MALTITOL SOLUTION	18	
MALTITOL SOLUTION		18	
Maltitol syrup	MALTITOL SOLUTION	18	
MANGO KERNEL OIL		17	
Meglumine	N-METHYLGLUCAMINE SOLUTION (70% OR LESS)	18	
dl-p-Mentha-1,8-diene	DIPENTENE	17	
MERCAPTOBENZOTHIAZOL, SODIUM SALT SOLUTION		17	
Mesitylene	TRIMETHYLBENZENE (ALL ISOMERS)	17	
MESITYL OXIDE		17	1229
Metaformaldehyde	1,3,5-TRIOXANE	17	
Metam-sodium	METAM SODIUM SOLUTION	17	
METAM SODIUM SOLUTION		17	
METHACRYLIC ACID		17	2531
alpha-Methacrylic acid	METHACRYLIC ACID	17	
METHACRYLIC ACID–ALKOXYPOLY(ALKYLENE OXIDE) METHACRYLATE COPOLYMER, SODIUM SALT AQUEOUS SOLUTION (45% OR LESS)		17	
Methacrylic acid, dodecyl ester	DODECYL METHACRYLATE	17	
Methacrylic acid, lauryl ester	DODECYL METHACRYLATE	17	
METHACRYLIC RESIN IN ETHYLENE DICHLORIDE		17	
METHACRYLONITRILE		17	3079
Methanal	FORMALDEHYDE SOLUTIONS (45% OR LESS)	17	
Methanamide	FORMAMIDE	17	
Methanamine	METHYLAMINE SOLUTIONS (42% OR LESS)	17	
Methane carboxylic acid	ACETIC ACID	17	
Methanecarboxylic acid	ACETIC ACID	17	
Methanoic acid	FORMIC ACID	17	
Methanol	METHYL ALCOHOL	17	
Methenamine	HEXAMETHYLENETETRAMINE SOLUTIONS	18	
3-METHOXY-1-BUTANOL		17	
3-Methoxybutan-1-ol	3-METHOXY-1-BUTANOL	17	
3-METHOXYBUTYL ACETATE		17	
2-Methoxyethanol	ETHYLENE GLYCOL MONOALKYL ETHERS	17	
2-(2-Methoxyethoxy)ethanol	POLY(2–8)ALKYLENE GLYCOL MONOALKYL (C_1–C_6) ETHER	17	

Index Name	Product Name	Chapter	UN Number
2-[2-(2-Methoxyethoxy)ethoxy]ethanol	POLY(2–8)ALKYLENE GLYCOL MONOALKYL (C$_1$–C$_6$) ETHER	17	
2-(2-Methoxyethoxy)ethyl acetate	POLY(2–8)ALKYLENE GLYCOL MONOALKYL (C$_1$–C$_6$) ETHER ACETATE	17	
2-Methoxyethyl acetate	ETHYLENE GLYCOL METHYL ETHER ACETATE	17	
2-Methoxy-2-methylbutane	*tert*-AMYL METHYL ETHER	17	
3-Methoxy-3-methylbutan-1-ol	3-METHYL-3-METHOXYBUTANOL	17	
3-Methoxy-3-methylbutyl alcohol	3-METHYL-3-METHOXYBUTANOL	17	
2-Methoxy-1-methylethyl acetate	PROPYLENE GLYCOL METHYL ETHER ACETATE	17	
N-(2-METHOXY-1-METHYLETHYL)-2-ETHYL-6-METHYLCHLOROACETANILIDE		17	
2-Methoxy-2-methylpropane	METHYL *tert*-BUTYL ETHER	17	
1-Methoxypropan-2-ol	PROPYLENE GLYCOL MONOALKYL ETHER	17	
1-Methoxy-2-propanol acetate	PROPYLENE GLYCOL METHYL ETHER ACETATE	17	
1-(2-Methoxypropoxy)propan-2-ol	POLY(2–8)ALKYLENE GLYCOL MONOALKYL (C$_1$–C$_6$) ETHER	17	
3-[3-(3-Methoxypropoxy)propoxy]propan-1-ol	POLY(2–8)ALKYLENE GLYCOL MONOALKYL (C$_1$–C$_6$) ETHER	17	
Methoxytriglycol	POLY(2–8)ALKYLENE GLYCOL MONOALKYL (C$_1$–C$_6$) ETHER	17	
Methylacetaldehyde	PROPIONALDEHYDE	17	
METHYL ACETATE		17	
Methylacetic acid	PROPIONIC ACID	17	
METHYL ACETOACETATE		17	
Methyl acetylacetate	METHYL ACETOACETATE	17	
beta-Methylacrolein	CROTONALDEHYDE	17	
METHYL ACRYLATE		17	1919
2-Methylacrylic acid	METHACRYLIC ACID	17	
2-Methylacrylic acid, dodecyl ester	DODECYL METHACRYLATE	17	
2-Methylacrylic acid, lauryl ester	DODECYL METHACRYLATE	17	
METHYL ALCOHOL		17	
METHYLAMINE SOLUTIONS (42% OR LESS)		17	1235
1-Methyl-2-aminobenzene	*o*-TOLUIDINE	17	
2-Methyl-1-aminobenzene	*o*-TOLUIDINE	17	
METHYLAMYL ACETATE		17	1233
METHYLAMYL ALCOHOL		17	2053
METHYL AMYL KETONE		17	1110
Methyl *n*-amyl ketone	METHYL AMYL KETONE	17	
2-Methylaniline	*o*-TOLUIDINE	17	
3-Methylaniline	*o*-TOLUIDINE	17	
o-Methylaniline	*o*-TOLUIDINE	17	
2-Methylbenzenamine	*o*-TOLUIDINE	17	
3-Methylbenzenamine	*o*-TOLUIDINE	17	
o-Methylbenzenamine	*o*-TOLUIDINE	17	
Methylbenzene	TOLUENE	17	
Methylbenzenediamine	TOLUENEDIAMINE	17	
Methylbenzol	TOLUENE	17	

Index Name	Product Name	Chapter	UN Number
2-Methyl-1,3-butadiene	ISOPRENE	17	
3-Methyl-1,3-butadiene	ISOPRENE	17	
2-Methylbutanal	VALERALDEHYDE (ALL ISOMERS)	17	
3-Methylbutanal	VALERALDEHYDE (ALL ISOMERS)	17	
1-Methylbutane	PENTANE (ALL ISOMERS)	17	
2-Methylbutane	PENTANE (ALL ISOMERS)	17	
Methyl butanoate	METHYL BUTYRATE	17	
2-Methyl-2-butanol	*tert*-AMYL ALCOHOL	17	
2-Methylbutan-2-ol	*tert*-AMYL ALCOHOL	17	
2-Methyl-4-butanol	ISOAMYL ALCOHOL	17	
3-Methyl-1-butanol	AMYL ALCOHOL, PRIMARY	17	
3-Methyl-1-butanol	ISOAMYL ALCOHOL	17	
3-Methylbutan-1-ol	AMYL ALCOHOL, PRIMARY	17	
3-Methylbutan-1-ol	ISOAMYL ALCOHOL	17	
3-Methylbutan-3-ol	*tert*-AMYL ALCOHOL	17	
3-Methylbut-1-ene	PENTENE (ALL ISOMERS)	17	
Methylbutenes	PENTENE (ALL ISOMERS)	17	
METHYLBUTENOL		17	
1-Methylbutyl acetate	AMYL ACETATE (ALL ISOMERS)	17	
2-Methyl-2-butyl alcohol	*tert*-AMYL ALCOHOL	17	
2-Methyl-4-butyl alcohol	ISOAMYL ALCOHOL	17	
3-Methyl-1-butyl alcohol	ISOAMYL ALCOHOL	17	
3-Methyl-3-butyl alcohol	*tert*-AMYL ALCOHOL	17	
METHYL *tert*-BUTYL ETHER		17	
METHYL BUTYL KETONE		17	1224
METHYLBUTYNOL		17	
2-Methyl-3-butyn-2-ol	2-METHYL-2-HYDROXY-3-BUTYNE	17	
2-Methyl-3-butyn-2-ol	METHYLBUTYNOL	17	
2-Methylbut-3-yn-2-ol	2-METHYL-2-HYDROXY-3-BUTYNE	17	
2-Methylbut-3-yn-2-ol	METHYLBUTYNOL	17	
2-Methylbutyraldehyde	VALERALDEHYDE (ALL ISOMERS)	17	
3-Methylbutyraldehyde	VALERALDEHYDE (ALL ISOMERS)	17	
METHYL BUTYRATE		17	1237
2-*beta*-Methyl 'carbitol'	POLY(2–8)ALKYLENE GLYCOL MONOALKYL (C_1–C_6) ETHER	17	
Methyl 'carbitol' acetate	POLY(2–8)ALKYLENE GLYCOL MONOALKYL (C_1–C_6) ETHER ACETATE	17	
Methyl 'cellosolve'	ETHYLENE GLYCOL MONOALKYL ETHERS	17	
Methyl 'cellosolve' acetate	ETHYLENE GLYCOL METHYL ETHER ACETATE	17	
Methylchloroform	1,1,1-TRICHLOROETHANE	17	
Methyl cyanide	ACETONITRILE	17	
METHYLCYCLOHEXANE		17	2296
METHYLCYCLOPENTADIENE DIMER		17	
Methyl-1,3-cyclopentadiene dimer	METHYLCYCLOPENTADIENE DIMER	17	
METHYLCYCLOPENTADIENYL MANGANESE TRICARBONYL		17	3281

Index Name	Product Name	Chapter	UN Number
METHYL DIETHANOLAMINE		17	
4-Methyl-1,3-dioxolan-2-one	PROPYLENE CARBONATE	18	
Methyl disulphide	DIMETHYL DISULPHIDE	17	
Methylenebis(4-cyanatobenzene)	DIPHENYLMETHANE DIISOCYANATE	17	
S,S′-Methylenebis[*N*-dialkyl(C$_4$–C$_8$)dithiocarbamate]	ALKYL DITHIOCARBAMATE (C$_{19}$–C$_{35}$)	17	
Methylenebis(phenyl isocyanate)	DIPHENYLMETHANE DIISOCYANATE	17	
4,4′-Methylenebis(phenyl isocyanate)	DIPHENYLMETHANE DIISOCYANATE	17	
Methylenebis(phenylene isocyanate)	DIPHENYLMETHANE DIISOCYANATE	17	
Methylenebis(*p*-phenylene isocyanate)	DIPHENYLMETHANE DIISOCYANATE	17	
Methylene bromide	DIBROMOMETHANE	17	
Methylene chloride	DICHLOROMETHANE	17	
Methylene dichloride	DICHLOROMETHANE	17	
4,4′-Methylenediphenyl diisocyanate	DIPHENYLMETHANE DIISOCYANATE	17	
Methylenedi-*p*-phenylene diisocyanate	DIPHENYLMETHANE DIISOCYANATE	17	
4,4′-Methylenediphenyl isocyanate	DIPHENYLMETHANE DIISOCYANATE	17	
2-Methylenepropionic acid	METHACRYLIC ACID	17	
Methyl ethanoate	METHYL ACETATE	17	
1-Methylethyl acetate	ISOPROPYL ACETATE	17	
1-Methylethylamine	ISOPROPYLAMINE	17	
2-METHYL-6-ETHYLANILINE		17	
1,4-Methyl ethyl benzene	ETHYLTOLUENE	17	
Methylethylcarbinol	*sec*-BUTYL ALCOHOL	18	
Methyl ethylene glycol	PROPYLENE GLYCOL	18	
Methylethylene glycol	PROPYLENE GLYCOL	18	
Methylethylene oxide	PROPYLENE OXIDE	17	
METHYL ETHYL KETONE		17	
N-(1-Methylethyl)propan-2-amine	DIISOPROPYLAMINE	17	
2-METHYL-5-ETHYLPYRIDINE		17	2300
METHYL FORMATE		17	1243
N-Methyl-*D*-glucamine	*N*-METHYLGLUCAMINE SOLUTION (70% OR LESS)	18	
N-METHYLGLUCAMINE SOLUTION (70% OR LESS)		18	
Methyl glycol	PROPYLENE GLYCOL	18	
5-Methyl-3-heptanone	ETHYL AMYL KETONE	17	
5-Methylheptan-3-one	ETHYL AMYL KETONE	17	
5-Methylhexan-2-one	METHYL AMYL KETONE	17	
Methylhexylcarbinol	OCTANOL (ALL ISOMERS)	17	
Methyl 2-hydroxybenzoate	METHYL SALICYLATE	17	
Methyl *o*-hydroxybenzoate	METHYL SALICYLATE	17	
2-METHYL-2-HYDROXY-3-BUTYNE		17	
2-Methyl-2-hydroxy-3-butyne	METHYLBUTYNOL	17	
2,2′-(Methylimino)diethanol	METHYL DIETHANOLAMINE	17	
N-Methyl-2,2′-iminodiethanol	METHYL DIETHANOLAMINE	17	
Methyl isoamyl ketone	METHYL AMYL KETONE	17	
Methyl isobutenyl ketone	MESITYL OXIDE	17	

Index Name	Product Name	Chapter	UN Number
Methylisobutylcarbinol	METHYLAMYL ALCOHOL	17	
Methylisobutylcarbinol acetate	METHYLAMYL ACETATE	17	
METHYL ISOBUTYL KETONE		17	
2-Methyllactonitrile	ACETONE CYANOHYDRIN	17	
Methyl mercaptopropionaldehyde	3-(METHYLTHIO)PROPIONALDEHYDE	17	
METHYL METHACRYLATE		17	1247
Methyl methanoate	METHYL FORMATE	17	
3-METHYL-3-METHOXYBUTANOL		17	
Methyl alpha-methylacrylate	METHYL METHACRYLATE	17	
7-Methyl-3-methylene-1,6-octadiene	MYRCENE	17	
Methyl 2-methylprop-2-enoate	METHYL METHACRYLATE	17	
METHYLNAPHTHALENE (MOLTEN)		17	
alpha-Methylnaphthalene	METHYLNAPHTHALENE (MOLTEN)	17	
beta-Methylnaphthalene	METHYLNAPHTHALENE (MOLTEN)	17	
(o- and p-) Methylnitrobenzene	o- OR p-NITROTOLUENES	17	
8-Methylnonan-1-ol	DECYL ALCOHOL (ALL ISOMERS)	17	
Methylolpropane	n-BUTYL ALCOHOL	18	
alpha-Methyl-omega-methoxypoly(ethylene oxide)	POLYETHYLENE GLYCOL DIMETHYL ETHER	17	
alpha-Methyl-omega-methoxypoly(oxy-1,2-ethanediyl)	POLYETHYLENE GLYCOL DIMETHYL ETHER	17	
alpha-Methyl-omega-methoxypoly(oxyethylene)	POLYETHYLENE GLYCOL DIMETHYL ETHER	17	
Methyloxirane	PROPYLENE OXIDE	17	
2-Methyl-2,4-pentanediol	HEXYLENE GLYCOL	18	
2-Methylpentane-2,4-diol	HEXYLENE GLYCOL	18	
Methylpentan-2-ol	METHYLAMYL ALCOHOL	17	
4-Methylpentanol-2	METHYLAMYL ALCOHOL	17	
4-Methylpentan-2-ol	METHYLAMYL ALCOHOL	17	
4-Methyl-2-pentanol acetate	METHYLAMYL ACETATE	17	
4-Methyl-2-pentanone	METHYL ISOBUTYL KETONE	17	
4-Methylpentan-2-one	METHYL ISOBUTYL KETONE	17	
2-Methylpentene	HEXENE (ALL ISOMERS)	17	
2-Methyl-1-pentene	HEXENE (ALL ISOMERS)	17	
2-Methylpent-1-ene	HEXENE (ALL ISOMERS)	17	
4-Methyl-1-pentene	HEXENE (ALL ISOMERS)	17	
4-Methyl-3-penten-2-one	MESITYL OXIDE	17	
4-Methylpent-3-en-2-one	MESITYL OXIDE	17	
4-Methyl-2-pentyl acetate	METHYLAMYL ACETATE	17	
Methylpentyl acetates	METHYLAMYL ACETATE	17	
Methyl tert-pentyl ether	tert-AMYL METHYL ETHER	17	
Methyl pentyl ketone	METHYL AMYL KETONE	17	
Methylphenylenediamine	TOLUENEDIAMINE	17	
2-Methyl-m-phenylenediamine	TOLUENEDIAMINE	17	
4-Methyl-m-phenylenediamine	TOLUENEDIAMINE	17	
Methylphenylene diisocyanate	TOLUENE DIISOCYANATE	17	
4-Methyl-1,3-phenylene diisocyanate	TOLUENE DIISOCYANATE	17	

Index Name	Product Name	Chapter	UN Number
4-Methyl-*m*-phenylene diisocyanate	TOLUENE DIISOCYANATE	17	
2-Methyl-2-phenylpropane	BUTYLBENZENE (ALL ISOMERS)	17	
2-Methylpropanal	BUTYRALDEHYDE (ALL ISOMERS)	17	
2-METHYL-1,3-PROPANEDIOL		17	
2-Methyl-1-propanol	ISOBUTYL ALCOHOL	17	
2-Methylpropan-1-ol	ISOBUTYL ALCOHOL	17	
2-Methyl-2-propanol	*tert*-BUTYL ALCOHOL	17	
2-Methylpropan-2-ol	*tert*-BUTYL ALCOHOL	17	
2-Methylprop-2-enenitrile	METHACRYLONITRILE	17	
2-Methylpropenoic acid	METHACRYLIC ACID	17	
alpha-Methylpropenoic acid	METHACRYLIC ACID	17	
2-Methylprop-1-enyl methyl ketone	MESITYL OXIDE	17	
2-Methylpropyl acrylate	BUTYL ACRYLATE (ALL ISOMERS)	17	
2-Methyl-1-propyl alcohol	ISOBUTYL ALCOHOL	17	
2-Methyl-2-propyl alcohol	*tert*-BUTYL ALCOHOL	17	
Methylpropylbenzene	*p*-CYMENE	17	
Methylpropylcarbinol	*sec*-AMYL ALCOHOL	17	
1-Methyl-1-propylethylene	HEXENE (ALL ISOMERS)	17	
2-Methylpropyl formate	ISOBUTYL FORMATE	17	
METHYL PROPYL KETONE		18	1249
2-METHYLPYRIDINE		17	2313
3-METHYLPYRIDINE		17	2313
4-METHYLPYRIDINE		17	2313
alpha-Methylpyridine	2-METHYLPYRIDINE	17	
1-Methyl-2-pyrrolidinone	*N*-METHYL-2-PYRROLIDONE	17	
1-Methylpyrrolidin-2-one	*N*-METHYL-2-PYRROLIDONE	17	
N-Methylpyrrolidinone	*N*-METHYL-2-PYRROLIDONE	17	
1-Methyl-2-pyrrolidone	*N*-METHYL-2-PYRROLIDONE	17	
N-METHYL-2-PYRROLIDONE		17	
METHYL SALICYLATE		17	
Methylstyrene	VINYLTOLUENE	17	
alpha-METHYLSTYRENE		17	2303
3-(METHYLTHIO)PROPIONALDEHYDE		17	
2-Methyltrimethylene glycol	2-METHYL-1,3-PROPANEDIOL	17	
Metolachlor	*N*-(2-METHOXY-1-METHYLETHYL)-2-ETHYL-6-METHYLCHLOROACETANILIDE	17	
Middle oil	CARBOLIC OIL	17	
Milk acid	LACTIC ACID	17	
Milk of magnesia	MAGNESIUM HYDROXIDE SLURRY	18	
Mineral jelly	PETROLATUM	17	
Mineral wax	PETROLATUM	17	
Mixed aliphatic oxygenated hydrocarbons, primary aliphatic alcohols and aliphatic ethers: mol wt: >200	OXYGENATED ALIPHATIC HYDROCARBON MIXTURE	17	
MOLASSES		18	
MOLYBDENUM POLYSULFIDE LONG CHAIN ALKYL DITHIOCARBAMIDE COMPLEX		17	

Index Name	Product Name	Chapter	UN Number
Monochlorobenzene	CHLOROBENZENE	17	
Monochlorobenzol	CHLOROBENZENE	17	
Monoethanolamine	ETHANOLAMINE	17	
Monoethylamine	ETHYLAMINE	17	
Monoethylamine solutions, 72% or less	ETHYLAMINE SOLUTIONS (72% OR LESS)	17	
Monoisopropanolamine	ISOPROPANOLAMINE	17	
Monoisopropylamine	ISOPROPYLAMINE	17	
Monomethylamine	METHYLAMINE SOLUTIONS (42% OR LESS)	17	
Monomethylamine solutions, 42% or less	METHYLAMINE SOLUTIONS (42% OR LESS)	17	
Monopropylamine	n-PROPYLAMINE	17	
Monopropylene glycol	PROPYLENE GLYCOL	18	
MORPHOLINE		17	2054
MOTOR FUEL ANTI-KNOCK COMPOUNDS (CONTAINING LEAD ALKYLS)		17	1649
Muriatic acid	HYDROCHLORIC ACID	17	
MYRCENE		17	
Naphtha, coal tar	COAL TAR NAPHTHA SOLVENT	17	
Naphtha (petroleum), Light Steam-cracked Aromatics	ALKYLBENZENE MIXTURES (CONTAINING AT LEAST 50% OF TOLUENE)	17	
NAPHTHALENE (MOLTEN)		17	2304
NAPHTHALENESULPHONIC ACID–FORMALDEHYDE COPOLYMER, SODIUM SALT SOLUTION		17	
Naphtha safety solvent	WHITE SPIRIT, LOW (15–20%) AROMATIC	17	
NEODECANOIC ACID		17	
Neodecanoic acid, 2,3-epoxypropyl ester	GLYCIDYL ESTER OF C_{10} TRIALKYLACETIC ACID	17	
Neodecanoic acid, glycidyl ester	GLYCIDYL ESTER OF C_{10} TRIALKYLACETIC ACID	17	
Neodecanoic acid vinyl ester	VINYL NEODECANOATE	17	
Neopentane	PENTANE (ALL ISOMERS)	17	
Neopentanoic acid	TRIMETHYLACETIC ACID	17	
Neopentylene glycol	2,2-DIMETHYLPROPANE-1,3-DIOL (MOLTEN OR SOLUTION)	17	
NITRATING ACID (MIXTURE OF SULPHURIC AND NITRIC ACIDS)		17	1796
NITRIC ACID (70% AND OVER)		17	2031, 2032
NITRIC ACID (LESS THAN 70%)		17	2031
Nitric acid, fuming	NITRIC ACID (70% AND OVER)	17	
Nitric acid, red fuming	NITRIC ACID (70% AND OVER)	17	
NITRILOTRIACETIC ACID, TRISODIUM SALT SOLUTION		17	
2,2′,2″-Nitrilotriethanol	TRIETHANOLAMINE	17	
Nitrilo-2,2′,2″-triethanol	TRIETHANOLAMINE	17	
2,2′,2″-Nitrilotriethanol	TRIETHANOLAMINE	17	
1,1′,1″-Nitrilotripropan-2-ol	TRIISOPROPANOLAMINE	17	
1,1′,1″-Nitrilotri-2-propanol	TRIISOPROPANOLAMINE	17	
1,1′,1″-Nitrilotripropan-2-ol	TRIISOPROPANOLAMINE	17	
NITROBENZENE		17	1662
Nitrobenzol	NITROBENZENE	17	

Index Name	Product Name	Chapter	UN Number
o-Nitrochlorobenzene	*o*-CHLORONITROBENZENE	17	
NITROETHANE		17	2842
NITROETHANE (80%)/NITROPROPANE (20%)		17	
NITROETHANE, 1-NITROPROPANE (EACH 15% OR MORE) MIXTURE		17	
ortho-Nitrophenol	*o*-NITROPHENOL (MOLTEN)	17	
2-Nitrophenol	*o*-NITROPHENOL (MOLTEN)	17	
2-Nitrophenol (molten)	*o*-NITROPHENOL (MOLTEN)	17	
o-Nitrophenol	*o*-NITROPHENOL (MOLTEN)	17	
o-NITROPHENOL (MOLTEN)		17	1663
1- OR 2-NITROPROPANE		17	2608
NITROPROPANE (60%)/NITROETHANE (40%) MIXTURE		17	
2-Nitrotoluene	*o*- OR *p*-NITROTOLUENES	17	
4-Nitrotoluene	*o*- OR *p*-NITROTOLUENES	17	
o-Nitrotoluene	*o*- OR *p*-NITROTOLUENES	17	
p-Nitrotoluene	*o*- OR *p*-NITROTOLUENES	17	
o- OR *p*-NITROTOLUENES		17	1664
NONANE (ALL ISOMERS)		17	1920
1-Nonanecarboxylic acid	DECANOIC ACID	17	
n-Nonane	NONANE (ALL ISOMERS)	17	
NONANOIC ACID (ALL ISOMERS)		17	
Nonanols	NONYL ALCOHOL (ALL ISOMERS)	17	
NON-EDIBLE INDUSTRIAL GRADE PALM OIL		17	
NONENE (ALL ISOMERS)		17	
NONYL ALCOHOL (ALL ISOMERS)		17	
Nonylcarbinol	DECYL ALCOHOL (ALL ISOMERS)	17	
Nonylene	NONENE (ALL ISOMERS)	17	
Nonyl hydride	NONANE (ALL ISOMERS)	17	
NONYL METHACRYLATE MONOMER		17	
NONYLPHENOL		17	
alpha-4-Nonylphenyl-*omega*-hydroxypoly(oxyethylene)	ALKARYL POLYETHERS (C$_9$–C$_{20}$)	17	
NONYLPHENOL POLY(4+)ETHOXYLATE		17	
Nopinen	*beta*-PINENE	17	
Nopinene	*beta*-PINENE	17	
NOXIOUS LIQUID, NF, (1) N.O.S. (TRADE NAME . . ., CONTAINS . . .) ST1, CAT. X		17	
NOXIOUS LIQUID, F, (2) N.O.S. (TRADE NAME . . ., CONTAINS . . .) ST1, CAT. X		17	
NOXIOUS LIQUID, NF, (3) N.O.S. (TRADE NAME . . ., CONTAINS . . .) ST2, CAT. X		17	
NOXIOUS LIQUID, F, (4) N.O.S. (TRADE NAME . . ., CONTAINS . . .) ST2, CAT. X		17	
NOXIOUS LIQUID, NF, (5) N.O.S. (TRADE NAME . . ., CONTAINS . . .) ST2, CAT. Y		17	
NOXIOUS LIQUID, F, (6) N.O.S. (TRADE NAME . . ., CONTAINS . . .) ST2, CAT. Y		17	

Index Name	Product Name	Chapter	UN Number
NOXIOUS LIQUID, NF, (7) N.O.S. (TRADE NAME . . ., CONTAINS . . .) ST3, CAT. Y		17	
NOXIOUS LIQUID, F, (8) N.O.S. (TRADE NAME . . ., CONTAINS . . .) ST3, CAT. Y		17	
NOXIOUS LIQUID, NF, (9) N.O.S. (TRADE NAME . . ., CONTAINS . . .) ST3, CAT. Z		17	
NOXIOUS LIQUID, F, (10) N.O.S. (TRADE NAME . . ., CONTAINS . . .) ST3, CAT. Z		17	
NOXIOUS LIQUID, (11) N.O.S. (TRADE NAME . . ., CONTAINS . . .) CAT. Z		18	
NON NOXIOUS LIQUID, (12) N.O.S. (TRADE NAME . . ., CONTAINS . . .) CAT. OS		18	
Octadecan-1-ol	ALCOHOLS (C_{13}+)	17	
1-Octadecanol	ALCOHOLS (C_{13}+)	17	
(Z)-Octadec-9-enamine	OLEYLAMINE	17	
cis-9-Octadecenoic acid	OLEIC ACID	17	
(Z)-Octadec-9-enoic acid	OLEIC ACID	17	
(Z)-Octadec-9-enoic acid	OLEIC ACID	17	
(Z)-Octadec-9-enylamine	OLEYLAMINE	17	
Octanal	OCTYL ALDEHYDES	17	
OCTANE (ALL ISOMERS)		17	1262
OCTANOIC ACID (ALL ISOMERS)		17	
OCTANOL (ALL ISOMERS)		17	
Octan-1-ol	OCTANOL (ALL ISOMERS)	17	
OCTENE (ALL ISOMERS)		17	
Octic acid	OCTANOIC ACID (ALL ISOMERS)	17	
Octoic acid	OCTANOIC ACID (ALL ISOMERS)	17	
Octyl acetate	n-OCTYL ACETATE	17	
n-OCTYL ACETATE		17	
Octyl acrylate	2-ETHYLHEXYL ACRYLATE	17	
Octyl adipate	DI-(2-ETHYLHEXYL) ADIPATE	17	
Octyl alcohol	OCTANOL (ALL ISOMERS)	17	
OCTYL ALDEHYDES		17	1191
Octylcarbinol	NONYL ALCOHOL (ALL ISOMERS)	17	
OCTYL DECYL ADIPATE		17	
Octyl decyl phthalate	DIALKYL (C_7–C_{13}) PHTHALATES	17	
Octylic acid	OCTANOIC ACID (ALL ISOMERS)	17	
Octyl nitrate	ALKYL (C_7–C_9) NITRATES	17	
Octyl nitrates (all isomers)	ALKYL (C_7–C_9) NITRATES	17	
Octyl phthalate	DIALKYL (C_7–C_{13}) PHTHALATES	17	
Oenanthic acid	n-HEPTANOIC ACID	17	
Oenanthylic acid	n-HEPTANOIC ACID	17	
Oil of Mirbane	NITROBENZENE	17	
Oil of Myrbane	NITROBENZENE	17	
Oil of turpentine	TURPENTINE	17	
Oil of vitriol	SULPHURIC ACID	17	
Oil of wintergreen	METHYL SALICYLATE	17	

Index Name	Product Name	Chapter	UN Number
Oleamine	OLEYLAMINE	17	
OLEFIN–ALKYL ESTER COPOLYMER (MOLECULAR WEIGHT 2000+)		17	
OLEFIN MIXTURES (C_5–C_7)		17	
OLEFIN MIXTURES (C_5–C_{15})		17	
OLEFINS (C_{13}+, ALL ISOMERS)		17	
alpha-OLEFINS (C_6–C_{18}) MIXTURES		17	
OLEIC ACID		17	
OLEUM		17	1831
OLEYLAMINE		17	
OLIVE OIL		17	
Orthophosphoric acid	PHOSPHORIC ACID	17	
Oxal	GLYOXAL SOLUTION (40% OR LESS)	17	
Oxaldehyde	GLYOXAL SOLUTION (40% OR LESS)	17	
3-Oxapentane-1,5-diol	DIETHYLENE GLYCOL	18	
1,4-Oxazinane	MORPHOLINE	17	
2-Oxetanone	*beta*-PROPIOLACTONE	17	
Oxoacetic acid	GLYOXYLIC ACID SOLUTION (50% OR LESS)	17	
Oxoethanoic acid	GLYOXYLIC ACID SOLUTION (50% OR LESS)	17	
2,2'-Oxybis(1-chloropropane)	2,2'-DICHLOROISOPROPYL ETHER	17	
2,2'-Oxybis(ethyleneoxy)diethanol	TETRAETHYLENE GLYCOL	17	
2,2'-Oxybispropane	ISOPROPYL ETHER	17	
2,2'-Oxydiethanol	DIETHYLENE GLYCOL	18	
1,1'-Oxydipropan-2-ol	DIPROPYLENE GLYCOL	17	
Oxyethanoic acid	GLYCOLIC ACID SOLUTION (70% OR LESS)	17	
OXYGENATED ALIPHATIC HYDROCARBON MIXTURE		17	1993
Oxymethylene	FORMALDEHYDE SOLUTIONS (45% OR LESS)	17	
PALM ACID OIL		17	
PALM FATTY ACID DISTILLATE		17	
PALM KERNEL ACID OIL		17	
PALM KERNEL OIL		17	
PALM KERNEL OLEIN		17	
PALM KERNEL STEARIN		17	
PALM MID FRACTION		17	
PALM OIL		17	
PALM OIL FATTY ACID METHYL ESTER		17	
PALM OLEIN		17	
PALM STEARIN		17	
Paraffin	PARAFFIN WAX	17	
Paraffin jelly	PETROLATUM	17	
Paraffin scale	PARAFFIN WAX	17	
n-Paraffins (C_{10}–C_{20})	*n*-ALKANES (C_{10}+)	17	
PARAFFIN WAX		17	
PARALDEHYDE		17	1264
PARALDEHYDE–AMMONIA REACTION PRODUCT		17	2920

Index Name	Product Name	Chapter	UN Number
Pear oil	AMYL ACETATE (ALL ISOMERS)	17	
Pelargonic acid	NONANOIC ACID (ALL ISOMERS)	17	
Pelargonic alcohol	NONYL ALCOHOL (ALL ISOMERS)	17	
PENTACHLOROETHANE		17	1669
Pentadecanol	ALCOHOLS (C_{13}+)	17	
Pentadec-1-ene	OLEFINS (C_{13}+, ALL ISOMERS)	17	
1-Pentadecene	OLEFINS (C_{13}+, ALL ISOMERS)	17	
Penta-1,3-diene	1,3-PENTADIENE	17	
1,3-PENTADIENE		17	
cis-1,3-Pentadiene	1,3-PENTADIENE	17	
cis-trans-1,3-Pentadiene	1,3-PENTADIENE	17	
(E)-1,3-Pentadiene	1,3-PENTADIENE	17	
trans-1,3-Pentadiene	1,3-PENTADIENE	17	
(Z)-1,3-Pentadiene	1,3-PENTADIENE	17	
Pentaethylene glycol	POLYETHYLENE GLYCOL	17	
PENTAETHYLENEHEXAMINE		17	
Pentalin	PENTACHLOROETHANE	17	
Pentamethylene	CYCLOPENTANE	17	
2,2,4,6,6-Pentamethyl-4-heptanethiol	tert-DODECANETHIOL	17	
Pentanal	VALERALDEHYDE (ALL ISOMERS)	17	
Pentane	PENTANE (ALL ISOMERS)	17	
PENTANE (ALL ISOMERS)		17	1265
Pentanedial solutions, 50% or less	GLUTARALDEHYDE SOLUTIONS (50% OR LESS)	17	
n-Pentane	PENTANE (ALL ISOMERS)	17	
PENTANOIC ACID		17	
n-PENTANOIC ACID (64%)/2-METHYLBUTYRIC ACID (36%) MIXTURE		17	
tert-Pentanoic acid	TRIMETHYLACETIC ACID	17	
Pentan-1-ol	n-AMYL ALCOHOL	17	
1-Pentanol	n-AMYL ALCOHOL	17	
Pentan-2-ol	sec-AMYL ALCOHOL	17	
2-Pentanol	sec-AMYL ALCOHOL	17	
Pentan-3-ol	sec-AMYL ALCOHOL	17	
3-Pentanol	sec-AMYL ALCOHOL	17	
1-Pentanol acetate	AMYL ACETATE (ALL ISOMERS)	17	
n-Pentanol	n-AMYL ALCOHOL	17	
sec-Pentanol	sec-AMYL ALCOHOL	17	
tert-Pentanol	tert-AMYL ALCOHOL	17	
Pentan-2-one	METHYL PROPYL KETONE	18	
2-Pentanone	METHYL PROPYL KETONE	18	
Pentasodium diethylenetriaminepentaacetate	DIETHYLENETRIAMINEPENTAACETIC ACID, PENTASODIUM SALT SOLUTION	17	
PENTENE (ALL ISOMERS)		17	
Pent-1-ene	PENTENE (ALL ISOMERS)	17	
n-Pentene	PENTENE (ALL ISOMERS)	17	

Index Name	Product Name	Chapter	UN Number
Pentenes	PENTENE (ALL ISOMERS)	17	
Pentyl acetate	AMYL ACETATE (ALL ISOMERS)	17	
sec-Pentyl acetate	AMYL ACETATE (ALL ISOMERS)	17	
Pentyl alcohol	*n*-AMYL ALCOHOL	17	
sec-Pentyl alcohol	*sec*-AMYL ALCOHOL	17	
tert-Pentyl alcohol	*tert*-AMYL ALCOHOL	17	
Pentyl propanoate	*n*-PENTYL PROPIONATE	17	
n-PENTYL PROPIONATE		17	1993
PERCHLOROETHYLENE		17	1897
Perchloromethane	CARBON TETRACHLORIDE	17	
Perhydroazepine	HEXAMETHYLENEIMINE	17	
PETROLATUM		17	
Petroleum jelly	PETROLATUM	17	
Phene	BENZENE AND MIXTURES HAVING 10% BENZENE OR MORE	17	
Phenic acid	PHENOL	17	
PHENOL		17	2312
2-Phenoxyethanol	ETHYLENE GLYCOL PHENYL ETHER	17	
Phenyl alkane(C$_{10}$–C$_{21}$)sulphonate	ALKYL SULPHONIC ACID ESTER OF PHENOL	17	
Phenylamine	ANILINE	17	
N-Phenyl aniline	DIPHENYLAMINE (MOLTEN)	17	
N-Phenylbenzenamine	DIPHENYLAMINE (MOLTEN)	17	
1-Phenylbutane	BUTYLBENZENE (ALL ISOMERS)	17	
2-Phenylbutane	BUTYLBENZENE (ALL ISOMERS)	17	
Phenyl carbinol	BENZYL ALCOHOL	17	
Phenyl 'cellosolve'	ETHYLENE GLYCOL PHENYL ETHER	17	
Phenyl chloride	CHLOROBENZENE	17	
1-Phenyldecane	ALKYL(C$_9$+)BENZENES	17	
1-Phenyldodecane	ALKYL(C$_9$+)BENZENES	17	
Phenylethane	ETHYLBENZENE	17	
Phenyl ether	DIPHENYL ETHER	17	
Phenylethylene	STYRENE MONOMER	17	
1-Phenylethylxylene	1-PHENYL-1-XYLYLETHANE	17	
Phenyl hydride	BENZENE AND MIXTURES HAVING 10% BENZENE OR MORE	17	
Phenyl hydroxide	PHENOL	17	
Phenylic acid	PHENOL	17	
Phenylmethane	TOLUENE	17	
Phenylmethanol	BENZYL ALCOHOL	17	
Phenylmethyl acetate	BENZYL ACETATE	17	
1-Phenylpropane	PROPYLBENZENE (ALL ISOMERS)	17	
2-Phenylpropane	PROPYLBENZENE (ALL ISOMERS)	17	
2-Phenylpropene	*alpha*-METHYLSTYRENE	17	
1-Phenyltetradecane	ALKYL(C$_9$+)BENZENES	17	
1-Phenyltridecane	ALKYL(C$_9$+)BENZENES	17	

Index Name	Product Name	Chapter	UN Number
1-Phenylundecane	ALKYL(C_9+)BENZENES	17	
Phenylxylylethane	1-PHENYL-1-XYLYLETHANE	17	
1-PHENYL-1-XYLYLETHANE		17	
1-Phenyl-1-(2,5-xylyl)ethane	1-PHENYL-1-XYLYLETHANE	17	
1-Phenyl-1-(3,4-xylyl)ethane	1-PHENYL-1-XYLYLETHANE	17	
PHOSPHATE ESTERS, ALKYL (C_{12}–C_{14}) AMINE		17	2053
L-alpha-Phosphatidyl choline	LECITHIN	18	
N-(Phosphonomethyl)glycine	GLYPHOSATE SOLUTION (NOT CONTAINING SURFACTANT)	17	
PHOSPHORIC ACID		17	1805
PHOSPHORUS, YELLOW OR WHITE		17	1381, 2447
Phthalandione	PHTHALIC ANHYDRIDE (MOLTEN)	17	
Phthalic acid anhydride	PHTHALIC ANHYDRIDE (MOLTEN)	17	
Phthalic acid, diundecyl ester	DIUNDECYL PHTHALATE	17	
PHTHALIC ANHYDRIDE (MOLTEN)		17	2214
2-Picoline	2-METHYLPYRIDINE	17	
3-Picoline	3-METHYLPYRIDINE	17	
4-Picoline	4-METHYLPYRIDINE	17	
alpha-Picoline	2-METHYLPYRIDINE	17	
beta-Picoline	3-METHYLPYRIDINE	17	
gamma-Picoline	4-METHYLPYRIDINE	17	
Pimelic ketone	CYCLOHEXANONE	17	
2-Pinene	alpha-PINENE	17	
2(10)-Pinene	beta-PINENE	17	
alpha-PINENE		17	2368
beta-PINENE		17	2368
PINE OIL		17	1272
2-Piperazin-1-ylethylamine	N-AMINOETHYLPIPERAZINE	17	
Piperylene	1,3-PENTADIENE	17	
Pivalic acid	TRIMETHYLACETIC ACID	17	
POLYACRYLIC ACID SOLUTION (40% OR LESS)		17	
POLYALKYL (C_{18}–C_{22}) ACRYLATE IN XYLENE		17	
POLY(2–8)ALKYLENE GLYCOL MONOALKYL (C_1–C_6) ETHER		17	
POLY(2–8)ALKYLENE GLYCOL MONOALKYL (C_1–C_6) ETHER ACETATE		17	
Poly (2-8) alkylene (C_2–C_3) glycols/Polyalkylene (C_2–C_{10}) glycol monoalkyl (C_1–C_4) ethers and their borate esters	BRAKE FLUID BASE MIX: POLY(2–8)ALKYLENE (C_2–C_3) GLYCOLS/POLYALKYLENE (C_2–C_{10}) GLYCOLS MONOALKYL (C_1–C_4) ETHERS AND THEIR BORATE ESTERS	17	
POLYALKYL (C_{10}–C_{20}) METHACRYLATE		17	
POLYALKYL (C_{10}–C_{18}) METHACRYLATE/ETHYLENE–PROPYLENE COPOLYMER MIXTURE		17	3257
POLYALUMINIUM CHLORIDE SOLUTION		18	
POLYBUTENE		17	
POLYBUTENYL SUCCINIMIDE		17	
POLY(2+)CYCLIC AROMATICS		17	

Index Name	Product Name	Chapter	UN Number
POLYETHER (MOLECULAR WEIGHT 1350+)		17	
POLYETHYLENE GLYCOL		17	
Poly(4–12)ethylene glycol alkyl(C_7–C_{11})phenyl ether	NONYLPHENOL POLY(4+)ETHOXYLATE	17	
POLYETHYLENE GLYCOL DIMETHYL ETHER		17	
Polyethylene glycols, mono(*p*-nonylphenyl) ether	ALKARYL POLYETHERS (C_9–C_{20})	17	
Poly[ethylene oxide]	POLYETHER (MOLECULAR WEIGHT 1350+)	17	
POLYETHYLENE POLYAMINES		17	
Polyethylene polyamines (in C_5–C_{20} paraffin oil)	POLYETHYLENE POLYAMINES (MORE THAN 50% C_5–C_{20} PARAFFIN OIL)	17	
POLYETHYLENE POLYAMINES (MORE THAN 50% C_5–C_{20} PARAFFIN OIL)		17	2734, 2735
POLYFERRIC SULPHATE SOLUTION		17	
Polyglucitol	HYDROGENATED STARCH HYDROLYSATE	18	
Polyglucitol syrup	HYDROGENATED STARCH HYDROLYSATE	18	
POLYGLYCERIN, SODIUM SALT SOLUTION (CONTAINING LESS THAN 3% SODIUM HYDROXIDE)		18	
POLY(IMINOETHYLENE)-GRAFT-*N*-POLY(ETHYLENEOXY) SOLUTION (90% OR LESS)		17	
POLYISOBUTENAMINE IN ALIPHATIC (C_{10}–C_{14}) SOLVENT		17	
POLYISOBUTENYL ANHYDRIDE ADDUCT		17	
Polyisobutylene	POLY(4+)ISOBUTYLENE	17	
POLY(4+)ISOBUTYLENE		17	
POLYMETHYLENE POLYPHENYL ISOCYANATE		17	2206, 2207
POLYOLEFIN (MOLECULAR WEIGHT 300+)		17	
POLYOLEFIN AMIDE ALKENEAMINE (C_{17}+)		17	
POLYOLEFIN AMIDE ALKENEAMINE BORATE (C_{28}–C_{250})		17	
POLYOLEFINAMINE (C_{28}–C_{250})		17	
POLYOLEFINAMINE IN ALKYL (C_2–C_4) BENZENES		17	
POLYOLEFINAMINE IN AROMATIC SOLVENT		17	
POLYOLEFIN AMINOESTER SALTS (MOLECULAR WEIGHT 2000+)		17	
POLYOLEFIN ANHYDRIDE		17	
POLYOLEFIN ESTER (C_{28}–C_{250})		17	
POLYOLEFIN PHENOLIC AMINE (C_{28}–C_{250})		17	
POLYOLEFIN PHOSPHOROSULPHIDE, BARIUM DERIVATIVE (C_{28}–C_{250})		17	
Poly[oxyethylene]	POLYETHER (MOLECULAR WEIGHT 1350+)	17	
Poly(oxyethyleneoxyethyleneoxyphthaloyl)	DIETHYLENE GLYCOL PHTHALATE	17	
POLY(20)OXYETHYLENE SORBITAN MONOOLEATE		17	
Poly[oxypropylene]	POLYETHER (MOLECULAR WEIGHT 1350+)	17	
Poly[(phenyl isocyanate)-co-formaldehyde]	POLYMETHYLENE POLYPHENYL ISOCYANATE	17	
Polyphenyl-polymethylene isocyanate	POLYMETHYLENE POLYPHENYL ISOCYANATE	17	
Poly[propene oxide]	POLYETHER (MOLECULAR WEIGHT 1350+)	17	
Polypropylene	POLY(5+)PROPYLENE	17	
POLY(5+)PROPYLENE		17	
POLYPROPYLENE GLYCOL		17	

Index Name	Product Name	Chapter	UN Number
Poly(propylene oxide)	POLYPROPYLENE GLYCOL	17	
POLYSILOXANE		17	
Poly(sodium carboxylatoethylene)	SODIUM POLY(4+)ACRYLATE SOLUTIONS	17	
Potassium chloride drilling brine	POTASSIUM CHLORIDE SOLUTION	17	
POTASSIUM CHLORIDE SOLUTION		17	
POTASSIUM FORMATE SOLUTIONS		18	
POTASSIUM HYDROXIDE SOLUTION		17	1814
POTASSIUM OLEATE		17	
POTASSIUM THIOSULPHATE (50% OR LESS)		17	
Propanal	PROPIONALDEHYDE	17	
Propan-1-amine	n-PROPYLAMINE	17	
2-Propanamine	ISOPROPYLAMINE	17	
Propane-1,2-diol	PROPYLENE GLYCOL	18	
1,2-Propanediol	PROPYLENE GLYCOL	18	
1,2-Propanediol cyclic carbonate	PROPYLENE CARBONATE	18	
Propanenitrile	PROPIONITRILE	17	
Propane-1,2,3-triol	GLYCERINE	18	
1,2,3-Propanetriol	GLYCERINE	18	
1,2,3-Propane trioltriacetate	GLYCERYL TRIACETATE	17	
Propanoic acid	PROPIONIC ACID	17	
Propanoic anhydride	PROPIONIC ANHYDRIDE	17	
Propanol	n-PROPYL ALCOHOL	17	
Propan-1-ol	n-PROPYL ALCOHOL	17	
1-Propanol	n-PROPYL ALCOHOL	17	
Propan-2-ol	ISOPROPYL ALCOHOL	18	
2-Propanol	ISOPROPYL ALCOHOL	18	
n-PROPANOLAMINE		17	
3-Propanolide	beta-PROPIOLACTONE	17	
n-Propanol	n-PROPYL ALCOHOL	17	
Propanone	ACETONE	18	
Propan-2-one	ACETONE	18	
2-Propanone	ACETONE	18	
Propenamide solution, 50% or less	ACRYLAMIDE SOLUTION (50% OR LESS)	17	
Propenenitrile	ACRYLONITRILE	17	
Propene oxide	PROPYLENE OXIDE	17	
2-Propenoic acid, homopolymer solution (40% or less)	POLYACRYLIC ACID SOLUTION (40% OR LESS)	17	
Propenoic acid	ACRYLIC ACID	17	
1-Propenol-3	ALLYL ALCOHOL	17	
Prop-2-en-1-ol	ALLYL ALCOHOL	17	
2-Propen-1-ol	ALLYL ALCOHOL	17	
Propenyl alcohol	ALLYL ALCOHOL	17	
Propiolactone	beta-PROPIOLACTONE	17	
beta-PROPIOLACTONE		17	
PROPIONALDEHYDE		17	1275

Index Name	Product Name	Chapter	UN Number
PROPIONIC ACID		17	1848
Propionic aldehyde	PROPIONALDEHYDE	17	
PROPIONIC ANHYDRIDE		17	2496
PROPIONITRILE		17	2404
beta-Propionolactone	*beta*-PROPIOLACTONE	17	
Propiononitrile	PROPIONITRILE	17	
Propionyl oxide	PROPIONIC ANHYDRIDE	17	
1-Propoxypropan-2-ol	PROPYLENE GLYCOL MONOALKYL ETHER	17	
Propyl acetate	*n*-PROPYL ACETATE	17	
n-PROPYL ACETATE		17	
Propyl acetone	METHYL BUTYL KETONE	17	
Propyl alcohol	*n*-PROPYL ALCOHOL	17	
2-Propyl alcohol	ISOPROPYL ALCOHOL	18	
n-PROPYL ALCOHOL		17	1274
sec-Propyl alcohol	ISOPROPYL ALCOHOL	18	
Propyl aldehyde	PROPIONALDEHYDE	17	
Propylamine	*n*-PROPYLAMINE	17	
n-PROPYLAMINE		17	1277
PROPYLBENZENE (ALL ISOMERS)		17	
n-Propylbenzene	PROPYLBENZENE (ALL ISOMERS)	17	
Propylcarbinol	*n*-BUTYL ALCOHOL	18	
Propylene aldehyde	CROTONALDEHYDE	17	
2,2'-[Propylenebis(nitrilomethylene)]diphenol	ALKYL (C_8–C_9) PHENYLAMINE IN AROMATIC SOLVENTS	17	
PROPYLENE CARBONATE		18	
Propylene chloride	1,2-DICHLOROPROPANE	17	
Propylene dichloride	1,2-DICHLOROPROPANE	17	
alpha,*alpha*'-(Propylenedinitrilo)di-*o*-cresol	ALKYL (C_8–C_9) PHENYLAMINE IN AROMATIC SOLVENTS	17	
Propylene epoxide	PROPYLENE OXIDE	17	
PROPYLENE GLYCOL		18	
1,2-Propylene glycol	PROPYLENE GLYCOL	18	
Propylene glycol *n*-butyl ether	PROPYLENE GLYCOL MONOALKYL ETHER	17	
Propylene glycol ethyl ether	PROPYLENE GLYCOL MONOALKYL ETHER	17	
Propylene glycol methyl ether	PROPYLENE GLYCOL MONOALKYL ETHER	17	
PROPYLENE GLYCOL METHYL ETHER ACETATE		17	
PROPYLENE GLYCOL MONOALKYL ETHER		17	
Propylene glycol monobutyl ether	PROPYLENE GLYCOL MONOALKYL ETHER	17	
Propylene glycol monomethyl ether	PROPYLENE GLYCOL MONOALKYL ETHER	17	
PROPYLENE GLYCOL PHENYL ETHER		17	
Propylene glycol propyl ether	PROPYLENE GLYCOL MONOALKYL ETHER	17	
Propylene glycol trimer	TRIPROPYLENE GLYCOL	17	
1,2-Propylene glycol trimer	TRIPROPYLENE GLYCOL	17	
Propylene glycol *beta*-monoethyl ether	PROPYLENE GLYCOL MONOALKYL ETHER	17	
PROPYLENE OXIDE		17	1280

Index Name	Product Name	Chapter	UN Number
PROPYLENE TETRAMER		17	2850
PROPYLENE TRIMER		17	2057
Propylethylene	PENTENE (ALL ISOMERS)	17	
Propyl methyl ketone	METHYL PROPYL KETONE	18	
n-Propyl-1-propanamine	DI-*n*-PROPYLAMINE	17	
Pseudobutylene glycol	BUTYLENE GLYCOL	17	
Pseudocumene	TRIMETHYLBENZENE (ALL ISOMERS)	17	
Pseudopinen	*beta*-PINENE	17	
Pseudopinene	*beta*-PINENE	17	
Pygas	PYROLYSIS GASOLINE (CONTAINING BENZENE)	17	
PYRIDINE		17	1282
Pyroacetic acid	ACETONE	18	
Pyroacetic ether	ACETONE	18	
PYROLYSIS GASOLINE (CONTAINING BENZENE)		17	
Pyrolysis gasoline (steam-cracked naphtha)	BENZENE AND MIXTURES HAVING 10% BENZENE OR MORE	17	
Pyrolysis gasoline, containing 10% or more benzene	BENZENE AND MIXTURES HAVING 10% BENZENE OR MORE	17	
Pyromucic aldehyde	FURFURAL	17	
RAPESEED OIL		17	
RAPE SEED OIL FATTY ACID METHYL ESTERS		17	
RESIN OIL, DISTILLED		17	
RICE BRAN OIL		17	
ROSIN		17	
Rubbing alcohol	ISOPROPYL ALCOHOL	18	
Safety solvent	WHITE SPIRIT, LOW (15–20%) AROMATIC	17	
SAFFLOWER OIL		17	
Saturated fatty acid (C_{13} and above)	FATTY ACID (SATURATED C_{13}+)	17	
SHEA BUTTER		17	
Silvite	POTASSIUM CHLORIDE SOLUTION	17	
Sludge acid	SULPHURIC ACID, SPENT	17	
Soda ash	SODIUM CARBONATE SOLUTION	17	
Soda lye	SODIUM HYDROXIDE SOLUTION	17	
SODIUM ACETATE SOLUTIONS		18	
Sodium acid sulphite	SODIUM HYDROGEN SULPHITE SOLUTION (45% OR LESS)	17	
Sodium alkylbenzene sulphonate	ALKYLBENZENE SULPHONIC ACID, SODIUM SALT SOLUTION	17	
SODIUM ALKYL (C_{14}–C_{17}) SULPHONATES (60–65% SOLUTION)		17	
SODIUM ALUMINOSILICATE SLURRY		17	
Sodium aminoacetate solution	GLYCINE, SODIUM SALT SOLUTION	17	
SODIUM BENZOATE		17	
Sodium 1,3-benzothiazole-2-thiolate solution	MERCAPTOBENZOTHIAZOL, SODIUM SALT SOLUTION	17	
Sodium 1,3-benzothiazol-2-yl sulphide solution	MERCAPTOBENZOTHIAZOL, SODIUM SALT SOLUTION	17	

Index Name	Product Name	Chapter	UN Number
Sodium bichromate	SODIUM DICHROMATE SOLUTION (70% OR LESS)	17	
Sodium bisulphide	SODIUM HYDROSULPHIDE SOLUTION (45% OR LESS)	17	
SODIUM BOROHYDRIDE (15% OR LESS)/SODIUM HYDROXIDE SOLUTION		17	
SODIUM CARBONATE SOLUTION		17	
SODIUM CHLORATE SOLUTION (50% OR LESS)		17	2428
Sodium cresylate	CRESYLIC ACID, SODIUM SALT SOLUTION	17	
SODIUM DICHROMATE SOLUTION (70% OR LESS)		17	
Sodium glycinate solution	GLYCINE, SODIUM SALT SOLUTION	17	
Sodium hydrate	SODIUM HYDROXIDE SOLUTION	17	
Sodium hydrogensulphide	SODIUM HYDROSULPHIDE SOLUTION (45% OR LESS)	17	
SODIUM HYDROGEN SULPHIDE (6% OR LESS)/SODIUM CARBONATE (3% OR LESS) SOLUTION		17	
SODIUM HYDROGEN SULPHITE SOLUTION (45% OR LESS)		17	2693
SODIUM HYDROSULPHIDE/AMMONIUM SULPHIDE SOLUTION		17	
SODIUM HYDROSULPHIDE SOLUTION (45% OR LESS)		17	2949
SODIUM HYDROXIDE SOLUTION		17	1824
SODIUM HYPOCHLORITE SOLUTION (15% OR LESS)		17	1791
Sodium lignosulphonate	LIGNINSULPHONIC ACID, SODIUM SALT SOLUTION	17	
Sodium mercaptan	SODIUM HYDROSULPHIDE SOLUTION (45% OR LESS)	17	
Sodium mercaptide	SODIUM HYDROSULPHIDE SOLUTION (45% OR LESS)	17	
Sodium methylcarbamodithioate	METAM SODIUM SOLUTION	17	
Sodium N-methyldithiocarbamate	METAM SODIUM SOLUTION	17	
Sodium methyldithiocarbamate solution	METAM SODIUM SOLUTION	17	
SODIUM NITRITE SOLUTION		17	1500
SODIUM PETROLEUM SULPHONATE		17	
SODIUM POLY(4+)ACRYLATE SOLUTIONS		17	
Sodium rhodanate	SODIUM THIOCYANATE SOLUTION (56% OR LESS)	17	
Sodium rhodanide	SODIUM THIOCYANATE SOLUTION (56% OR LESS)	17	
Sodium salt of sulphonated naphthalene–formaldehyde condensate	NAPHTHALENESULPHONIC ACID–FORMALDEHYDE COPOLYMER, SODIUM SALT SOLUTION	17	
SODIUM SILICATE SOLUTION		17	
SODIUM SULPHATE SOLUTIONS		18	
SODIUM SULPHIDE SOLUTION (15% OR LESS)		17	1385
SODIUM SULPHITE SOLUTION (25% OR LESS)		17	
Sodium sulphocyanate	SODIUM THIOCYANATE SOLUTION (56% OR LESS)	17	
Sodium sulphocyanide	SODIUM THIOCYANATE SOLUTION (56% OR LESS)	17	
Sodium sulphydrate	SODIUM HYDROSULPHIDE SOLUTION (45% OR LESS)	17	
Sodium tetrahydroborate (15% or less)/sodium hydroxide solution	SODIUM BOROHYDRIDE (15% OR LESS)/SODIUM HYDROXIDE SOLUTION	17	
SODIUM THIOCYANATE SOLUTION (56% OR LESS)		17	
Sodium tolyl oxides	CRESYLIC ACID, SODIUM SALT SOLUTION	17	
d-Sorbite	SORBITOL SOLUTION	18	
d-Sorbitol	SORBITOL SOLUTION	18	
SORBITOL SOLUTION		18	

Index Name	Product Name	Chapter	UN Number
SOYABEAN OIL		17	
Spirit of turpentine	TURPENTINE	17	
Spirits of wine	ETHYL ALCOHOL	18	
Stoddard solvent	WHITE SPIRIT, LOW (15–20%) AROMATIC	17	
STYRENE MONOMER		17	2055
Styrol	STYRENE MONOMER	17	
Suberane	CYCLOHEPTANE	17	
Sulfonic acid, alkane(C_{10}–C_{21}) phenyl ester	ALKYL SULPHONIC ACID ESTER OF PHENOL	17	
SULPHOHYDROCARBON (C_3–C_{88})		17	
SULPHOLANE		17	
SULPHONATED POLYACRYLATE SOLUTION		18	
SULPHUR (MOLTEN)		17	2448
SULPHURIC ACID		17	1830
Sulphuric acid, fuming	OLEUM	17	
SULPHURIC ACID, SPENT		17	1832
Sulphuric chlorohydrin	CHLOROSULPHONIC ACID	17	
Sulphuric ether	DIETHYL ETHER	17	
SULPHURIZED FAT (C_{14}–C_{20})		17	
SULPHURIZED POLYOLEFINAMIDE ALKENE (C_{28}–C_{250}) AMINE		17	
SUNFLOWER SEED OIL		17	
Sweet-birch oil	METHYL SALICYLATE	17	
TALL OIL, CRUDE		17	
TALL OIL, DISTILLED		17	
TALL OIL FATTY ACID (RESIN ACIDS LESS THAN 20%)		17	
TALL OIL PITCH		17	
TALLOW		17	
TALLOW FATTY ACID		17	
Tar acids	CRESOLS (ALL ISOMERS)	17	
Tar camphor	NAPHTHALENE (MOLTEN)	17	
Terebenthene	beta-PINENE	17	
3,6,9,12-Tetraazatetradecamethylenediamine	PENTAETHYLENEHEXAMINE	17	
3,6,9,12-Tetraazatetradecane-1,14-diamine	PENTAETHYLENEHEXAMINE	17	
1,3,5,7-Tetraazatricyclo[3.3.1.1^{3,7}]decane	HEXAMETHYLENETETRAMINE SOLUTIONS	18	
TETRACHLOROETHANE		17	1702
1,1,2,2-Tetrachloroethane	TETRACHLOROETHANE	17	
sym-Tetrachloroethane	TETRACHLOROETHANE	17	
Tetrachloroethylene	PERCHLOROETHYLENE	17	
1,1,2,2-Tetrachloroethylene	PERCHLOROETHYLENE	17	
Tetrachloromethane	CARBON TETRACHLORIDE	17	
Tetradecan-1-ol	ALCOHOLS (C_{13}+)	17	
1-Tetradecanol	ALCOHOLS (C_{13}+)	17	
Tetradecene	OLEFINS (C_{13}+, ALL ISOMERS)	17	
Tetradecylbenzene	ALKYL(C_9+)BENZENES	17	
TETRAETHYLENE GLYCOL		17	

Index Name	Product Name	Chapter	UN Number
TETRAETHYLENEPENTAMINE		17	2320
Tetraethyllead	MOTOR FUEL ANTI-KNOCK COMPOUNDS (CONTAINING LEAD ALKYLS)	17	
Tetraethylplumbane	MOTOR FUEL ANTI-KNOCK COMPOUNDS (CONTAINING LEAD ALKYLS)	17	
TETRAETHYL SILICATE MONOMER/OLIGOMER (20% IN ETHANOL)		18	
3a,4,7,7a-Tetrahydro-3,5-dimethyl-4,7-methano-1*H*-indene	METHYLCYCLOPENTADIENE DIMER	17	
TETRAHYDROFURAN		17	2056
TETRAHYDRONAPHTHALENE		17	
1,2,3,4-Tetrahydronapthalene	TETRAHYDRONAPHTHALENE	17	
Tetrahydro-1,4-oxazine	MORPHOLINE	17	
Tetrahydro-2*H*-1,4-oxazine	MORPHOLINE	17	
2*H*-Tetrahydro-1,4-oxazine	MORPHOLINE	17	
Tetrahydrothiophene-1-dioxide	SULPHOLANE	17	
Tetrahydrothiophene 1,1-dioxide	SULPHOLANE	17	
Tetralin	TETRAHYDRONAPHTHALENE	17	
TETRAMETHYLBENZENE (ALL ISOMERS)		17	
1,2,3,4-Tetramethylbenzene	TETRAMETHYLBENZENE (ALL ISOMERS)	17	
1,2,3,5-Tetramethylbenzene	TETRAMETHYLBENZENE (ALL ISOMERS)	17	
1,2,4,5-Tetramethylbenzene	TETRAMETHYLBENZENE (ALL ISOMERS)	17	
Tetramethylene cyanide	ADIPONITRILE	17	
Tetramethylene dicyanide	ADIPONITRILE	17	
Tetramethylene glycol	BUTYLENE GLYCOL	17	
Tetramethylene oxide	TETRAHYDROFURAN	17	
Tetramethylene sulphone	SULPHOLANE	17	
Tetramethyllead	MOTOR FUEL ANTI-KNOCK COMPOUNDS (CONTAINING LEAD ALKYLS)	17	
Tetrapropylbenzene	ALKYL(C$_9$+)BENZENES	17	
Tetrapropylenebenzene	DODECYLBENZENE	17	
Tetryl formate	ISOBUTYL FORMATE	17	
Thiacyclopentane-1,1-dioxide	SULPHOLANE	17	
4-Thiapentanal	3-(METHYLTHIO)PROPIONALDEHYDE	17	
Thiocyclopentane-1,1-dioxide	SULPHOLANE	17	
Thiophan sulphone	SULPHOLANE	17	
Thiosulphuric acid, dipotassium salt	POTASSIUM THIOSULPHATE (50% OR LESS)	17	
TITANIUM DIOXIDE SLURRY		17	
Titanium(IV) oxide	TITANIUM DIOXIDE SLURRY	17	
TOLUENE		17	1294
TOLUENEDIAMINE		17	1709
2,4-Toluenediamine	TOLUENEDIAMINE	17	
2,6-Toluenediamine	TOLUENEDIAMINE	17	
TOLUENE DIISOCYANATE		17	2078
2-Toluidine	*o*-TOLUIDINE	17	
o-TOLUIDINE		17	1708

Index Name	Product Name	Chapter	UN Number
Toluol	TOLUENE	17	
o-Tolylamine	o-TOLUIDINE	17	
2,4-Tolylenediamine	TOLUENEDIAMINE	17	
2,6-Tolylenediamine	TOLUENEDIAMINE	17	
Tolylenediisocyanate	TOLUENE DIISOCYANATE	17	
2,4-Tolylene diisocyanate	TOLUENE DIISOCYANATE	17	
m-Tolylene diisocyanate	TOLUENE DIISOCYANATE	17	
Toxilic anhydride	MALEIC ANHYDRIDE	17	
Treacle	MOLASSES	18	
Triacetin	GLYOXAL SOLUTION (40% OR LESS)	17	
3,6,9-Triazaundecamethylenediamine	TETRAETHYLENEPENTAMINE	17	
3,6,9-Triazaundecane-1,11-diamine	TETRAETHYLENEPENTAMINE	17	
TRIBUTYL PHOSPHATE		17	
1,2,3-TRICHLOROBENZENE (MOLTEN)		17	
1,2,4-TRICHLOROBENZENE		17	2321
sym-Trichlorobenzene	1,2,4-TRICHLOROBENZENE	17	
1,2,3-Trichlorobenzol	1,2,3-TRICHLOROBENZENE (MOLTEN)	17	
1,1,1-TRICHLOROETHANE		17	2831
1,1,2-TRICHLOROETHANE		17	
beta-Trichloroethane	1,1,2-TRICHLOROETHANE	17	
Trichloroethene	TRICHLOROETHYLENE	17	
TRICHLOROETHYLENE		17	1710
Trichloromethane	CHLOROFORM	17	
1,2,3-TRICHLOROPROPANE		17	
1,1,2-TRICHLORO-1,2,2-TRIFLUOROETHANE		17	
TRICRESYL PHOSPHATE (CONTAINING 1% OR MORE ortho-ISOMER)		17	2574
TRICRESYL PHOSPHATE (CONTAINING LESS THAN 1% ortho-ISOMER)		17	
TRIDECANE		17	
TRIDECANOIC ACID		17	
Tridecanol	ALCOHOLS (C_{13}+)	17	
Tridecene	OLEFINS (C_{13}+, ALL ISOMERS)	17	
Tridecoic acid	TRIDECANOIC ACID	17	
TRIDECYL ACETATE		17	
Tridecyl alcohol	ALCOHOLS (C_{13}+)	17	
Tridecylbenzene	ALKYL(C_9+)BENZENES	17	
Tridecylic acid	FATTY ACID (SATURATED C_{13}+)	17	
Tridecylic acid	TRIDECANOIC ACID	17	
Tri(dimethylphenyl) phosphate	TRIXYLYL PHOSPHATE	17	
TRIETHANOLAMINE		17	
TRIETHYLAMINE		17	1296
TRIETHYLBENZENE		17	
TRIETHYLENE GLYCOL		18	
Triethylene glycol butyl ether	POLY(2–8)ALKYLENE GLYCOL MONOALKYL(C_1–C_6) ETHER	17	

Index Name	Product Name	Chapter	UN Number
Triethylene glycol ethyl ether	POLY(2–8)ALKYLENE GLYCOL MONOALKYL(C$_1$–C$_6$) ETHER	17	
Triethylene glycol methyl ether	POLY(2–8)ALKYLENE GLYCOL MONOALKYL(C$_1$–C$_6$) ETHER	17	
Triethylene glycol monobutyl ether	POLY(2–8)ALKYLENE GLYCOL MONOALKYL(C$_1$–C$_6$) ETHER	17	
TRIETHYLENETETRAMINE		17	2259
TRIETHYL PHOSPHATE		17	
TRIETHYL PHOSPHITE		17	2323
Triformol	1,3,5-TRIOXANE	17	
Triglycol	TRIETHYLENE GLYCOL	18	
Tri(2-hydroxyethyl)amine	TRIETHANOLAMINE	17	
Trihydroxypropane	GLYCERINE	18	
Trihydroxytriethylamine	TRIETHANOLAMINE	17	
TRIISOPROPANOLAMINE		17	
TRIISOPROPYLATED PHENYL PHOSPHATES		17	
TRIMETHYLACETIC ACID		17	
TRIMETHYLAMINE SOLUTION (30% OR LESS)		17	1297
Trimethylaminomethane	BUTYLAMINE (ALL ISOMERS)	17	
TRIMETHYLBENZENE (ALL ISOMERS)		17	
1,2,3-Trimethylbenzene	TRIMETHYLBENZENE (ALL ISOMERS)	17	
1,2,4-Trimethylbenzene	TRIMETHYLBENZENE (ALL ISOMERS)	17	
1,3,5-Trimethylbenzene	TRIMETHYLBENZENE (ALL ISOMERS)	17	
uns-Trimethylbenzene	TRIMETHYLBENZENE (ALL ISOMERS)	17	
2,6,6-Trimethylbicyclo[3.1.1]hept-2-ene	alpha-PINENE	17	
Trimethylcarbinol	tert-BUTYL ALCOHOL	17	
1,1,3-Trimethyl-3-cyclohexene-5-one	ISOPHORONE	17	
3,5,5-Trimethylcyclohex-2-enone	ISOPHORONE	17	
3,5,5-Trimethylcyclohex-2-en-1-one	ISOPHORONE	17	
3,3'-Trimethylenedioxydipropan-1-ol	TRIPROPYLENE GLYCOL	17	
TRIMETHYLOLPROPANE PROPOXYLATED		17	
2,2,4-Trimethylpentane	OCTANE (ALL ISOMERS)	17	
2,2,4-TRIMETHYL-1,3-PENTANEDIOL DIISOBUTYRATE		17	
2,2,4-Trimethylpentane-1,3-diol diisobutyrate	2,2,4-TRIMETHYL-1,3-PENTANEDIOL DIISOBUTYRATE	17	
2,2,4-TRIMETHYL-1,3-PENTANEDIOL-1-ISOBUTYRATE		17	
2,4,4-Trimethylpentene-1	DIISOBUTYLENE	17	
2,4,4-Trimethylpent-1-ene	DIISOBUTYLENE	17	
2,4,4-Trimethylpentene-2	DIISOBUTYLENE	17	
2,4,4-Trimethylpent-2-ene	DIISOBUTYLENE	17	
2,4,6-Trimethyl-1,3,5-trioxane	PARALDEHYDE	17	
2,4,6-Trimethyl-s-trioxane	PARALDEHYDE	17	
Trioxan	1,3,5-TRIOXANE	17	
1,3,5-TRIOXANE		17	
sym-Trioxane	1,3,5-TRIOXANE	17	
5,8,11-Trioxapentadecane	DIETHYLENE GLYCOL DIBUTYL ETHER	17	
3,6,9-Trioxaundecane	DIETHYLENE GLYCOL DIETHYL ETHER	17	

Index Name	Product Name	Chapter	UN Number
Trioxin	1,3,5-TRIOXANE	17	
Trioxymethylene	1,3,5-TRIOXANE	17	
Tripropylene	PROPYLENE TRIMER	17	
TRIPROPYLENE GLYCOL		17	
Tripropylene glycol methyl ether	POLY(2–8)ALKYLENE GLYCOL MONOALKYL(C_1–C_6) ETHER	17	
Tris(dimethylphenyl) phosphate	TRIXYLYL PHOSPHATE	17	
N,N,N-Tris(2-hydroxyethyl)amine	TRIETHANOLAMINE	17	
Tris(2-hydroxy-2-methylethyl)ammonium 2,4-dichlorophenoxyacetate	2,4-DICHLOROPHENOXYACETIC ACID, TRIISOPROPANOLAMINE SALT SOLUTION	17	
Tris(2-hydroxypropyl)amine	TRIISOPROPANOLAMINE	17	
Tris(2-hydroxy-1-propyl)amine	TRIISOPROPANOLAMINE	17	
Trisodium 2-[carboxylatomethyl(2-hydroxyethyl)amino]ethyliminodi(acetate)	N-(HYDROXYETHYL)ETHYLENEDIAMINETRIACETIC ACID, TRISODIUM SALT SOLUTION	17	
Trisodium N-(carboxymethyl)-N'-(2-hydroxyethyl)-N,N'-ethylenediglycine	N-(HYDROXYETHYL)ETHYLENEDIAMINETRIACETIC ACID, TRISODIUM SALT SOLUTION	17	
Trisodium N-(2-hydroxyethyl)ethylenediamine-N,N',N'-triacetate	N-(HYDROXYETHYL)ETHYLENEDIAMINETRIACETIC ACID, TRISODIUM SALT SOLUTION	17	
Trisodium nitrilotriacetate solution	NITRILOTRIACETIC ACID, TRISODIUM SALT SOLUTION	17	
Tritolyl phosphate, containing less than 1% ortho-isomer	TRICRESYL PHOSPHATE (CONTAINING LESS THAN 1% ortho-ISOMER)	17	
Tritolyl phosphate, containing 1% or more ortho-isomer	TRICRESYL PHOSPHATE (CONTAINING 1% OR MORE ortho-ISOMER)	17	
Trixylenyl phosphate	TRIXYLYL PHOSPHATE	17	
TRIXYLYL PHOSPHATE		17	
TUNG OIL		17	
TURPENTINE		17	1299
Turpentine oil	TURPENTINE	17	
Turps	TURPENTINE	17	
Type A Zeolite	SODIUM ALUMINOSILICATE SLURRY	17	
Undecane	n-ALKANES (C_{10}+)	17	
1-Undecanecarboxylic acid	LAURIC ACID	17	
UNDECANOIC ACID		17	
Undecan-1-ol	UNDECYL ALCOHOL	17	
Undec-1-ene	1-UNDECENE	17	
1-UNDECENE		17	
UNDECYL ALCOHOL		17	
Undecylbenzene	ALKYL(C_9+)BENZENES	17	
Undecylic acid	UNDECANOIC ACID	17	
n-Undecylic acid	UNDECANOIC ACID	17	
Urea, ammonia liquor	UREA/AMMONIUM NITRATE SOLUTION (CONTAINING LESS THAN 1% FREE AMMONIA)	17	
Urea, ammonium carbamate solutions	UREA/AMMONIUM NITRATE SOLUTION (CONTAINING LESS THAN 1% FREE AMMONIA)	17	
UREA/AMMONIUM NITRATE SOLUTION		17	
UREA/AMMONIUM NITRATE SOLUTION (CONTAINING LESS THAN 1% FREE AMMONIA)		17	
UREA/AMMONIUM PHOSPHATE SOLUTION		17	

Index Name	Product Name	Chapter	UN Number
UREA SOLUTION		17	
Valeral	VALERALDEHYDE (ALL ISOMERS)	17	
VALERALDEHYDE (ALL ISOMERS)		17	2058
n-Valeraldehyde	VALERALDEHYDE (ALL ISOMERS)	17	
Valerianic acid	PENTANOIC ACID	17	
Valeric acid	PENTANOIC ACID	17	
n-Valeric acid	PENTANOIC ACID	17	
Valeric aldehyde	VALERALDEHYDE (ALL ISOMERS)	17	
Valerone	DIISOBUTYL KETONE	17	
Varnoline	WHITE SPIRIT, LOW (15–20%) AROMATIC	17	
VEGETABLE ACID OILS		17	
VEGETABLE FATTY ACID DISTILLATES		17	
VEGETABLE PROTEIN SOLUTION (HYDROLYSED)		18	
Vinegar acid	ACETIC ACID	17	
Vinegar naphtha	ETHYL ACETATE	17	
VINYL ACETATE		17	1301
Vinylbenzene	STYRENE MONOMER	17	
Vinylcarbinol	ALLYL ALCOHOL	17	
Vinyl cyanide	ACRYLONITRILE	17	
Vinyl ethanoate	VINYL ACETATE	17	
VINYL ETHYL ETHER		17	1302
Vinylformic acid	ACRYLIC ACID	17	
VINYLIDENE CHLORIDE		17	1303
VINYL NEODECANOATE		17	
VINYLTOLUENE		17	2618
Vinyl trichloride	1,1,2-TRICHLOROETHANE	17	
Vitriol brown oil	OLEUM	17	
WATER		18	
Water glass	SODIUM SILICATE SOLUTION	17	
WAXES		17	
White bole	KAOLIN SLURRY	18	
White caustic	SODIUM HYDROXIDE SOLUTION	17	
WHITE SPIRIT, LOW (15–20%) AROMATIC		17	1300
White tar	NAPHTHALENE (MOLTEN)	17	
Wine	ALCOHOLIC BEVERAGES, N.O.S.	18	
Wintergreen oil	METHYL SALICYLATE	17	
Wood alcohol	METHYL ALCOHOL	17	
Wood naphtha	METHYL ALCOHOL	17	
Wood spirit	METHYL ALCOHOL	17	
XYLENES		17	1307
XYLENES/ETHYLBENZENE (10% OR MORE) MIXTURE		17	
XYLENOL		17	2261
2,3-Xylenol	XYLENOL	17	
2,4-Xylenol	XYLENOL	17	

Index Name	Product Name	Chapter	UN Number
2,5-Xylenol	XYLENOL	17	
2,6-Xylenol	XYLENOL	17	
3,4-Xylenol	XYLENOL	17	
3,5-Xylenol	XYLENOL	17	
Xylols	XYLENES	17	
ZINC ALKARYL DITHIOPHOSPHATE (C_7–C_{16})		17	
ZINC ALKENYL CARBOXAMIDE		17	
ZINC ALKYL DITHIOPHOSPHATE (C_3–C_{14})		17	
Zinc bromide drilling brine	DRILLING BRINES (CONTAINING ZINC SALTS)	17	

Chapter 20

Transport of liquid chemical wastes

20.1   Preamble

20.1.1   Maritime transport of liquid chemical wastes could present a threat to human health and to the environment.

20.1.2   Liquid chemical wastes shall, therefore, be transported in accordance with relevant international conventions and recommendations and, in particular, where it concerns maritime transport in bulk, with the requirements of this Code.

20.2   Definitions

For the purpose of this chapter:

20.2.1   *Liquid chemical wastes* are substances, solutions or mixtures, offered for shipment, containing or contaminated with one or more constituents which are subject to the requirements of this Code and for which no direct use is envisaged but which are carried for dumping, incineration or other methods of disposal other than at sea.

20.2.2   *Transboundary movement* means maritime transport of wastes from an area under the national jurisdiction of one country to or through an area under the national jurisdiction of another country, or to or through an area not under the national jurisdiction of any country, provided at least two countries are concerned by the movement.

20.3   Applicability

20.3.1   The requirements of this chapter are applicable to the transboundary movement of liquid chemical wastes in bulk by seagoing ships and shall be considered in conjunction with all other requirements of this Code.

20.3.2   The requirements of this chapter do not apply to:

.1   wastes derived from shipboard operations which are covered by the requirements of MARPOL 73/78; and

.2   substances, solutions or mixtures containing or contaminated with radioactive materials which are subject to the applicable requirements for radioactive materials.

20.4   Permitted shipments

20.4.1   Transboundary movement of wastes is permitted to commence only when:

.1   notification has been sent by the competent authority of the country of origin, or by the generator or exporter through the channel of the competent authority of the country of origin, to the country of final destination; and

.2   the competent authority of the country of origin, having received the written consent of the country of final destination stating that the wastes will be safely incinerated or treated by other methods of disposal, has given authorization to the movement.

20.5   Documentation

20.5.1   In addition to the documentation specified in 16.2 of this Code, ships engaged in transboundary movement of liquid chemical wastes shall carry on board a waste movement document issued by the competent authority of the country of origin.

20.6   Classification of liquid chemical wastes

20.6.1   For the purpose of the protection of the marine environment, all liquid chemical wastes transported in bulk shall be treated as Category X noxious liquid substances, irrespective of the actual evaluated category.

20.7   Carriage and handling of liquid chemical wastes

20.7.1   Liquid chemical wastes shall be carried in ships and cargo tanks in accordance with the minimum requirements for liquid chemical wastes specified in chapter 17, unless there are clear grounds indicating that the hazards of the wastes would warrant:

.1   carriage in accordance with the ship type 1 requirements; or

.2   any additional requirements of this Code applicable to the substance or, in the case of a mixture, its constituent presenting the predominant hazard.

Chapter 21

Criteria for assigning carriage requirements for products subject to the IBC Code

21.1 Introduction

21.1.1 The following criteria are guidelines for the determination of pollution classification and assignment of appropriate carriage requirements for bulk liquid cargoes being considered as candidates for entry into the IBC Code or annexes 1, 3 or 4 of MEPC.2/Circulars.

21.1.2 In developing such criteria, every effort has been made to follow the criteria and cut-off points developed under the Global Harmonized System (GHS).

21.1.3 Although the criteria are intended to be closely defined in order to establish a uniform approach, it must be emphasized that these are guidelines only and, where human experience or other factors indicates the need for alternative arrangements, these shall always be taken into account. Where deviations from the criteria have been recognized, they shall be properly recorded with justifications.

21.2 Contents

21.2.1 This chapter contains the following:

.1   minimum safety and pollution criteria for products subject to chapter 17 of the IBC Code;

.2   criteria used to assign the minimum carriage requirements for products which meet the safety or pollution criteria to make them subject to chapter 17 of the IBC Code;

.3   criteria used for special requirements in chapter 15 of the IBC Code to be included in *column o* of chapter 17 of the IBC Code;

.4   criteria used for special requirements in chapter 16 of the IBC Code to be included in *column o* of chapter 17 of the IBC Code; and

.5   definitions of properties used within this chapter.

21.3 Minimum safety and pollution criteria for products subject to chapter 17 of the IBC Code

21.3.1 Products are deemed to be hazardous and subject to chapter 17 of the IBC Code if they meet one or more of the following criteria:

.1   inhalation $LC_{50} \leq 20$ mg/ℓ/4 h (see definitions in 21.7.1.1);

.2   dermal $LD_{50} \leq 2000$ mg/kg (see definitions in 21.7.1.2);

.3   oral $LD_{50} \leq 2000$ mg/kg (see definitions in 21.7.1.3);

.4   toxic to mammals by prolonged exposure (see definitions in 21.7.2);

.5   cause skin sensitization (see definitions in 21.7.3);

.6   cause respiratory sensitization (see definitions in 21.7.4);

.7   corrosive to skin (see definitions in 21.7.5);

.8   have a Water Reactive Index (WRI) of ≥ 1 (see definitions in 21.7.6);

.9   require inertion, inhibition, stabilization, temperature control or tank environmental control in order to prevent a hazardous reaction (see definitions in 21.7.10);

.10 flashpoint < 23°C; and have an explosive/flammability range (expressed as a percentage by volume in air) of ≥ 20%;

.11 autoignition temperature of ≤ 200°C; and

.12 classified as pollution category X or Y or meeting the criteria for rules 11 to 13 under 21.4.5.1.

21.4 Criteria used to assign the minimum carriage requirements for products which meet the minimum safety or pollution criteria to make them subject to chapter 17 of the IBC Code

21.4.1 *Column a* – Product Name

21.4.1.1 The International Union of Pure and Applied Chemistry (IUPAC) name shall be used as far as possible but, where this is unnecessarily complex, then a technically correct and unambiguous alternative chemical name may be used.

21.4.2 *Column b* – *Deleted.*

21.4.3 *Column c* – Pollution Category

21.4.3.1 *Column c* identifies the pollution category assigned to each product under Annex II of MARPOL 73/78.

21.4.4 *Column d* – Hazards

21.4.4.1 An "S" is assigned to *column d* if any of the safety criteria described in paragraphs 21.3.1.1 to 21.3.1.11 are met.

21.4.4.2 A "P" is assigned to *column d* if the product meets the criteria for assigning Ship Type 1 to 3 as defined by rules 1 to 14 in paragraph 21.4.5.

21.4.5 *Column e* – Ship Type

21.4.5.1 The basic criteria for assigning Ship Types based on the GESAMP Hazard Profile are shown in the table below. An explanation of the details in the columns is provided in appendix 1 of MARPOL Annex II. Selected rules, identified in this table, are specified in section 21.4.5.2 for assigning specific Ship Types.

Rule number	A1	A2	B1	B2	D3	E2	Ship Type
1			≥5				**1**
2	≥ 4	NR	4		CMRTNI		
3	≥ 4	NR			CMRTNI		**2**
4			4				
5	≥ 4		3				
6		NR	3				
7				≥ 1			
8						Fp	
9					CMRTNI	F	
10			≥ 2			S	
11	≥ 4						**3**
12		NR					
13			≥ 1				
14	All other category Y Substances						
15	All other category Z Substances All "Other Substances" (OS)						**NA**

21.4.5.2 The Ship Type is assigned according to the following criteria:

Ship Type 1:
Inhalation $LC_{50} \leq 0.5$ mg/ℓ/4 h; and/or
Dermal $LD_{50} \leq 50$ mg/kg; and/or
Oral $LD_{50} \leq 5$ mg/kg; and/or
Autoignition temperature $\leq 65^\circ$C; and/or
Explosive range $\geq 50\%$ v/v in air and the flashpoint $< 23^\circ$C; and/or
Rules 1 or 2 of the table shown in 21.4.5.1.

Ship Type 2:
Inhalation $LC_{50} > 0.5$ mg/ℓ/4 h – ≤ 2 mg/ℓ/4 h; and/or
Dermal $LD_{50} > 50$ mg/kg – ≤ 1000 mg/kg; and/or
Oral $LD_{50} > 5$ mg/kg – ≤ 300 mg/kg; and/or
WRI $= 2$;
Autoignition temperature $\leq 200^\circ$C; and/or
Explosive range $\geq 40\%$ v/v in air and the flashpoint $< 23^\circ$C; and/or
Any of the rules 3 to 10 of the table shown in 21.4.5.1.

Ship Type 3:
Any of the minimum safety or pollution criteria for bulk liquid cargoes subject to chapter 17 of the IBC Code not meeting the requirements for ship types 1 or 2 and not meeting rule 15 of the table shown in 21.4.5.1.

21.4.6 *Column f – Tank type*

21.4.6.1 The tank type is assigned according to the following criteria:

Tank type 1G: Inhalation $LC_{50} \leq 0.5$ mg/ℓ/4 h; and/or
Dermal $LD_{50} \leq 200$ mg/kg; and/or
Autoignition temperature $\leq 65^\circ$C; and/or
Explosive range $\geq 40\%$ v/v in air and the flashpoint $<23^\circ$C; and/or
WRI $= 2$.

Tank type 2G: Any of the minimum safety or pollution criteria for bulk liquid cargoes subject to chapter 17 of the IBC Code not meeting the requirements for tank type 1G.

21.4.7 *Column g – Tank vents*

21.4.7.1 The tank venting arrangements are assigned according to the following criteria:

Controlled: Inhalation $LC_{50} \leq 10$ mg/ℓ/4 h; and/or
Toxic to mammals by prolonged exposure; and/or
Respiratory sensitizer; and/or
Special carriage control needed; and/or
Flashpoint $\leq 60^\circ$C;
Corrosive to skin (≤ 4 h exposure).

Open: Any of the minimum safety or pollution criteria for bulk liquid cargoes subject to chapter 17 of the IBC Code not meeting the requirements for controlled tank vents.

21.4.8 *Column h – Tank environmental control*

21.4.8.1 The tank environmental control conditions are assigned according to the following criteria:

Inert: Autoignition temperature $\leq 200^\circ$C; and/or
Reacts with air to cause a hazard; and/or
Explosive range $\geq 40\%$ and the flashpoint $< 23^\circ$C.

Dry: WRI ≥ 1

Pad: Only applies to specific products identified on a case-by-case basis.

Vent: Only applies to specific products identified on a case-by-case basis.

No: Where the above criteria do not apply (inerting requirements may be required under SOLAS).

21.4.9 *Column i* – Electrical equipment

21.4.9.1 If the flashpoint of the product is ≤ 60°C or the product is heated to within 15°C of its flashpoint then the electrical equipment required are assigned according to the following criteria, otherwise '–' is assigned in column i' and i''.

.1 *Column i'* – Temperature class:

T1   Autoignition temperature ≥ 450°C
T2   Autoignition temperature ≥ 300°C but < 450°C
T3   Autoignition temperature ≥ 200°C but < 300°C
T4   Autoignition temperature ≥ 135°C but < 200°C
T5   Autoignition temperature ≥ 100°C but < 135°C
T6   Autoignition temperature ≥ 85°C but < 100°C

.2 *Column i''* – Apparatus group:

Apparatus group	MESG at 20°C (mm)	MIC ratio product/methane
IIA	≥ 0.9	> 0.8
IIB	> 0.5 to < 0.9	≥ 0.45 to ≤ 0.8
IIC	≤ 0.5	< 0.45

.2.1   The tests shall be carried out in accordance with the procedures described in IEC 60079-1-1: 2002 and IEC 79-3.

.2.2   For gases and vapours it is sufficient to make only one determination of either the Maximum Experimental Safe Gap (MESG) or the Minimum Igniting Current (MIC) provided that:

for Group IIA: the MESG is > 0.9 mm or the MIC ratio is > 0.9.

for Group IIB: the MESG is ≥ 0.55 mm and ≤ 0.9 mm; or the MIC ratio is ≥ 0.5 and ≤ 0.8.

for Group IIC: the MESG is < 0.5 mm or the MIC ratio is < 0.45.

.2.3   It is necessary to determine both the MESG and the MIC ratio when:

.1   the MIC ratio determination only has been made, and the ratio is between 0.8 and 0.9, when an MESG determination will be required;

.2   the MIC ratio determination only has been made, and the ratio is between 0.45 and 0.5, when an MESG determination will be required; or

.3   the MESG only has been found, and is between 0.5 mm and 0.55 mm, when an MIC ratio determination will be required.

.3 *Column i'''* – Flashpoint:

> 60°C: Yes
≤ 60°C: No
Non-flammable: NF

21.4.10 *Column j* – Gauging

21.4.10.1 The type of gauging equipment permitted is assigned according to the following criteria:

Closed: Inhalation LC_{50} ≤ 2 mg/ℓ/4 h; and/or
Dermal LD_{50} ≤ 1000 mg/kg; and/or
Toxic to mammals by prolonged exposure; and/or
Respiratory sensitizer; and/or
Corrosive to skin (≤ 3 min exposure).

Restricted: Inhalation LC_{50} > 2 – ≤ 10 mg/ℓ/4 h; and/or
Special carriage control indicates inerting required; and/or
Corrosive to skin (> 3 min – ≤ 1 h exposure); and/or
Flashpoint ≤ 60°C.

Open: Any of the minimum safety or pollution criteria for bulk liquid cargoes subject to chapter 17 of the IBC Code not meeting the requirements for closed or restricted gauging.

21.4.11   *Column k* – **Vapour detection**

21.4.11.1   The type of vapour detection equipment required is determined by the following criteria:

Toxic (T):   Inhalation $LC_{50} \leq$ 10 mg/ℓ/4 h, and/or
                    Respiratory sensitizer; and/or
                    Toxic by prolonged exposure.

Flammable (F):   Flashpoint $\leq 60^\circ$C

No: Where the above criteria do not apply.

21.4.12   *Column l* – **Fire protection equipment**

21.4.12.1   The appropriate fire-fighting media are defined as being appropriate according to the following criteria related to the properties of the product:

Solubility > 10% (> 100 000 mg/ℓ):   A   Alcohol-resistant foam.

Solubility < 10% (< 100 000 mg/ℓ):   A   Alcohol-resistant foam; and/or
                                            B   Regular foam.

WRI = 0:   C   Water spray (generally used as a coolant and can be used with A and/or B providing that the WRI = 0).

WRI $\geq$ 1:   D   Dry chemical.

No: No requirements under this Code.

Note: all appropriate media shall be listed.

21.4.13   *Column m* – *Deleted.*

21.4.14   *Column n* – **Emergency Equipment**

21.4.14.1   The requirement to have personnel emergency equipment on board is identified by 'Yes' in *column n* according to the following criteria:

Inhalation $LC_{50} \leq$ 2 mg/ℓ/4 h; and/or
Respiratory sensitizer; and/or
Corrosive to skin ($\leq$ 3 min exposure); and/or
WRI = 2.

No: indicates that the above criteria do not apply.

21.5   Criteria for special requirements in chapter 15 to be included in *column o*

21.5.1   The assignment of special requirements in *column o* shall normally follow clear criteria based on the data supplied in the reporting form. Where it is considered appropriate to deviate from such criteria, this shall be clearly documented in such a way that it can easily be retrieved on demand.

21.5.2   The criteria for making reference to the special requirements identified in chapters 15 and 16 are defined below with comments where relevant.

21.5.3   **Paragraphs 15.2 to 15.10 and 15.20**

21.5.3.1   Paragraphs 15.2 to 15.10 and 15.20 identify specific products by name with special carriage requirements that cannot be easily accommodated in any other way.

21.5.4   **Paragraph 15.11 – Acids**

21.5.4.1   Paragraph 15.11 applies to all acids unless they:

.1   are organic acids – when only paragraphs 15.11.2 to 15.11.4 and paragraphs 15.11.6 to 15.11.8 apply; or

.2   do not evolve hydrogen – when paragraph 15.11.5 need not apply.

21.5.5   Paragraph 15.12 – Toxic products

21.5.5.1   All of paragraph 15.12 is added to *column o* according to the following criteria:

Inhalation $LC_{50} \leq 2$ mg/ℓ/4 h; and/or
the product is a respiratory sensitizer; and/or
the product is toxic to mammals by prolonged exposure.

21.5.5.2   Paragraph 15.12.3 is added to *column o* according to the following criteria:

Inhalation $LC_{50} > 2 - \leq 10$ mg/ℓ/4 h; and/or
Dermal $LD_{50} \leq 1000$ mg/kg; and/or
Oral $LD_{50} \leq 300$ mg/kg.

21.5.5.3   Paragraph 15.12.4 is added to *column o* according to the following criterion:

Inhalation $LC_{50} > 2 - \leq 10$ mg/ℓ/4 h.

21.5.6   Paragraph 15.13 – Cargoes protected by additives

21.5.6.1   The requirement to assign paragraph 15.13 to *column o* is based on the information related to the products tendency to polymerize, decompose, oxidize or undergo other chemical changes which may cause a hazard under normal carriage conditions and which would be prevented by the addition of appropriate additives.

21.5.7   Paragraph 15.14 – Cargoes with a vapour pressure greater than atmospheric at 37.8°C

21.5.7.1   The requirement to assign paragraph 15.14 to *column o* is based on the following criterion:

Boiling point $\leq 37.8°C$.

21.5.8   Paragraph 15.16 – Cargo contamination

21.5.8.1   Paragraph 15.16.1 is deleted.

21.5.8.2   Paragraph 15.16.2 is added to *column o* according to the following criterion:
WRI ≥ 1.

21.5.9   Paragraph 15.17 – Increased ventilation requirements

21.5.9.1   Paragraph 15.17 shall be added to *column o* according to the following criteria:

Inhalation $LC_{50} > 0.5 - \leq 2$ mg/ℓ/4 h; and/or
Respiratory sensitizer; and/or
Toxic to mammals by prolonged exposure; and/or
Corrosive to skin (≤ 1 h exposure time).

21.5.10   Paragraph 15.18 – Special cargo pump-room requirements

21.5.10.1   Paragraph 15.18 shall be added to *column o* according to the following criterion:

Inhalation $LC_{50} \leq 0.5$ mg/ℓ/4 h.

21.5.11   Paragraph 15.19 – Overflow control

21.5.11.1   Paragraph 15.19 shall be added to *column o* according to the following criteria:

Inhalation $LC_{50} \leq 2$ mg/ℓ/4 h; and/or
Dermal $LD_{50} \leq 1000$ mg/kg; and/or
Oral $LD_{50} \leq 300$ mg/kg; and/or
Respiratory sensitizer; and/or
Corrosive to skin (≤ 3 min exposure); and/or
Autoignition temperature $\leq 200°C$; and/or
Explosive range $\geq 40\%$ v/v in air and flashpoint $< 23°C$; and/or
Classified as ship type 1 on pollution grounds.

21.5.11.2   Only paragraph 15.19.6 shall apply if the product has any of the following properties:

Inhalation $LC_{50} > 2$ mg/ℓ/4 h – ≤ 10 mg/ℓ/4 h; and/or
Dermal $LD_{50} > 1000$ mg/kg – ≤ 2000 mg/kg; and/or
Oral $LD_{50} > 300$ mg/kg – ≤ 2000 mg/kg; and/or
Skin sensitizer; and/or
Corrosive to skin (> 3 min – ≤ 1 h exposure); and/or
Flashpoint $\leq 60^{\circ}$C; and/or
Classified as ship type 2 on pollution grounds; and/or
Pollution category X or Y.

21.5.12   Paragraph 15.21 – Temperature sensors

21.5.12.1   Paragraph 15.21 is added to *column o* according to the heat sensitivity of the product. This requirement is related to pumps in cargo pump-rooms only.

21.6   Criteria for special requirements in chapter 16 to be included in *column o*

21.6.1   Paragraphs 16.1 to 16.2.5 and 16.3 to 16.5

21.6.1.1   These apply to all cargoes and so are not referenced specifically in *column o*.

21.6.2   Paragraph 16.2.6

21.6.2.1   Paragraph 16.2.6 is added to *column o* for products which meet the following criteria:

Pollution Category X or Y and viscosity ≥ 50 mPa·s at 20°C.

21.6.3   Paragraph 16.2.9

21.6.3.1   Paragraph 16.2.9 is added to *column o* for products which meet the following criterion:

Melting point $\geq 0^{\circ}$C.

21.6.4   Paragraph 16.6 – Cargo not to be exposed to excessive heat

21.6.4.1   Paragraphs 16.6.2 to 16.6.4 are added to *column o* for products which are identified as requiring temperature control during carriage.

21.7   Definitions

21.7.1   Acute mammalian toxicity

21.7.1.1   *Acutely toxic by inhalation* *

Inhalation toxicity (LC_{50})	
Hazard level	mg/ℓ/4 h
High	≤ 0.5
Moderately high	$> 0.5 – \leq 2$
Moderate	$> 2 – \leq 10$
Slight	$> 10 – \leq 20$
Negligible	> 20

---

* All inhalation toxicity data are assumed to be associated with vapours and not mists or sprays, unless indicated otherwise.

21.7.1.2 *Acutely toxic in contact with skin*

Dermal toxicity (LD$_{50}$)	
Hazard Level	mg/kg
High	≤ 50
Moderately high	$> 50 - \leq 200$
Moderate	$> 200 - \leq 1000$
Slight	$> 1000 - \leq 2000$
Negligible	> 2000

21.7.1.3 *Acutely toxic if swallowed*

Oral toxicity (LD$_{50}$)	
Hazard Level	mg/kg
High	≤ 5
Moderately High	$> 5 - \leq 50$
Moderate	$> 50 - \leq 300$
Slight	$> 300 - \leq 2000$
Negligible	> 2000

21.7.2 **Toxic to mammals by prolonged exposure**

21.7.2.1 A product is classified as *toxic by prolonged exposure* if it meets any of the following criteria: it is known to be, or suspected of being, a carcinogen, a mutagen, reprotoxic, neurotoxic, immunotoxic or exposure below the lethal dose is known to cause specific organ oriented systemic toxicity (TOST) or other related effects.

21.7.2.2 Such effects may be identified from the GESAMP Hazard Profile of the product or other recognized sources of such information.

21.7.3 **Skin sensitization**

21.7.3.1 A product is classified as a *skin sensitizer*:

   .1 if there is evidence in humans that the substance can induce sensitization by skin contact in a substantial number of persons; or

   .2 where there are positive results from an appropriate animal test.

21.7.3.2 When an adjuvant type test method for skin sensitization is used, a response of at least 30% of the animals is considered as positive. For a non-adjuvant test method a response of at least 15% of the animals is considered positive.

21.7.3.3 When a positive result is obtained from the Mouse Ear Swelling Test (MEST) or the Local Lymph Node Assay (LLNA), this may be sufficient to classify the product as a skin sensitizer.

21.7.4 **Respiratory sensitization**

21.7.4.1 A product is classified as a *respiratory sensitizer*:

   .1 if there is evidence in humans that the substance can induce specific respiratory hypersensitivity; and/or

   .2 where there are positive results from an appropriate animal test; and/or

.3 where the product is identified as a skin sensitizer and there is no evidence to show that it is not a respiratory sensitizer.

21.7.5 Corrosive to skin*

Hazard level	Exposure time to cause full thickness necrosis of skin	Observation time
Severely corrosive to skin	$\leq$ 3 min	$\leq$ 1 h
Highly corrosive to skin	> 3 min – $\leq$ 1 h	$\leq$ 14 days
Moderately corrosive to skin	> 1 h – $\leq$ 4 h	$\leq$ 14 days

21.7.6 Water reactive substances

21.7.6.1 These are classified into three groups as follows:

Water reactive index (WRI)	Definition
2	Any chemical which, in contact with water, may produce a toxic, flammable or corrosive gas or aerosol
1	Any chemical which, in contact with water, may generate heat or produce a non-toxic, non-flammable or non-corrosive gas
0	Any chemical which, in contact with water, would not undergo a reaction to justify a value of 1 or 2

21.7.7 Air reactive substances

21.7.7.1 Air reactive substances are products which react with air to cause a potentially hazardous situation, e.g., the formation of peroxides which may cause an explosive reaction.

21.7.8 Electrical apparatus – Temperature Class (for products which either have a flashpoint of $\leq$ 60°C or are heated to within 15°C of their flashpoint)

21.7.8.1 The Temperature Class is defined by the International Electrotechnical Commission (IEC) as:

The highest temperature attained under practical conditions of operation within the rating of the apparatus (and recognized overloads, if any, associated therewith) by any part of any surface, the exposure of which to an explosive atmosphere may involve a risk.

21.7.8.2 The Temperature Class of the electrical apparatus is assigned by selecting the Maximum Surface Temperature which is closest to, but less than, the product's autoignition temperature (see 21.4.9.1.1).

21.7.9 Electrical apparatus – Apparatus group (for products with a flashpoint of $\leq$ 60°C)

21.7.9.1 This refers to intrinsically safe and associated electrical apparatus for explosive gas atmospheres which the IEC divide into the following groups:

Group I: for mines susceptible to firedamp (not used by IMO); and

Group II: for applications in other industries – further sub-divided according to its Maximum Experimental Safe Gap (MESG) and/or the Minimum Igniting Current (MIC) of the gas/vapour into groups IIA, IIB and IIC.

21.7.9.2 This property cannot be determined from other data associated with the product; it has to be either measured or assigned by assimilation with related products in an homologous series.

---

* Products that are corrosive to skin are, for the purpose of assigning relevant carriage requirements, deemed to be corrosive by inhalation.

21.7.10 Special carriage control conditions

21.7.10.1 Special carriage control conditions refer to specific measures that need to be taken in order to prevent a hazardous reaction. They include:

.1 **Inhibition:** the addition of a compound (usually organic) that retards or stops an undesired chemical reaction such as corrosion, oxidation or polymerization;

.2 **Stabilization:** the addition of a substance (stabilizer) that tends to keep a compound, mixture or solution from changing its form or chemical nature. Such stabilizers may retard a reaction rate, preserve a chemical equilibrium, act as antioxidants, keep pigments and other components in emulsion form or prevent the particles in colloidal suspension from precipitating;

.3 **Inertion:** the addition of a gas (usually nitrogen) in the ullage space of a tank that prevents the formation of a flammable cargo/air mixture;

.4 **Temperature control:** the maintenance of a specific temperature range for the cargo in order to prevent a hazardous reaction or to keep the viscosity low enough to allow the product to be pumped; and

.5 **Padding and venting:** only applies to specific products identified on a case-by-case basis.

21.7.11 Flammable cargoes

21.7.11.1 A cargo is defined as flammable according to the following criteria:

IBC Code descriptor	Flashpoint (degrees Centigrade)
Highly flammable	< 23
Flammable	≤ 60 but ≥ 23

21.7.11.2 It should be noted that flashpoints of mixtures and aqueous solutions need to be measured unless all of the components are non-flammable.

21.7.11.3 It should be noted that the carriage of bulk liquid cargoes which have a flashpoint of $\leq 60°C$ is subject to other SOLAS regulations.

Appendix
Model form of International Certificate of Fitness for the Carriage of Dangerous Chemicals in Bulk

INTERNATIONAL CERTIFICATE OF FITNESS FOR THE CARRIAGE OF DANGEROUS CHEMICALS IN BULK

(Official seal)

Issued under the provisions of the

INTERNATIONAL CODE FOR THE CONSTRUCTION AND EQUIPMENT OF SHIPS
CARRYING DANGEROUS CHEMICALS IN BULK
(resolutions MSC.176(79) and MEPC.119(52))

under the authority of the Government of

....

(full official designation of country)

by ....

*(full designation of the competent person or organization
recognized by the Administration)*

Particulars of ship*

Name of ship ....

Distinctive number or letters ....

IMO Number† ....

Port of registry ....

Gross tonnage ....

Ship Type (Code paragraph 2.1.2) ....

Date on which keel was laid or on which the ship was at a similar stage of construction or (in the case of a converted ship) date on which conversion to chemical tanker was commenced ....

The ship also complies fully with the following amendments to the Code:

....

....

---

* Alternatively, the particulars of the ship may be placed horizontally in boxes.
† In accordance with IMO ship identification number scheme adopted by the Organization by resolution A.600(15).

The ship is exempted from compliance with the following provisions of the Code:

. . . .

. . . .

THIS IS TO CERTIFY:

1   That the ship has been surveyed in accordance with the provisions of section 1.5 of the Code;

2   That the survey showed that the construction and equipment of the ship and the condition thereof are in all respects satisfactory and that the ship complies with the relevant provisions of the Code;

3   That the ship has been provided with a Manual in accordance with appendix 4 of Annex II of MARPOL 73/78 as called for by regulation 14 of Annex II, and that the arrangements and equipment of the ship prescribed in the Manual are in all respects satisfactory;

4   That the ship meets the requirements for the carriage in bulk of the following products, provided that all relevant operational provisions of the Code and Annex II of MARPOL 73/78 are observed:

Product	Conditions of carriage (tank numbers etc.)	Pollution Category
Continued on attachment 1, additional signed and dated sheets. * Tank numbers referred to in this list are identified on attachment 2, signed and dated tank plan.		

5   That, in accordance with 1.4/2.8.2 *, the provisions of the Code are modified in respect of the ship in the following manner:

. . . .

6   That the ship must be loaded:

.1   in accordance with the loading conditions provided in the approved loading manual, stamped and dated . . . . and signed by a responsible officer of the Administration, or of an organization recognized by the Administration; *

.2   in accordance with the loading limitations appended to this Certificate. *

Where it is required to load the ship other than in accordance with the above instruction, then the necessary calculations to justify the proposed loading conditions shall be communicated to the certifying Administration who may authorize in writing the adoption of the proposed loading condition.†

---

* Delete as appropriate.

† Instead of being incorporated in the Certificate, this text may be appended to the Certificate if signed and stamped.

This Certificate is valid until *(dd/mm/yyyy)*: . . . . *
subject to surveys in accordance with 1.5 of the Code.

Completion date of the survey on which this certificate is based: . . . .
(dd/mm/yyyy)

Issued at . . . .
(Place of issue of certificate)

(dd/mm/yyyy) . . . .
(Date of issue)   *(Signature of duly authorized official
issuing the certificate)*

(Seal or stamp of the authority, as appropriate)

Notes on completion of Certificate:

1   The Certificate can be issued only to ships entitled to fly the flags of States which are both a Contracting Government to the 1974 SOLAS Convention and a Party to MARPOL 73/78.

2   Ship Type: Any entry under this column must relate to all relevant recommendations, e.g., an entry "Type 2" means Type 2 in all respects prescribed by the Code.

3   Products: Products listed in chapter 17 of the Code, or which have been evaluated by the Administration in accordance with 1.1.6 of the Code, shall be listed. In respect of the latter "new" products, any special requirements provisionally prescribed shall be noted.

4   Products: The list of products the ship is suitable to carry shall include the noxious liquid substances of Category Z which are not covered by the Code and shall be identified as "chapter 18 Category Z".

---

* Insert the date of expiry as specified by the Administration in accordance with 1.5.6.1 of the Code. The day and the month of this day correspond to the anniversary date as defined in 1.3.3 of the Code, unless amended in accordance with 1.5.6.8 of the Code.

ENDORSEMENT FOR ANNUAL AND INTERMEDIATE SURVEYS

THIS IS TO CERTIFY that at a survey required by 1.5.2 of the Code the ship was found to comply with the relevant provisions of the Code.

Annual survey: Signed: ....
(Signature of duly authorized official)

Place: ....

Date *(dd/mm/yyyy)* ....

(Seal or stamp of the authority, as appropriate)

Annual/Intermediate* survey: Signed: ....
(Signature of duly authorized official)

Place: ....

Date *(dd/mm/yyyy)* ....

(Seal or stamp of the authority, as appropriate)

Annual/Intermediate* survey: Signed: ....
(Signature of duly authorized official)

Place: ....

Date *(dd/mm/yyyy)* ....

(Seal or stamp of the authority, as appropriate)

Annual survey: Signed: ....
(Signature of duly authorized official)

Place: ....

Date *(dd/mm/yyyy)* ....

(Seal or stamp of the authority, as appropriate)

---

* Delete as appropriate.

ANNUAL/INTERMEDIATE SURVEY IN ACCORDANCE WITH PARAGRAPH 1.5.6.8.3

THIS IS TO CERTIFY that, at an annual/intermediate* survey in accordance with paragraph 1.5.8.6.3 of the Code, the ship was found to comply with the relevant provisions of the Convention.

Signed: . . . .
(Signature of duly authorized official)

Place: . . . .

Date *(dd/mm/yyyy)* . . . .

(Seal or stamp of the authority, as appropriate)

ENDORSEMENT TO EXTEND THE CERTIFICATE IF VALID FOR LESS THAN 5 YEARS WHERE PARAGRAPH 1.5.6.3 APPLIES

The ship complies with the relevant provisions of the Convention, and this Certificate shall, in accordance with paragraph 1.5.6.3 of the Code, be accepted as valid until *(dd/mm/yyyy)*: . . . .

Signed: . . . .
(Signature of duly authorized official)

Place: . . . .

Date *(dd/mm/yyyy)* . . . .

(Seal or stamp of the authority, as appropriate)

ENDORSEMENT WHERE THE RENEWAL SURVEY HAS BEEN COMPLETED AND PARAGRAPH 1.5.6.4 APPLIES

The ship complies with the relevant provisions of the Convention, and this Certificate shall, in accordance with paragraph 1.5.6.4 of the Code, be accepted as valid until *(dd/mm/yyyy)*: . . . .

Annual survey:

Signed: . . . .
(Signature of duly authorized official)

Place: . . . .

Date *(dd/mm/yyyy)* . . . .

(Seal or stamp of the authority, as appropriate)

* Delete as appropriate.

ENDORSEMENT TO EXTEND THE VALIDITY OF THE CERTIFICATE UNTIL REACHING THE PORT OF SURVEY OR FOR A PERIOD OF GRACE WHERE PARAGRAPH 1.5.6.5 OR 1.5.6.6 APPLIES

This Certificate shall, in accordance with paragraph 1.5.6.5/1.5.6.6* of the Code, be accepted as valid until *(dd/mm/yyyy)*: . . . .

Signed: . . . .
(Signature of duly authorized official)

Place: . . . .

Date *(dd/mm/yyyy)* . . . .

(Seal or stamp of the authority, as appropriate)

ENDORSEMENT FOR ADVANCEMENT OF ANNIVERSARY DATE WHERE PARAGRAPH 1.5.6.8 APPLIES

In accordance with paragraph 1.5.6.8 of the Code, the new anniversary date is *(dd/mm/yyyy)*: . . . .

Signed: . . . .
(Signature of duly authorized official)

Place: . . . .

Date *(dd/mm/yyyy)* . . . .

(Seal or stamp of the authority, as appropriate)

In accordance with paragraph 1.5.6.8, the new anniversary date is *(dd/mm/yyyy)*: . . . .

Signed: . . . .
(Signature of duly authorized official)

Place: . . . .

Date *(dd/mm/yyyy)* . . . .

(Seal or stamp of the authority, as appropriate)

---

* Delete as appropriate.

ATTACHMENT 1 TO THE INTERNATIONAL CERTIFICATE OF FITNESS
FOR THE CARRIAGE OF DANGEROUS CHEMICALS IN BULK

Continued list of products to those specified in section 4, and their conditions of carriage.

Products	Conditions of carriage (tank numbers etc.)	Pollution Category

Date . . . .
    (dd/mm/yyyy)   *(Signature of official issuing the Certificate*
    (as for Certificate)   *and/or seal of issuing authority)*

**ATTACHMENT 2 TO THE INTERNATIONAL CERTIFICATE OF FITNESS
FOR THE CARRIAGE OF DANGEROUS CHEMICALS IN BULK**

TANK PLAN (specimen)

Name of ship: . . . .

Distinctive number or letters: . . . .

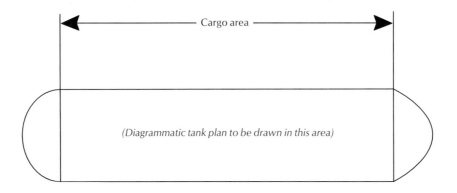

Date . . . .　　　　　　　　　　　　. . . . .
　　　(dd/mm/yyyy)　　　　　　　　　　　　　　*(Signature of official issuing the Certificate*
　　(as for Certificate)　　　　　　　　　　　　　　*and/or seal of issuing authority)*

STANDARDS AND GUIDELINES
RELEVANT TO THE IBC CODE

MSC-MEPC.2/Circ.4 of 2 June 2006

Early application of the amendments to the fire protection requirements of the revised IBC Code

1   The Marine Environment Protection Committee, at its fifty-second session (11 to 15 October 2004), and the Maritime Safety Committee, at its seventy-ninth session (1 to 10 December 2004), adopted amendments to the International Code for the Construction and Equipment of Ships Carrying Dangerous Chemicals in Bulk (revised IBC Code) by resolutions MEPC.119(52) and MSC.176(79), respectively, which are expected to enter into force on 1 January 2007.

2   The Marine Environment Protection Committee, at its fifty-third session (18 to 22 July 2005) and the Maritime Safety Committee, at its eighty-first session (10 to 19 May 2006), approved, in principle, proposed amendments to the fire protection requirements of the aforementioned revised IBC Code, as set out in the annex, with a view to adoption by MEPC 56 and MSC 83*.

3   Considering that early implementation of the proposed amendments would be of benefit to the industry and other interested parties, the Committees invited Contracting Governments to the 1974 SOLAS Convention and Parties to MARPOL 73/78 to:

.1   apply the proposed amendments to the revised IBC Code, referred to in paragraph 2 above, to ships flying their flags on or after 1 January 2007, pending their formal entry into force; and

.2   accept ships flying the flags of other States, constructed and equipped in accordance with the revised IBC Code and the aforementioned proposed amendments.

Annex
Draft amendments to the
International Code for the Construction and Equipment
of Ships Carrying Dangerous Chemicals in Bulk
(2004 Amendments to the IBC Code (Resolutions MEPC.119(52)
and MSC.176(79))

Chapter 11
Fire protection and fire extinction

11.1   Application

1   *In paragraph 11.1.1, subparagraphs .4 to .6 are replaced by the following subparagraphs:*

".4   regulation 10.5.6 shall apply to ships of 2,000 gross tonnage and over;

.5   the provisions of 11.3 shall apply in lieu of regulation 10.8;

.6   the provisions of 11.2 shall apply in lieu of regulation 10.9;

.7   regulation 4.5.10 shall apply to ships of 500 gross tonnage and over, replacing "hydrocarbon gases" by "flammable vapours" in the regulation; and

.8   regulations 13.3.4 and 13.4.3 shall apply to ships of 500 gross tonnage and over."

---

* The amendment was adopted by MSC at its eighty-second session in December 2006. The resolution is MSC.219(82).

2   *In paragraph 11.1, the following new paragraph 11.1.4 is added:*

"11.1.4 In lieu of the provisions of SOLAS regulation II-2/1.6.7, the requirements of regulations II-2/4.5.10.1.1 and 4.5.10.1.4 and a system for continuous monitoring of the concentration of flammable vapours shall be fitted on ships of 500 gross tonnage and over which were constructed before [the date of entry into force of the amendment] by the date of the first scheduled dry-docking after [the date of entry into force of the amendment], but not later than [3 years after the date of entry into force of the amendment]. Sampling points or detector heads should be located in suitable positions in order that potentially dangerous leakages are readily detected. When the flammable vapour concentration reaches a pre-set level which shall not be higher than 10% of the lower flammable limit, a continuous audible and visual alarm signal shall be automatically effected in the pump-room and cargo control room to alert personnel to the potential hazard. However, existing monitoring systems already fitted having a pre-set level not greater than 30% of the lower flammable limit may be accepted. Notwithstanding the above provisions, the Administration may exempt ships not engaged on international voyages from those requirements."

MSC/Circ.879//MEPC/Circ.348
of 19 November 1998, corrected by Corr.1

Equivalency arrangements for the carriage
of styrene monomer

1   The Maritime Safety Committee, at its sixty-ninth session, and the Marine Environment Protection Committee, at its forty-second session, agreed that, in accordance with the provisions off paragraph 1.4 of the IBC Code, the carriage of styrene monomer under the conditions indicated below should be considered as equivalent to that identified in paragraph 15.13.5 of the IBC Code.

2   Contracting Governments to the 1974 SOLAS Convention and Parties to MARPOL 73/78 are therefore advised that they may transport styrene monomer in a chemical tanker with cargo tanks over 3,000 m^3 fitted with an IGS (Inert Gas System), provided that the oxygen content inside those tanks is maintained between 2% and 8% and that the following operational measures are observed:

   .1   upon completion of loading and taking of product samples, the vapour space is checked to ensure that the oxygen level is within acceptable limits (2% to 8%). Although levels as low as 2% are adequate, levels of oxygen between 6% and 8% are preferred;

   .2   during the voyage, the vapour space oxygen content is monitored and recorded at least twice per day, at least 8 hours apart; and

   .3   temperature and pressure readings of the cargo tanks are monitored and recorded at least twice per day, at least 8 hours apart.

MSC/Circ.1100//MEPC/Circ.407 of 27 August 2003

Recommendation for the use of a standard format for the cargo information required by chapter 16 of the IBC Code

1   The Maritime Security Committee, at its seventy-sixth session (2 to 13 December 2002), and the Marine Environment Protection Committee, at its forty-ninth session (14 to 18 July 2003), recognizing the need for a standard set of occupational health data for seafarers that covers the substances to which they are likely to become exposed on board tankers, agreed that a standard format should be used to provide seafarers with clear, concise and accurate occupational health information.

2   Therefore, the Committees, noting that the United Nations Sub-Committee for the Globally Harmonized System of Classification and Labelling of Chemicals has developed a single, globally harmonized system to address classification of chemicals, labels, and safety data by consumers, workers, transport workers and emergency responders, agreed that, in addition to the provisions of paragraph 16.2 of the International Code for the Construction and Equipment of Ships Carrying Dangerous Chemicals in Bulk (IBC Code), any cargo offered for shipment in bulk which is subject to chapters 17 and 18 of the IBC Code should be accompanied by safety data sheets based on the format contained in chapter 1.5 of the Globally Harmonized System for Hazard Classification and Communication.*

3   Member Governments are invited to bring the above recommendation to the attention of shipowners, shipoperators and other parties involved in the transportation of such cargo.

---

* United Nations Publication, Sales No: E.03.II.E.25; ISBN: 92-1-116840-6.

MSC-MEPC.2/Circ.3 of 5 June 2006

Guidelines on the basic elements of a shipboard occupational health and safety programme

1   The Maritime Safety Committee, at its eighty-first session (10 to 19 May 2006), and the Marine Environment Protection Committee, at its fifty-third session (18 to 22 July 2005), recognizing the need to provide guidance to personnel or consultants who are implementing, improving or auditing the effectiveness of shipboard health and safety programmes, approved Guidelines on the basic elements of a shipboard occupational health and safety programme, as set out in the annex.

2   Member Governments are invited to bring the annexed Guidelines to the attention of all parties concerned so that they may use them when implementing, improving or auditing the effectiveness of a shipboard occupational health and safety programme.

3   The Committees, recognizing the need to provide guidance for shipowners and ship managers for implementing the ISM Code, agreed that these guidelines would provide relevant information related to occupational health and safety on board ships.

Annex
Guidelines on the basic elements of a shipboard occupational health and safety programme

1   Purpose

These guidelines describe the basic elements of a shipboard occupational health and safety programme (SOHSP). The elements set out in the appendices are applicable to all vessel types and are fundamental pieces of a systematic occupational health and safety programme, which may be used by company line managers, health and safety personnel or consultants who are implementing, improving or auditing the effectiveness of a shipboard occupational health and safety programme.

2   Application

These guidelines do not set specific performance or technical criteria, but recommend that companies set policies and objectives and develop procedures for managing their occupational health and safety programme. Companies should consider their unique organization, culture and hazards on their vessels and the possible effects of their operations. The elements are intentionally flexible and may be adapted to address any size of operation or any vessel type. However, it should be noted that, although the standard is aimed at the shipboard occupational health and safety programmes, some of the elements address activities and commitments that must be completed or made by shoreside personnel (e.g., executive management commitment and provision of adequate resources). Key to the effectiveness of the programme is the implementation of each element within an interconnected system.

3   Basic elements

3.1   Executive Management commitment and leadership

Executive management commitment and leadership is a precondition for an effective SOHSP. Executive management commitment and leadership includes, but is not limited to: (a) integrating occupational health and safety into the management structure and fabric of the company; (b) developing an occupational health and safety policy; (c) developing occupational health and safety objectives; (d) providing resources to achieve the objectives; (e) defining stewardship responsibilities, and providing authority to carry out those responsibilities, and (f) establishing accountability for occupational health and safety as a part of job performance reviews. Further guidance is provided in appendix 1.

3.2   Employee participation

Employees from all levels, including crew members, officers, masters, persons in charge, and shoreside personnel, should be directly involved with the SOHSP. Shipboard and shoreside employees should be involved in developing, implementing, evaluating, and modifying the SOHSP. Employees should also participate in setting occupational health and safety objectives and performance criteria. This involvement might be through employee membership on safety committees that provide input to management for the development of occupational health and safety policy, debate and set occupational health and safety goals, measure and evaluate performance, and recommend modifications to the programme based on their evaluation. Shoreside and shipboard employees should work together to achieve occupational health and safety goals. For example, shoreside personnel should participate on vessel safety committees since their decisions affect vessel operations and ultimately the occupational health and safety of vessel personnel. In large companies, individual vessel safety committees might submit recommendations to an over-arching safety committee that evaluates the recommendations and sets policy to apply appropriate recommendations to the entire fleet. Further guidance is provided in appendix 2.

3.3 Hazard anticipation, identification, evaluation and control

The core function of any occupational health and safety programme is prevention. Occupational health and safety hazards, including fire, reactivity, chemical and physical hazards, need to be anticipated and prevented from occurring. Hazards and unsafe operating procedures need to be identified and addressed so they will not endanger employees or the public, and will not damage the vessel, cargo or third-party property. Potential hazards should be systematically anticipated, identified, evaluated and controlled. Tools such as job hazard analysis, industrial hygiene exposure assessments, and risk assessment/management methodologies enable the evaluation and control of hazards. Further guidance is provided in appendix 3.

3.4 Training

Employees should receive training appropriate for their duties and responsibilities so that they may work safely and not endanger their shipmates or the public. In addition, employees who have specific occupational health and safety responsibilities (generally supervisors with responsibility for the safety of others, but also non-supervisors who are assigned to safety committees or as crew member representatives) should receive training to enable them to carry out their occupational health and safety programme responsibilities. Further guidance is provided in appendix 4.

3.5 Record keeping

Company records sufficient to demonstrate the effectiveness of the occupational health and safety programme should be maintained. Data that enables trend or pattern analysis for root causes is particularly desirable. For example, results of audits that evaluate effectiveness of the occupational health and safety management programme should be maintained. Records that indicate that industrial hygiene exposure assessments have been conducted and appropriate controls have been implemented should be maintained. Current job safety analyses and corresponding standard operating procedures with safe work practices should be documented. Injury and illness data should be maintained to enable the identification of trends and patterns that associate the injury or illness with a common cause, which can be addressed. Training topics, lesson outlines and attendees should be documented. Where appropriate, such records should permit evaluation of the programme on individual vessels as well as across an entire fleet. Further guidance is provided in appendix 5.

3.6 Contract or third-party personnel

When contract or third-party personnel are on board to perform work, vessel personnel should provide information regarding potential hazards on the vessel that may affect the contract or third-party personnel. Potential hazards related to the work conducted by contract or third-party personnel should be provided to the vessel owner/operator and/or the master/person-in-charge. Each employer should provide appropriate information regarding vessel and work hazards to their own employees. For example, exchange of information on chemical hazards might be accomplished by exchanging appropriate safety data sheets (SDS), then each employer can inform their own employees of the hazards identified in the SDS. Further guidance is provided in appendix 6.

3.7 Fatality, injury, illness and incident investigation

Personnel injuries, occupational illnesses, and "near miss" incidents should be promptly investigated. The current incident and other similar occurrences should be analysed to identify the primary (root) cause and any contributing factors. The investigation report, setting forth primary cause, contributing factors, and corrective measures, should be presented to management. Follow-up action which specifically addresses the report's recommendations for corrective action should be undertaken and documented. Further guidance is provided in appendix 7.

3.8 Systematic programme evaluation and continuous improvement

Maintaining an effective occupational health and safety programme is an ongoing process. The SOHSP should have systems for detecting, reporting, and correcting non-conformities to the programme. Some type of "formalized" evaluation should also be conducted on a periodic basis consistent with other aspects of the vessel's management plan. The evaluation should determine whether the SOHSP is appropriate for the vessel and its operations, that actual practices are consistent with the programmes and procedures in the SOHSP, and that the SOHSP is effective. Comparison of data and records (refer to appendix 5, Record keeping) to performance objectives and criteria (refer to appendix 1, paragraph 3, health and safety objectives) can provide important indicators of the effectiveness of the SOHSP. Further guidance is provided in appendix 8.

Appendix 1
Management commitment and leadership

1 Occupational health and safety programmes are most effective when they are integrated into the management structure of a company, rather than treated as an "add on" programme. Examples of integrated occupational health and safety efforts include:

  .1 developing standard operating procedures (SOPs), written to the education level of the person who must follow the SOP, that integrate safe work practices and basic operational functions;

  .2 making design review by qualified occupational health and safety personnel an element of the acquisition procedures; and

  .3 making consultation with qualified occupational health and safety personnel a part of the process when making changes to operations.

2 Executive management sets the tone for the entire SOHSP through their policy regarding occupational health and safety. Examples of values that can be stated and commitments that can be made in company policy include:

  .1 a statement that the company will make every effort to provide a safe and healthy workplace and that working safely is a condition of employment;

  .2 statements that convey how important each crewmember is to the vessel as a fellow worker and as a company resource:

    "The basic safety policy of this company is that no task is so important that an employee must violate a safety rule or put himself or herself at risk of injury or illness in order to get it done.";

  .3 a written commitment to provide resources necessary to implement the occupational health and safety programme could also be included in the policy statement; and

  .4 management can demonstrate commitment to the occupational health and safety policies through word and action. For example, managers visiting vessels should follow safety rules and standard operating procedures, including use of hearing protection, safety glasses, safety shoes, protective clothing, etc.

3 Setting and attaining occupational health and safety objectives demonstrates a company's commitment to improvement of occupational health and safety performance. Objectives provide a target against which those who are responsible for occupational health and safety may measure their progress. Quantifiable objectives are desirable since often "What gets measured gets done." (Refer to appendix 8, Systematic shipboard occupational health and safety evaluation, for examples of performance measures and an overall programme audit). Occupational health and safety objectives may include:

  .1 eliminate Lost Time Incidents;

  .2 report "near miss" incidents or problems, evaluate, and, if appropriate, implement changes to prevent a more serious incident or accident in the future;

  .3 develop and implement a programme of evaluations through drills and other means (for example, simulators) to ensure that personnel are competent to carry out their duties;

  .4 improve the occupational health and safety programme by reviewing, considering and implementing appropriate published industry practices and other recognized standards;

  .5 complete periodic comprehensive (or area-specific) hazard review;

  .6 reduce exposure levels to airborne vapours to acceptable levels through appropriate controls;

  .7 complete annual respiratory fit-testing on schedule;

  .8 develop and implement acute toxic exposure procedures addressing first aid procedures, obtaining additional emergency medical assistance, and appropriate medical surveillance tests (for example, S-phenylmercapturic acid in urine following a potential benzene over-exposure); and

.9 develop and implement an occupational health medical surveillance plan.*

4 Company management holds the authority to dedicate necessary resources to achieve occupational health and safety objectives. Necessary resources may include:

.1 access to occupational health and safety information;

.2 training, including classroom and on-the-job training, that cover topics identified by the company's risk-assessment process as well as those required by international or national standards. These topics would include, but not be limited to, existing chemical and mechanical hazards;

.3 qualified occupational health and safety professionals, either on the company staff or hired as consultants;

.4 capital investments in engineering controls; and

.5 personal protective equipment.

5 Defining stewardship responsibilities and providing authority to carry out those responsibilities is an essential component of management commitment. For example:

.1 Company management should:

.1.1 designate a shoreside person who has access to the executive management of the company and is responsible to ensure essential occupational health and safety issues are clearly communicated to executive management of the company, and decisions regarding those issues are clearly communicated back to the vessel;

.1.2 ensure adequate resources of time, funds for occupational health and safety equipment, training and expertise are available to effectively implement the programme throughout the company;

.1.3 ensure that a safety committee or other mechanism to adequately involve crewmembers in occupational health and safety issues is created on each vessel;

.1.4 ensure that the elements of the shipboard occupational health and safety programme are integrated and systematically implemented throughout the company and on each vessel;

.1.5 ensure that objectives are developed and performance measures are reported from each vessel;

.1.6 ensure that all appropriate programmes are developed and implemented, including, but not limited, to respiratory protection, hearing protection, confined space entry, and lock out–tag out;

.1.7 set a good example for employees by following established safety rules on vessels and by staying current on training commensurate with duties; and

.1.8 report unsafe practices or conditions observed while on a vessel to the supervisor of the area;

.2 Master/person-in-charge/operator should:

.2.1 ensure each crewmember receives an initial vessel orientation, covering company safety policy, emergency procedures, access and egress, fire fighting, job hazards, and information on hazardous materials, before beginning work. Document the completion of this orientation;

.2.2 ensure each crewmember is competent to perform a task or job by requiring a pre-job explanation and/or walk-through of all procedures, including safe work practices, before starting work on that project or equipment. Require pre-job refresher training if the employee cannot demonstrate this competence;

.2.3 ensure each crewmember has been issued and received training on the use of required personal protective equipment (PPE) before starting work on a project requiring PPE;

.2.4 complete periodic walk-around occupational health and safety checks of the vessel accompanied by appropriate personnel, including those who have responsibilities or work in certain areas (e.g., Chief engineer and an oiler in engine spaces or First mate and able-bodied seaman on deck);

.2.5 periodically observe work performance of employees for compliance with safety rules contained or documented in the SOHSP;

---

* **Note:** The intent of this medical surveillance plan is to ensure employees are not over-exposed to hazards on the job, including chemicals, radiation, noise, etc. This section is not intended to address physical standards related to watchkeeping published elsewhere.

.2.6 set a good example for subordinates by following established safety rules and attending training as appropriate;

.2.7 complete a preliminary investigation of all accidents and report findings to company management; and

.2.8 provide information to company management suggesting changes to company-wide standard operating procedures or equipment that will improve employee safety;

.3 Officers/other management personnel should act as the master's or person-in-charge's representative, and implement examples listed for the master in areas over which they exercise supervision (e.g., First Mate responsible for "deck" personnel and Chief Engineer responsible for "engineers").

6   Management should establish accountability for occupational health and safety as part of job performance reviews. Performance reporting regarding health is as important and should be as routine within the company as reports regarding timeliness of delivery, cargo loss or contamination, or citations regarding violations of regulations.

Appendix 2
Employee participation

1   Full participation in developing, implementing, evaluating and continually improving the SOHSP helps those on board the vessel to see the SOHSP as something that is the result of a value they share with vessel owners/operators. Personnel directly involved with the work are often the best source of information on health or safety hazards and often can suggest effective methods for abating those hazards. Shoreside personnel need to be directly and heavily involved with the SOHSP because they are integral in setting the rules and schedules for vessel operation. Shoreside personnel also represent the vessel to management and are the link to the resources and authority necessary for the success of the SOHSP. Specific ways that crewmembers, officers, and shoreside personnel can contribute to the SOHSP include:

    .1   participating in periodic vessel inspections;

    .2   evaluating occupational health and safety programme materials;

    .3   developing standard operating procedures that incorporate safe working practices;

    .4   conducting job safety/hazard analyses (JSAs/JHAs);

    .5   reviewing and analysing injury and illness data;

    .6   participating in risk-assessment and risk-management activities;

    .7   participating in accident/incident/problem investigations;

    .8   developing solutions to occupational health and safety complaints and disputes;

    .9   evaluating occupational health and safety training activities; and

    .10   evaluating the occupational health and safety management programme.

2   Line or operations personnel, including crewmembers, officers and shoreside personnel outside the occupational health and safety staff, may need training in occupational health and safety techniques such as job safety/hazard analysis, reviewing injury and illness data for trends, risk assessment and investigations. This initial training investment enables those who do the work to meaningfully participate in identifying and solving occupational health and safety problems. Those crewmembers, officers and shoreside personnel who receive additional training in occupational health and safety and actively participate in the development of the vessel and/or company SOHSP also become occupational health and safety "champions" among their peers. Additional information on training is provided in appendix 4.

3   Since occupational health and safety objectives and performance may directly affect crewmembers' and officers' current and/or future occupational health and safety, they should be involved in setting those objectives and performance criteria. This participation may be accomplished through occupational health and safety committee involvement, labour negotiations, or other mechanism suitable to the specific company. Refer to appendix 1, paragraph 3, for examples of occupational health and safety objectives and performance criteria.

4   Employees should:

    .1   fully understand (including underlying principles) and follow established standard operating procedures and safety rules;

    .2   report unsafe conditions or actions to supervisor as soon as they become aware of them;

    .3   report all injuries to supervisor promptly;

    .4   report all accidents, near misses or problems to supervisor promptly;

    .5   use personal protective equipment (PPE) in good working condition where it is required;

    .6   do not remove or defeat any safety device or safeguard;

.7 encourage shipmates by words and behaviour to follow standard operating procedures and use safe work practices on the job; and

.8 make suggestions to supervisor or safety committee representative about changes to operating procedures, work practices or equipment that will improve safety.

Appendix 3
Hazard anticipation, identification, evaluation and control

1   Potential hazards on the vessel and created by the vessel should be systematically anticipated, identified, evaluated and controlled. Hazards that should be discovered, evaluated and controlled by the SOHSP include hazards addressed by the organization and by the Administration, and other hazards that are causing or likely to cause illness, death or serious physical harm to workers or the public. Types of hazards to consider may include:

     .1   hazardous atmospheres due to oxygen deficiency, flammable or toxic gases or vapours, and biological agents;

     .2   chemical hazards and the proper handling of vessel-generated hazardous wastes;

     .3   physical hazards, including noise, vibration, radiation, electricity, uncontrolled mechanical energy, shifting cargoes that may engulf a crewmember;

     .4   ergonomic factors, including fatigue, workstation design, and poor team practices;

     .5 collisions, groundings, or rammings and their resultant impacts; and

     .6 drowning.

2   Methods of anticipation include:

     .1   systematic requirements for vessel and equipment design and modification review by qualified occupational health and safety personnel;

     .2   periodic management review of the vessel and its operation, its equipment, and its fitness-for-purpose;

     .3   a procurement system that automatically requires consideration of occupational health and safety aspects of items ordered;

     .4   consideration of fitness for current conditions; and

     .5   systematic review of vessel and shoreside team practices.

3   Methods of identifying hazards include:

     .1   vessel inspections;

     .2   industrial hygiene exposure assessments of chemical and biological hazards, including inhalation and dermal exposure routes, and physical hazards such as vibration and ergonomic hazards;

     .3   job safety analyses, including risk assessment, both statistical and expert-opinion-based;

     .4   employee hazardous condition notification system, including easy-to-understand labelling system for all possible mechanical and chemical hazards; and

     .5   review of available occupational health and safety data to identify trends.

4   Methods of hazard evaluation include:

     .1   comparison of industrial hygiene exposure levels to standards identified in the SOHSP (e.g., standards required by regulation or prudent levels adopted by the company in the absence of regulatory requirements); and

     .2   risk analysis tools:

         .2.1   hazard effects and control analysis;

         .2.2   hazard control analysis;

         .2.3   fault-tree analysis of possibilities based on expert opinion;

         .2.4   management oversight and risk analysis; and

         .2.5   task hazard analysis.

5   Methods of hazard control are hierarchical. In order of preference, they include:

.1   inherent safe design and verification of matching of design output to design requirements;

.2   material substitution such as:

    .2.1   non-hazardous insulation for asbestos lagging;

    .2.2   citrus-based cleaning agents for solvent-based cleaning agents; and

    .2.3   non-toxic paint for toxic paint.

.3   Engineering controls such as:

    .3.1   closed gauging;

    .3.2   vapour recovery systems; and

    .3.3   climate-controlled spaces such as control booths in engine-rooms.

.4   Administrative controls such as:

    .4.1   systematic review for fitness of vessel for operations;

    .4.2   standard operating procedures that incorporate safe work practices. Some activities that might require standard operating procedures with integrated safe work practices include:

        .4.2.1   machinery start-up and shut-down operations;

        .4.2.2   emergency response to machinery failures;

        .4.2.3   getting underway and entering port operations;

        .4.2.4   cargo loading and unloading operations;

        .4.2.5   response to unplanned or emergency situations during cargo operations;

        .4.2.6   man-overboard procedures;

        .4.2.7   lifeboat launching procedures;

        .4.2.8   watchkeeping procedures;

        .4.2.9   team working procedures such as:

            .1   bridge resource management taught in simulators with practice by actual team members; and

            .2   pre-job planning and briefings;

        .4.2.10   job hazard/safety analyses (JHAs/JSAs);

        .4.2.11   emergency procedures; and

        .4.2.12   systematic inspection of incoming equipment and equipment in use to ensure conformation to specifications identified in the SOHSP (for example, personal protective equipment).

    .4.3   an easy-to-understand labelling system for all possible mechanical and chemical hazards;

    .4.4   occupational medical surveillance programmes tailored to vessel and cargo hazards; and

    .4.5   specific programmes that need special attention within the overall SOHSP:

        .4.5.1   respiratory protection programme;

        .4.5.2   hearing loss prevention programme;

        .4.5.3   safe lifting procedures; and

        .4.5.4   permit-to-work programmes for operations such as:

            .1   lock out and tag out;

            .2   tank or hold cleaning operations;

            .3   confined space entry;

            .4   hot-work operations, including a gas-freeing programme; and

            .5   working aloft.

.5   occupational health and safety equipment control, calibration, and maintenance procedures;

.6   security procedures to control entry and exit of personnel to and from the vessel;

.7   basic safety rules such as:

    .7.1   You shall not do things which are unsafe in order to get the job done. If a necessary activity is unsafe, report it to your supervisor so it can be evaluated and alternate methods developed.

    .7.2   Mechanical guards must be kept in place at all times when machinery is being operated. Do not remove or disable any safety device!

.7.3 No person may operate a piece of equipment unless they have been trained and are authorized. Notify your supervisor that you need training if you are asked to perform a function you did not learn in meeting the requirements for your level.

.7.4 Use your personal protective equipment whenever it is required.

.7.5 Obey all safety warning signs.

.7.6 Smoking is only permitted in designated locations and may be entirely prohibited at certain times, such as during cargo transfer operations.

.7.7 Good housekeeping is an important part of accident prevention. Replace all tools and supplies after use. Do not allow rubbish or debris to accumulate where they will become a hazard;

.8 employee assistance and wellness programmes;

.9 pre-employment chemical tests for dangerous drugs;

.10 incentive programmes such as:

.10.1 safety awards;

.10.2 bonuses; and

.10.3 vessel competitions;

.11 disciplinary policy that provides for progressive consequences depending on the severity and/or repetition of the violation of a safety rule;

.12 personal protective equipment such as:

.12.1 safety glasses, goggles, hearing protection, safety shoes, protective clothing, chemical protective bootees, respiratory protection; and

.12.2 impervious gloves for food handlers, as appropriate; and

.13 preventive maintenance of the vessel and equipment and basic housekeeping programmes.

Appendix 4
Training

1   Training to enable all employees to recognize hazards and to take appropriate precautions should include:

    .1 general orientation to the company;

    .2 overview of the company's occupational health and safety programme;

    .3 vessel orientation, including access and egress;

    .4 emergency procedures in case of fire, confined space entry incident, release of hazardous chemicals or cargo, and over-exposure;

    .5 the nature of potential hazards to which employees may be exposed during routine tasks and how to recognize symptoms of exposure;

    .6 use of protective measures, such as standard operating procedures that incorporate safe work practices, and protective equipment and clothing (refer to appendix 3, paragraph 5, hazard control);

    .7 specific programmes, including respiratory protection, confined space entry, hearing loss prevention, lock-out–tag-out, fall protection, safe lifting, occupational health and safety equipment control, calibration and maintenance; and

    .8 recognition and control of fatigue.

2   Additional training for those with specific health or safety responsibilities may include:

    .1 risk assessment and risk management, including:

        .1.1 occupational health and safety data trend analysis;

        .1.2 job safety analysis; and

        .1.3 shipboard watch implications,

    .2 fatality, injury, illness, "near miss" incident, and problem investigation and root cause analysis.

3   Effective worker protection programmes do not stop at initial training. Effective programmes evaluate the success of the training provided and offer refresher training on both a routine and as-needed basis.

4   Elaborate training programmes solely related to occupational health and safety are not always needed. Integrating consideration of occupational health and safety protection into all organizational activities is the key to effectiveness. Occupational health and safety information should be integrated into other training about performance requirements and job practices.

Appendix 5
Record keeping

1   Records are needed to document hazard control efforts such as job hazard analyses, industrial hygiene sampling, and training. Data-collection systems that enable trend analysis help in identifying injuries and illnesses with common causes. A review of shipboard personnel injury and illness experienced over a period of time may reveal patterns of injury and illness with common causes, which can be addressed. Similarly, a review of accidents, "near miss" incidents or problems over time can reveal patterns of dangerous practice, which need correction to assure safety. The correlation of changes in injury, illness and "near miss" incidents or problem experience can be used to make changes in the occupational health and safety programme. Operations, work processes, and personnel may help to identify potential causes and likelihood of personnel accidents, injuries, and illnesses, and danger or risk to the public. Audits that evaluate the effectiveness of the occupational health and safety programme can be used to identify weak points in the system.

2   Examples of records that should be maintained include:

    .1   death, injury, illness, accident, "near miss" incident, and problem data, including:

        .1.1   investigation reports and root-cause analysis (see also appendix 7, Fatality, injury, illness and incident investigation); and

        .1.2   injury, illness, "near miss" and problem rates;

    .2   hazardous condition notifications and abatement actions;

    .3   crewmember safety suggestions;

    .4   industrial hygiene monitoring results for both personal and area samples;

    .5   job safety analyses;

    .6   safety committee reports;

    .7   safety inspection reports or log entries;

    .8   medical surveillance data (aimed at identifying exposures so that proper interventions, including improvement of hazard controls, may be initiated);

    .9   training (refer to appendix 4 for a discussion of recommended training):

        .9.1   record training outline, date and attendance; and

        .9.2   record completion of courses such as fire fighting and confined space entry schools; and

    .10 occupational health and safety management programme audits (refer to appendix 8 for an example).

3   The extent of record keeping necessary to document the effectiveness of the programme will vary depending on the size of the company, level and nature of exposure to hazards on the vessel, and other factors. The records should be maintained as long as necessary in light of their intended use.

4   Records of individual ships should also be shared with other ships and analysed as a larger base of data to gain information on frequency of problems to better identify trends.

Appendix 6
Contract or third-party personnel

1   The vessel owner/operator and/or the master/person-in-charge should provide information on applicable elements of the company's occupational health and safety programme concerning vessel hazards, safety rules, standard operating procedures, and emergency procedures with contract or third-party personnel who may be exposed to vessel or cargo hazards.

2   The contractor or third party should inform his/her employees of the applicable elements of the vessel's occupational health and safety programme and of any known vessel or cargo hazards to which his/her employees may be exposed. The contract or third-party person-in-charge should also direct his/her employees to follow the occupational health and safety rules of the vessel to the extent that they meet or exceed the contractor's or third party's own requirements.

3   The contract or third-party person-in-charge should inform the vessel's master or person-in-charge of any occupational health and safety hazards presented by their work and how they will address those hazards. The contract or third-party person-in-charge should also inform the vessel personnel of any other occupational health and safety hazards in the course of their work on the vessel.

4   During the initial exchange of information regarding vessel hazards and hazards presented by the work intended, the actions of the contractor or third party toward the occupational health and safety of the vessel crew and their own employees should be clearly identified. Likewise, the actions of the vessel personnel toward the occupational health and safety of the contractor or third party should be clearly identified. Emergency procedures should be clearly agreed upon in advance.

Appendix 7
Fatality, injury, illness and incident investigation

1   The objective of an investigation is to prevent related incidents from recurring. An investigation should identify the circumstances of the injury, illness or incident and reveal the proximate causes, contributing factors, and root causes by gathering and analysing information and drawing conclusions. Identification and correction of causes may prevent similar incidents from recurring. Furthermore, identifying and correcting a true root cause may prevent other, apparently unrelated, incidents, giving even more return on the effort expended to identify root causes. For example, if a problem with the company's training system was identified as the root cause for a confined-space incident, then correcting the entire training system may prevent an injury that would have been caused by an untrained person improperly operating a piece of machinery.

2   Start the investigation as soon as possible after the incident occurs. Interview workers involved in the incident and all witnesses. Discover situations leading up to the incident, including several days before. These situations may include contributing factors. (Human factors, including fatigue, often are found as root or contributing factors and may accumulate over a period of time.) Examine the location of the incident and identify factors associated with the incident. Interview other company personnel as needed to determine root causes. Document the investigation and recommendations.

3   The final report should include:

.1   a summary outlining the basic facts of the incident;

.2   a narrative detailing the circumstances of the casualty or near incident;

.3   analysis and comment that lead to logical conclusions or findings, establishing all the factors, including root cause(s), that contributed to the incident; and

.4   immediate and long-term recommendations aimed at preventing similar accidents and correcting root causes.

4   It may be helpful to categorize investigation data. An example of a one-page form divided into information categories is provided. Additional pages might be used to record the summary, narrative, analysis and recommendations.

☐ Fatality,	☐ Injury,	☐ Illness, or	☐ Incident investigation	Date:		Time:	
Vessel name:	Type of vessel:		Class. Society:	Vessel location:	Temp:	Wind speed:	Sea state:

Vessel operation at time of incident:

☐ Discharging cargo	☐ Loading cargo
☐ Gas-freeing tanks	☐ Stripping tanks
☐ Cleaning tanks	☐ Receiving fuel
☐ Mooring at dock	☐ Replenishment at sea
☐ Transit harbour	☐ Transit restricted channel
☐ Resource exploration	☐ Resource production
☐ Trawling	☐ Underway at sea

Employee name:　　　　　　**Employee ID No.:**

Employee position on vessel:

☐ Deck crew	☐ Deck officer
☐ Engineering crew	☐ Engineering officer
☐ Master	☐ Steward
☐ Tankerman	☐ Person-In-Charge
☐ OIM	☐ Platform worker
☐ Passenger	☐ Gov. employee
☐ Longshore/harbour worker	☐ Visitor

Nature of fatality, injury or illness:

☐ Thermal burn	☐ Allergic reaction	☐ Asphyxia
☐ Electrical burn (shock)	☐ Chemical burn	☐ Concussion
☐ Abrasion	☐ Aggravated old injury	☐ Strain
☐ Blister	☐ Bruise	☐ Sprain
☐ Cut	☐ Drowning	☐ Hernia
☐ Fracture	☐ Haemorrhoid	☐ Blot clot
☐ Infectious disease	☐ Puncture	☐ Other _____
☐ Unknown	☐ Heat stroke	

Part of body injured:

☐ Back	☐ Chest	☐ Ankle	☐ Arm	☐ Other _____
☐ Groin	☐ Hand	☐ Eye	☐ Finger	
☐ Knee	☐ Leg	☐ Foot	☐ Head	
☐ Shoulder	☐ Stomach	☐ Hip	☐ Neck	
☐ Multiple injuries	☐ Cardiovascular	☐ Trunk	☐ Lung	

Location when injured/at time of near miss: ☐ Unknown

☐ Aft area	☐ Cargo tank	☐ Engine stores
☐ Pump-room	☐ Engine-room	☐ Galley
☐ Deck, open	☐ Forepeak	☐ Laundry rooms
☐ Fire room	☐ Fuel tank	☐ Mid-ship area
☐ Forward area	☐ Mast, boom, rigging	☐ Offices
☐ Machinery spaces	☐ Paint locker	☐ Passageway
☐ Quarters	☐ Shaft alley	☐ Steering space
☐ Ballast tank	☐ Cofferdam	☐ Windlass room
☐ Void	☐ Drilling platform	☐ Other _____
☐ Mud pit	☐ Cargo hold	
☐ Bridge	☐ Deck stores	

Root (cause(s)):

☐ Management commitment	☐ Record keeping
☐ Employee involvement	☐ Contract/third party
☐ Hazard identification, evaluation, control	☐ Investigation
☐ Training	☐ Systematic evaluation

Lead investigator: _____ **Captain/PIC:** _____

Related vessel casualty:

☐ Allision	☐ Fire or explosion
☐ Collision	☐ Machinery damage
☐ Strand/grounding	☐ Capsize
☐ Failure: hull, watertight doors, ports, etc.	☐ Listing
	☐ Other _____

Nature of accident or incident:

☐ Slip/fall – stairs	☐ Slip/fall – gangway
☐ Slip/fall – deck	☐ Slip/fall – other _____
☐ Fall, same level	☐ Fall, into water
☐ struck, falling object	☐ Struck, flying object
☐ Struck, moving object	☐ Bumped, fixed object
☐ Struck, vessel	☐ Struck, other _____
☐ Pinched/crushed	☐ Cut, bruise
☐ Sprain/strain	☐ Overexertion
☐ Caught in lines	☐ Burned, non-electric
☐ Burned, electric	☐ Scalded
☐ Hypothermia	☐ Hyperthermia
☐ Diving accident	☐ Asphyxiation
☐ Acute toxic exposure	☐ Chronic toxic exposure
☐ Disappeared	☐ Other _____

Activity person undertaking when accident occurred:

☐ Deck duty	☐ Engine duty
☐ Drilling	☐ Fishing
☐ Handling cargo	☐ Handling lines
☐ Operating machinery	☐ Repairing machinery
☐ Steward duty	☐ Passenger
☐ Off duty – exercising	☐ Off duty

Proximate and contributory cause(s) of accident or incident:

☐ Intoxication, alcohol	☐ Intoxication, narcotics
☐ Adverse weather	☐ Faulty planning
☐ Command problem	☐ Haste
☐ Excessive task/work load	☐ Task time problem
☐ Inappropriate policy	☐ Boredom, inattention
☐ Carelessness	☐ Judgement error
☐ Cognitive function error	☐ Inadequate training
☐ Fatigue	☐ Untimely info flow
☐ Inaccurate info flow	☐ Design – control interface
☐ Design – emergency systems	☐ Design – general layout
☐ Design – workstation	☐ Psychological factors
☐ Physical factors	☐ Deck cluttered
☐ Deck slippery	☐ Equipment failure
☐ Failure to use PFD	☐ NO PFD available,
☐ Chemical reaction or release	☐ Failure to use PPE
☐ No/Inad. PPE available	☐ Inadequate/missing guard
☐ Improper maintenance	☐ Insufficient ventilation
☐ Improper supervision	☐ Misuse of tools/equipment
☐ Improper lighting	☐ Improper tools/equipment
☐ Improper load/storage	☐ Material failure
☐ Inadequate/missing rail	☐ Mooring line surge

Signature
Lead investigator _____　　Date _____

Signature
Captain/PIC _____　　Date _____

Statement of	☐ Injured/ill person	☐ Witness	☐ Supervisor	☐ Investigator

(Attach extra sheets, drawings, information if needed)

Name: (print)	Signature:	Date:

Appendix 8
Systematic shipboard occupational health and safety evaluation

1   Tools that may help with programme evaluation include:

    .1   trend analysis of fatality, injury, illness and "near miss" incident statistics;

    .2   trend analysis of records of "unsafe acts or behaviours";

    .3   review of vessel safety committee reports and recommendations; and

    .4   review of hazardous condition notifications and abatement actions.

2   Performance measures that may assist in programme evaluation include:

    .1   lost time incident rate;

    .2   fatality rate;

    .3   acute toxic exposure incidents per 1,000 employee work hours;

    .4   number of non-conformities with standard operating procedures per 100 employee work hours;

    .5   percentage of training required by SOHSP completed on schedule;

    .6   percentage of annual respiratory fit testing completed on schedule; and

    .7   percentage of annual medical monitoring examinations completed on schedule.

3   The following audit tool may be used to evaluate a SOHSP. The elements scored in the audit tool are the first seven elements of a SOHSP. Some elements are further divided into factors that are individually scored. The auditor should objectively score the vessel's SOHSP on each of the individual factors and elements after obtaining the necessary information to do so.

    .1   Calculate the overall score, after scoring each element, as follows:

        .1.1   the score for the Management Commitment and Leadership Element is the lower of the two scores of the General and Implementation Factors;

        .1.2   the score for the Employee Participation Element is the lower of the two scores for the General and Hazard Reporting Factors;

        .1.3   the score for the Hazard Anticipation, Identification, Evaluation and Control Element is the average of all six Factors; and

        .1.4   the scores for single-Factor Elements are the scores for the Factor;

    .2   The overall score is the average score of the seven Element scores and may be assigned a "verbal" description based upon the score.

SCORE	Level of Shipboard Occupational Health and Safety Programme
5	Outstanding Programme
4	Superior Programme
3	Basic Programme
2	Developmental Programme
1	No programme or ineffective programme

Programme Element	Absent or ineffective (1)	Develop- mental (2)	Basic (3)	Superior (4)	Outstanding (5)
Management Commitment and Leadership					
General					
Implementation					
Overall score for element		Lowest of 2 sections			
Employee Participation					
General					
Hazard Reporting					
Overall score for element		Lowest of 2 sections			
Hazard Anticipation, Identification, Evaluation, & Control					
Anticipation, Identification, & Evaluation					
Control – General					
Control – Maintenance					
Control – Medical Programme					
Control – Emergency Preparedness – Planning & Drills					
Control – Emergency Preparedness – First Aid					
Overall score for element		Average of 6 sections			
Health and Safety Training					
General					
Overall score for element		Score of 1 section			
Record Keeping					
Data Collection and Analysis					
Overall score for element		Score of 1 section			
Contract and Third-Party Personnel					
General					
Overall score for element		Score of 1 section			
Fatality, Injury, Illness & Accident Investigation					
General					
Overall score for element		Score of 1 section			
Overall Programme score		Average of 7 Elements rounded			

Attached tables provide the verbal descriptions for the numeric indicators above.

MANAGEMENT COMMITMENT AND LEADERSHIP	
General	
Management commitment and leadership is a precondition for an effective SOHSP	
1	Management demonstrates no policy, goals, objectives, or interest in occupational health and safety issues on this vessel.
2	Management sets and communicates occupational health and safety policy and goals, but remains detached from all other occupational health and safety efforts.
3	Management follows all occupational health and safety rules, and gives visible support to the occupational health and safety efforts of others.
4	Management participates in significant aspects of the ship's occupational health and safety programme. Such as ship inspections, incident reviews, and programme reviews. Incentive programmes that discourage reporting of accidents, symptoms, injuries, or hazards are absent. Other incentive programmes may be present.
5	Ship occupational health and safety issues are regularly included on agendas of management operations meetings. Management clearly demonstrates – by involvement, support, and example – the primary importance of occupational health and safety. Performance is consistent and sustained or has improved over time.

MANGEMENT COMMITMENT AND LEADERSHIP	
Implementation	

Implementation means tools, provided by management, that include:

- *resources:*
  - *budget*
  - *information*
  - *expertise/training*
  - *personnel*
- *defined and assigned responsibilities*
- *commensurate authority to carry out responsibilities*
- *accountability*

1	Tools to implement an occupational health and safety programme are inadequate or missing.
2	Some tools to implement an occupational health and safety programme are adequate and effectively used; others are ineffective or inadequate. Management assigns responsibility for implementing a ship occupational health and safety programme to identified person(s). Management's designated representative has authority to direct abatement of hazards that can be corrected without major capital expenditure.
3	Tools to implement an occupational health and safety programme are adequate, but are not all effectively used. Management representative has some expertise in hazard recognition and applicable standards. Management keeps or has access to applicable standards on the unit, and seeks appropriate guidance for interpretation of the standards. Management representative has authority to order/purchase occupational health and safety equipment.
4	All tools to implement an occupational health and safety programme are more than adequate and effectively used. Written safety procedures, policies, and interpretations are updated based on reviews of the occupational health and safety programme. Occupational health and safety expenditures, including training costs and personnel, are identified in the vessel budget. Hazard abatement is an element in management (officers/persons-in-charge/supervisors) performance evaluation.
5	All tools necessary to implement a good health and safety programme are more than adequate and effectively used. Management occupational health and safety representative has expertise appropriate to vessel size and operation, and has access to professional advice when needed. Occupational health and safety budgets and funding procedures are reviewed periodically for adequacy.

EMPLOYEE PARTICIPATION	
General	
Employee participation provides the means through which those who actually do the work identify hazards, recommend and monitor abatement, and otherwise participate in their own protection	
1	Worker participation in workplace occupational health and safety concerns is not encouraged. Incentive programmes are present which have the effect of discouraging reporting of incidents, injuries, potential hazards or symptoms. Employees/employee representatives are not involved in the shipboard occupational health and safety programme.
2	Workers and their representatives can participate freely in occupational health and safety activities on the unit without fear of reprisal. Procedures are in place for communication between employer and workers on occupational health and safety matters. Workers are able to refuse or stop work that they reasonably believe involves imminent danger. Workers are paid while performing safety activities.
3	Workers and their representatives are involved in the occupational health and safety programme, are involved in inspection of work areas, and are permitted to observe monitoring and receive results. Workers and representatives have access to information regarding the shipboard occupational health and safety programme, including occupational health and safety data trend analysis, job task analysis, and industrial hygiene sampling data. A documented procedure is in place for raising complaints of hazards or discrimination and receiving timely employer response.
4	Workers and their representatives participate in workplace analysis, inspections and investigations, and development of control strategies throughout the vessel, and have necessary training and education to participate in such activities. Workers and their representatives have access to all pertinent occupational health and safety information, including safety reports and audits. Workers are informed of their right to refuse job assignments that pose serious hazards to them pending management response.
5	Workers and their representatives participate fully in development of the occupational health and safety programme and conduct of training and education. Workers participate in audits, programme reviews conducted by management or third parties, and collection of samples for monitoring purposes, and have necessary training and education to participate in such activities. Employer encourages and authorizes employees to stop activities that present potentially serious occupational health and safety hazards.

EMPLOYEE PARTICIPATION	
Hazard Reporting	
A reliable hazard reporting system enables employees, without fear of reprisal, to notify management of conditions that appear hazardous and to receive timely and appropriate responses	
1	No formal hazard reporting system exists, or employees are reluctant to report hazards.
2	Employees are instructed to report hazards to management. Supervisors are instructed and are aware of a procedure for evaluating and responding to such reports. Employees use the system with no risk of reprisals.
3	A formal system for hazard reporting exists. Employee reports of hazards are documented, corrective action is scheduled, and records are maintained.
4	Employees are periodically instructed in hazard identification and reporting procedures. Management conducts surveys of employee observations of hazards to ensure that the system is working. Results are documented.
5	Management responds to reports of hazards in writing within specified time frames. The workforce readily identifies and self-corrects hazards; they are supported by management to do so.

HAZARD ANTICIPATION, IDENTIFICATION, EVALUATION AND CONTROL	
Anticipation, Identification and Evaluation	
Anticipation and identification and evaluation of hazards involves systematic review of vessel and equipment design, review of the vessel and equipment fitness for current conditions and operations, a procurement system that requires consideration of occupational health and safety aspects of items ordered, vessel inspections, exposure assessments, job safety analyses, mechanisms for employees to report hazardous conditions and review of occupational health and safety data and records to identify trends	
1	No system or requirement exists for hazard review of planned/changed/new equipment or operations. There are no requirements to consider occupational health and safety aspect of items purchased for the vessel. There is no evidence of comprehensive inspections for safety or health hazards, exposure assessments, routine job safety analysis or occupational health and safety data trend analysis.
2	The person-in-charge of operation and/or equipment changes considers occupational health and safety implications of the changes, but has not had appropriate training to be able to identify all occupational health and safety consequences of the changes. The person responsible for procurement considers occupational health and safety issues, but has not been trained on hazards that may be encountered. Inspections for occupational health and safety hazards are conducted by vessel and corporate personnel, but only in response to accidents or complaints. The employer has identified principal occupational health and safety standards appropriate for the vessel. Supervisors dedicate time to observing work practices and other occupational health and safety conditions in work areas where they have responsibility.
3	Competent person(s) determine occupational health and safety consequences of proposed changes in high-hazard operations or equipment before the changes occur, and appropriate precautions are implemented. Competent person(s) determine occupational health and safety hazards of all items procured, and appropriate precautions are taken when the item is used. Vessel and corporate personnel with specific training in occupational health and safety hazards conduct vessel inspections. Items in need of correction are documented. Inspections include compliance with relevant regulations, industry standards and practices. Time periods for corrections are set. Current hazard analyses are written (where appropriate) for all high-hazard jobs and processes; analyses are communicated to and understood by affected employees. Hazard analyses are conducted for jobs/tasks/workstations where injury or illnesses have been recorded.
4	Competent person(s) in consultation with a qualified professional determines occupational health and safety consequences of all proposed changes in operations or equipment before the changes occur, and appropriate precautions are implemented. Competent person(s) determine occupational health and safety hazards of all items requested for procurement, identify appropriate substitutions for hazardous items, or ensure appropriate precautions are taken if a substitute cannot be identified. A qualified professional conducted a vessel inspection within the last five years, and competent person(s), trained in items identified by the qualified professional, conduct periodic inspections and appropriate corrective actions are taken promptly. The inspections are planned, with key observations or check points defined and results documented. Corrections are documented through follow-up inspections. Results are available to workers. Current hazard analyses are documented for all work areas and are communicated and available to all employees.
5	Qualified professionals in consultation with certified occupational health and safety professional(s) analyse occupational health and safety consequences of all proposed changes in operations or equipment, identify substitutions if possible or ensure appropriate precautions are implemented as the change occurs. Competent person(s) in consultation with qualified professional(s) or certified occupational health and safety professional(s), as needed, identify occupational health and safety hazards of all items requested for procurement and obtain substitutes for hazardous items. Regular inspections are planned and overseen by certified safety or health professionals. Statistically valid random audits of compliance with all elements of the shipboard occupational health and safety programme are conducted. Observations are analysed to evaluate progress. Documented workplace hazard evaluations are conducted by certified occupational health and safety professional(s). Corrective action is documented and hazard inventories are updated.

HAZARD ANTICIPATION, IDENTIFICATION, EVALUATION AND CONTROL	
Control – General	
Workforce exposure to all current and potential hazards should be prevented or controlled by using engineering controls whenever feasible and appropriate, work practices and administrative controls, and personal protective equipment	
1	Hazard control is seriously lacking or absent from the vessel.
2	Hazard controls are generally in place, but effectiveness and completeness vary. Serious hazards may still exist. Employer has achieved general compliance with applicable standards regarding hazards with a significant probability of causing serious physical harm. Hazards that have caused past injuries on the vessel have been corrected.
3	Appropriate controls (engineering, work practice, and administrative controls, and PPE) are in place for significant hazards. Some serious hazards may exist. Employer is generally in compliance with voluntary standards, industry practices, and manufacturers' and suppliers' safety recommendations. Documented reviews determining the need for machine guarding, energy lockout, ergonomics programme. Materials handling procedures, blood-borne pathogen programme. Confined space entry programme. Hazard communication, and other generally applicable programmes have been conducted. The overall programme tolerates occasional deviations.
4	Hazard controls are fully in place, and are known and supported by the workforce. Few serious hazards exist. The employer requires strict and complete compliance with all applicable regulations, consensus standards and industry practices and recommendations. All deviations are identified and causes determined.
5	Hazard controls are fully in place and continually improved upon, based on workplace experience and general knowledge. Documented reviews of needs are conducted by certified occupational health and safety professionals.

HAZARD ANTICIPATION, IDENTIFICATION, EVALUATION AND CONTROL	
Control – Maintenance	
An effective shipboard occupational health and safety programme will provide for vessel and equipment maintenance, so that hazardous breakdowns are prevented	
1	No preventive maintenance programme is in place; breakdown maintenance is the rule.
2	There is a preventive maintenance schedule, but it does not cover everything and may be allowed to slide or performance is not documented. Safety devices on machinery and equipment are generally checked before each shift.
3	A preventive maintenance schedule is implemented for areas where it is most needed; it is followed under normal circumstances. Manufacturers' and industry recommendations and consensus standards for maintenance frequency are followed. Breakdown repairs for safety-related items are expedited. Safety device checks are documented. Ventilation system function is observed periodically.
4	The employer has effectively implemented a preventive maintenance schedule that applies to all equipment. Vessel experience is used to improve safety-related preventative maintenance scheduling.
5	There is a comprehensive safety and preventive maintenance programme that maximizes equipment reliability.

HAZARD ANTICIPATION, IDENTIFICATION, EVALUATION AND CONTROL	
Control – Medical Programme	
An effective shipboard occupational health and safety programme will include a suitable medical programme where it is appropriate for the nature of the hazards	
1	Management is unaware of, or unresponsive to, occupational medical surveillance needs. Required medical surveillance, monitoring and reporting are absent or inadequate.
2	Required medical surveillance, monitoring, removal, and reporting responsibilities for applicable standards are assigned and carried out, but results may be incomplete or inadequate.
3	Medical surveillance, removal, monitoring, and reporting comply with applicable standards. Employees report early signs/symptoms of job-related injury or illness and receive appropriate treatment.
4	Healthcare providers provide follow-up on employee treatment protocols and are involved in hazard identification and control on the vessel. Medical surveillance addresses conditions not covered by specific standards. Employee concerns about medical treatment are documented and responded to.
5	Healthcare providers periodically observe the work areas and activities and are fully involved in hazard identification and training.

HAZARD ANTICIPATION, IDENTIFICATION, EVALUATION AND CONTROL	
Control – Emergency Preparedness – Planning and Drills	
There should be appropriate planning, training/drills, and equipment for response to emergencies	
1	Little or no effort to prepare for emergencies.
2	Emergency response plans for fire, chemical, and weather emergencies as required by regulation are present. Training is conducted as required by the applicable regulation. Some deficiencies may exist.
3	Persons with specific training have prepared emergency response plans. Appropriate alarm systems are present. Employees are trained in emergency procedures. The emergency response extends to spills and incidents in routine operation. Adequate supply of spill control and PPE appropriate to hazards on ship is available.
4	Abandon-ship drills are conducted in accordance no less than annually. The plan is reviewed by a qualified occupational health and safety professional.
5	Vessel personnel with emergency response assignments have adequate training. All potential emergencies have been identified. Emergency response plans and performance are re-evaluated at least annually and after each significant incident. Procedures for terminating an emergency response condition are clearly defined.

HAZARD ANTICIPATION, IDENTIFICATION, EVALUATION AND CONTROL	
Control – Emergency Preparedness – First Aid	
First aid/emergency care should be readily available to minimize harm if an injury or illness occurs	
1	First aid/emergency care cannot be ensured.
2	First aid/emergency care is available on every shift.
3	Personnel with appropriate first aid skills commensurate with likely hazards on the vessel and as required by applicable regulations are available. Management documents and evaluates response time on a continuing basis.
4	Personnel with **certified** first aid skills are always available on-ship; their level of training is appropriate to the hazards of the work being done. Adequacy of first aid is formally reviewed after significant incidents.
5	Personnel trained in advanced first aid and/or emergency medical care are always available on ship.

OCCUPATIONAL HEALTH AND SAFETY TRAINING	
General	
Occupational health and safety training should cover the occupational health and safety responsibilities of all personnel who work on the vessel or affect its operations. It is most effective when incorporated into other training about performance requirements and job practices. It should include all subjects and areas necessary to address the hazards on the vessel	
1	Vessel personnel depend on experience and peer training to meet needs. Master/person-in-charge/others in supervisory positions demonstrate little or no involvement in occupational health and safety training responsibilities.
2	Some orientation training is given to new hires. Some safety training materials (e.g., pamphlets, posters, videotapes) are available or are used periodically at safety meetings, but there is little or no documentation of training or assessment of worker knowledge for a given topic. Masters/persons-in-charge and others in supervisory positions generally demonstrate awareness of occupational health and safety responsibilities, but have limited training themselves or involvement in the ship's training programme.
3	Training includes regulatory rights and access to information. Training required by regulations is provided to all vessel employees. Supervisors attend training in all subjects provided to employees under their direction. Vessel personnel can generally demonstrate the skills/knowledge necessary to perform their jobs safely. Records of training are kept and training is evaluated to ensure it is effective.
4	Knowledgeable persons conduct occupational health and safety training that is scheduled, assessed, and documented, and addresses all necessary technical topics. Employees are trained to recognize hazards, violations of regulations, and vessel practices. Employees are trained to report violations to management. Training is followed up with performance observation and feedback. All crew – including supervisors and masters/persons-in-charge – can demonstrate preparedness for participation in the overall occupational health and safety programme. There are easily retrievable scheduling and record-keeping systems.
5	Knowledgeable persons conduct occupational health and safety training that is scheduled, assessed, and documented. Training covers all necessary topics and situations, whether addressed in regulations or not, and includes all persons on the vessel (unlicensed personnel to the master or person-in-charge, contractors, and temporary employees). Employees participate in creating ship-specific training methods and materials. Employees are trained to recognize inadequate responses to reported programme violations. Retrievable record-keeping system provides for appropriate retraining, makeup training, and modifications to training as the result of evaluations.

	RECORD KEEPING
	Data Collection and Analysis
	*An effective shipboard occupational health and safety programme will collect and analyse injury, illness, and "near miss" incident data for indications of sources and locations of hazards, and jobs that experience higher numbers of incidents. By analysing injury, illness and "near miss" incident trends over time, patterns with common causes can be identified and prevented*
1	Little or no collection and/or analysis of injury, illness or "near miss" incident data. Exposure monitoring is not conducted or documented.
2	Injury, illness and "near miss" incident data are collected and analysed, but not widely used for prevention. Relevant forms are completed for all reportable marine casualties. Exposure records and analysis are organized and are available to safety personnel.
3	Injury, illness, and "near miss" incident logs and exposure records are kept, are audited by shoreside management personnel, and are essentially accurate and complete. Rates are calculated so as to identify high-risk areas and jobs. Liability claims are analysed and the results are used in the programme. Significant analytical findings are used for prevention.
4	Shoreside management and vessel master/person-in-charge and supervisors can identify the frequent and most severe problem areas, the high-risk areas and job classifications, and any exposures that exceed relevant or company standards. Data are fully analysed and effectively communicated to employees. Injury, illness and "near miss" incident data are audited and certified by a responsible person.
5	All levels of management and the workforce are aware of results of data analyses and resulting preventive activity. External audits of accuracy of injury, illness and "near miss" incident data, including review of all available data sources, are conducted. Scientific analysis of health information, including non-occupational databases, is included where appropriate in the programme.

	CONTRACT AND THIRD-PARTY PERSONNEL
	General
	An effective occupational health and safety programme protects all personnel on the vessel, including the employees of contractors, subcontractors and third-party personnel. It is the responsibility of shoreside management and the vessel master or person-in-charge to address contractor safety and third-party safety
1	Shoreside management and the vessel master or person-in-charge make no provision to include contractors and third-party personnel within the scope of the vessel's occupational health and safety programme.
2	Vessel safety policy requires contractor and third-party personnel to conform to applicable regulations and other legal requirements.
3	The master/person-in-charge designates a representative to monitor contractor and third-party occupational health and safety practices, and that individual has authority to stop contractor practices that expose host or contractor employees to hazards. Management informs contractor and employees of hazards present at the facility.
4	Shoreside management investigates a contractor's occupational health and safety record as one of the bidding criteria. Shoreside management contacts third-party personnel management if necessary to correct unsafe third-party behaviour.
5	The vessel's occupational health and safety programme ensures protection of everyone aboard, including full-time employees, temporary employees, contractors, and third-party personnel.

FATALITY, INJURY, ILLNESS AND INCIDENT INVESTIGATION	
General	
An effective shipboard occupational health and safety programme will provide for investigation of accidents and "near miss" incidents, so that their causes, and the means for their prevention, are identified	
1	No investigation of accidents, injuries, near misses, or other incidents is conducted.
2	Some investigation of incidents takes place, but root cause may not be identified, and correction may be inconsistent. Supervisors prepare injury reports for lost time incidents greater than 72 hours.
3	All "recordable incidents" are documented in a log. Reports are generally prepared with cause identification and corrective measures prescribed.
4	"Recordable incidents" are always investigated, and effective prevention is implemented. Reports and recommendations are available to employees. Trained safety personnel systematically review quality and completeness of investigations.
5	All loss-producing accidents and "near misses" are investigated for root causes by teams or individuals that include trained safety personnel and employees.

MSC/Circ.1116 of 2 June 2004

Unified interpretations of the IBC and IGC Codes

1   The Maritime Safety Committee, at its seventy-eighth session (12 to 21 May 2004), with a view to ensuring uniform application of the provisions of the IBC and IGC Codes containing vague wording which is open to diverging interpretations, approved the unified interpretations relating to cargo tank venting systems set out in the annex.

2   Member Governments are invited to use the annexed unified interpretations as guidance when applying relevant provisions of the IBC and IGC Codes for ships constructed on or after 1 July 2004 and to bring them to the attention of all parties concerned.

Annex
Unified interpretations of the IBC and IGC Codes*

International Code for the Construction and Equipment of Ships Carrying Dangerous Chemicals in Bulk (IBC Code)

Chapter 8
Cargo tank venting and gas-freeing arrangements

Paragraph 8.3.2 – By-passing of P/V valves

By-passing of P/V valves is allowed during cargo operations for cargoes which do not require a vapour return system, provided that the vent-line outlet is fitted with flame arresters and is located at the required height above the deck level. However, by-passing of high-velocity valves is not permitted.

Paragraph 8.3.3.2[†] – Area classification and selection of electrical equipment

1   Areas on an open deck, or semi-enclosed spaces on an open deck, within a vertical cylinder of unlimited height and 6 m radius centred upon the centre of the outlet, and within a hemisphere of 6 m radius below the outlet, which permit the flow of large volumes of vapour, air or inert gas mixtures during loading/discharging/ballasting are defined as Zone 1.

Permitted electrical equipment: Certified safe type equipment for Zone 1.

2   Areas within 4 m beyond the zone specified in paragraph 1 above are defined as Zone 2.

Permitted electrical equipment:

.1   certified safe type equipment for Zone 1;

.2   equipment of a type which ensures the absence of sparks, arcs and of "hot spots" during its normal operation;

.3   equipment having an enclosure filled with a liquid dielectric, when required by the application, or encapsulated;

.4   pressured equipment; and

.5   equipment specifically designed for Zone 2 (for example type "n" protection in accordance with IEC 60079-15).

---

* The interpretation of the IGC Code has been omitted from this publication.
† This corresponds with paragraph 8.3.4.2 of the IBC Code as amended in 2004 by resolutions MEPC.119(52) and MSC.176(79).

MSC/Circ.1095 of 18 June 2003

Revised minimum safety standards for ships carrying liquids in bulk containing benzene

1   The Maritime Safety Committee, at its sixty-first session (7 to 11 December 1992), recognized that chronic exposure to very low concentrations of benzene vapours in air, of the order of a few parts per million, may cause leukaemia.

2   The Committee, at its sixty-sixth session (28 May to 6 June 1996), desiring to protect the health of seafarers and to keep it at a level similar to that of shore-based workers engaged in similar tasks, approved MSC/Circ.752, by means of which it:

   .1   approved minimum safety standards for ships carrying mixtures the benzene content of which is 0.5 per cent or more; and

   .2   invited Member Governments to apply the standards as soon as possible.

3   The Committee, at its seventy-seventh session (28 May to 6 June 2003), noting that the diseases caused by the aforementioned exposure were still a source of great concern, agreed that MSC/Circ.752 was in need of revision, in particular with respect to cargo operations, which pose the largest risk of crew exposure to vapours from the products carried, and approved Revised minimum safety standards for ships carrying liquids in bulk containing benzene, as set out in the annex, which also includes an example of precautions to be given to the crew in connection with loading and gas-freeing operations.

4   Member Governments are invited to apply the annexed Revised minimum safety standards for ships carrying liquids in bulk containing benzene, including precautions to be given to the crew in connection with loading and gas-freeing operations appended thereto, as soon as possible.

5   MSC/Circ.752 is hereby revoked.

Annex
Revised minimum safety standards for ships carrying liquids in bulk containing benzene

Chronic exposure to very low concentrations of benzene vapours in air may *inter alia* cause leukaemia. In order to protect the health of seafarers to the same level as that of shore-based workers performing comparable tasks, measures should be taken for all ships carrying bulk liquids containing benzene the content of which is 0.5% or more by mass. The following measures should be included as indicated hereunder.

1 Information to the master

1.1 Prior to loading, the shipper should provide both to the master and the Company, as defined in the ISM Code, a Material Safety Data Sheet (MSDS), formatted in accordance with resolution MSC.150(77), for cargoes containing benzene.

1.2 The cargoes that may contain benzene are, for example, the cargoes listed in appendix I to Annex I to MARPOL 73/78, and the following bulk liquids:

.1 benzene and benzene mixtures;

.2 naphtha, varnish makers and paints (75%); and

.3 white spirit.

2 Information to the crew

2.1 It is the responsibility of the master and the Company that the crew is made aware of any work situation concerning operations involving liquids in bulk containing benzene that may impose a risk to their health. The crew should be informed of relevant safety precautions prior to cargo operations.

2.2 The appendix gives an example of precautions to be given to the crew in connection with loading and gas-freeing operations.

3 Occupational exposure limits*

3.1 Crewmember exposure to airborne concentrations of benzene vapours should be within the following limits:

.1 a Time-Weighted Average (TWA) of one part of benzene per million parts of air by volume (1 ppm), over an eight-hour period, which covers the time a person is assumed to work in any 24-hour period; and

.2 a Short-Term Exposure Limit (STEL) of five parts of benzene per million parts of air (5 ppm) over any 15-minute period.

4 Air quality monitoring

4.1 The airborne concentration of benzene vapour should be measured by a trained[†] and properly protected person with an approved instrument, before any crewmember is authorized to work in a given area. Such measuring should be continued whilst there is a risk of exposure to benzene vapours.

4.2 Alternative methods giving the same degree of safety may also be considered acceptable.

---

* Refer to the latest editions of the *Tanker Safety Guide (Chemicals)* (ICS) and the *International Safety Guide for Oil Tankers & Terminals (ISGOTT)* (ICS, OCIMF and IAPH).

[†] See also paragraph 8.

5 Personal protection

.1 Safety equipment

Ships carrying mixtures the benzene content of which is 0.5% or more should carry safety equipment equivalent to what is required in paragraph 14.2 of the IBC Code.

.2 Equipment for cargo operations on deck

Whenever direct or representative measurements indicate that the exposure limits are exceeded during normal cargo handling operations,* crew required to work in the affected area should wear appropriate respiratory equipment to be used in accordance with the manufacturers' instructions. Such equipment is indicated below;[†] however, the crewmember may select a higher level of protection:

.2.1 *Half face piece:* in areas where the airborne concentration of benzene vapours is expected to exceed 1 ppm but not more than 10 ppm;

.2.2 *Full face (filter) piece with cartridge:* in areas where the airborne concentration of benzene vapours is expected to exceed 10 ppm but not more than 50 ppm;

.2.3 *Air-supplied respirators:* in areas where the airborne concentration of benzene vapours is expected to exceed 50 ppm, but not more than 100 ppm;

.2.4 *Pressure-demand breathing apparatus and full protective clothing, resistant to chemical attack:*[‡] in areas where the airborne concentration of benzene is expected to be greater than 100 ppm; and

.2.5 *Personal protective equipment:* eye protection, impervious gloves and a protective apron should be readily available to crewmembers while sampling and gauging or when skin contact with the cargo is likely.

6 Maintenance of equipment for personal protection

The equipment for personal protection should be maintained and replaced in accordance with the manufacturers' instructions and in accordance with paragraph 14.2.6 of the IBC Code. Maintenance records should be kept on board.

7 Entering into enclosed spaces

Explicit instructions[§] from the master or a responsible officer are required before any entry into hazardous enclosed spaces. The hazards likely to be encountered should be evaluated and it should be ensured that all precautionary measures are taken. It should also be ensured that a responsible person is in attendance during the period of entry and while the space is occupied.

8 Training[**]

Crewmembers who might be exposed to benzene vapours should be given proper training, which should include:

.1 the respiratory hazard and the effect on the wearer if the respirator is not used properly;

.2 the engineering and administrative controls being used and the need for respirators to provide protection;

.3 the reason for selecting a particular type of respirator;

.4 the function, capabilities, and limitations of the selected respirator; and

.5 the method of donning the respirator and checking that it fits and is operational.

---

* The recommendations regarding air-purifying masks apply to operational uses of respiratory equipment for the purposes of protection during normal cargo handling operations and are not to be confused with those provisions specified in 14.3.1 of the IBC Code as amended by resolutions MEPC.119(52) and MSC.176(79).

† There are existing standards for respiratory protection equipment. These standards include: American National Standard for Respiratory Protection (ANSI Z88.2-1992); and the British Standard for Respiratory Protective Devices, Valved Filtering Half Masks to Protect Against Gases or Gases and Particles (BS EN 405:1993).

‡ Refer to SOLAS regulation II/2-19.

§ Refer to Recommendations for entering enclosed spaces aboard ships, adopted by the Organization by resolution A.864(20).

**Refer to the provisions of the International Convention on Standards of Training, Certification and Watchkeeping for Seafarers, 1978, as amended, and in particular to the "Mandatory minimum requirements for the training and qualification of masters, officers and ratings on tankers" – regulation V/1 of the annex to that Convention – and to section A-V/1 of the STCW Code (paragraphs 15 to 21).

---

9   Medical monitoring

Crewmembers potentially exposed to benzene vapour inhalation should be submitted to a programme of regular suitable medical checks on their health. The results of such checks should be kept on record under normal confidential practices in the medical profession.

10   Ship/shore connections

Prior to disconnecting, efficient and complete draining* and purging of all pipes, hoses and hard arms used for cargo handling should be ensured.

11   Precautions during cargo operations

Cargo loading, tank cleaning and gas-freeing are those procedures on board a tanker that expose the crew to the largest risk of exposure to vapours from the products carried, both in the accommodation and on open deck. It is, therefore, essential during these operations that all:

.1   openings to the accommodation are closed or battened down;

.2   ventilation in the accommodation is either re-circulated or shut down; and

.3   work on deck follows the provisions given in paragraph 5.2.

12   Controlled tank venting system

12.1   Vapours displaced from the tank during loading, tank cleaning, tank breathing and gas-freeing should be emitted through a controlled tank venting system complying with either SOLAS regulation II-2/16.3.2, or paragraph 8.3.2 of the IBC Code, or paragraph 2.14.2 of the BCH Code, as applicable.

12.2   Whenever a vapour emission control system is available ashore, vapours displaced from the tank during loading should be returned to that system (vapour return).

13   Cargo measurements and sampling

All cargo-related measurements (e.g., ullage, temperature and sampling) should be carried out in a closed mode to minimize the risk of exposing the crew and shore personnel to harmful vapours. When this is not possible, personal protection equipment should be worn.

14   Contaminated clothes

Working clothes should not be brought into the accommodation. Therefore, whenever possible, all working clothes should be removed and put in designated lockers prior to the crew entering the accommodation. The IBC Code, chapter 14, and the BCH Code, paragraph 3.16, deal extensively with personnel protection, including storage of protective equipment and working clothes.

---

* **Note:** In accordance with MARPOL regulation II/18(4) of Annex II as amended in 2004, drainage back into the cargo tanks is not allowed.

IBC CODE

Appendix
Example of precautions to be given to the crew in connection with loading and gas-freeing operations

1   All doors leading from the outside to the accommodation and to the engine-room should be closed and kept closed during these operations. Only one door on the windward side/nearest to the cargo control room* is to be used as an access.

2   All doors inside the accommodation shall be kept closed during the operation.

3   The ventilation to the accommodation shall be stopped/re-circulated* and the fire flaps kept closed.

4   Vapour concentrations on deck shall be measured prior to any work being undertaken.

5   The crew working on deck shall wear appropriate protective equipment.

6   Only work related to cargo handling is allowed on deck.

7   Presence of personnel in the engine-room shall be kept to a minimum during these operations.

8   Bring no working clothes into the accommodation.

---

* To be modified as appropriate to the actual ship.

Resolution MEPC.148(54)

adopted on 24 March 2006

Revised Guidelines for the transport of vegetable oils in deeptanks or in independent tanks specially designed for the carriage of such vegetable oils in general dry cargo ships

THE MARINE ENVIRONMENT PROTECTION COMMITTEE,

RECALLING article 38(a) of the Convention on the International Maritime Organization concerning the function of the Committee conferred upon it by international conventions for the prevention and control of marine pollution,

RECALLING ALSO resolution MEPC.118(52) by which it adopted the revised Annex II of the International Convention for the Prevention of Pollution from Ships, 1973, as modified by the Protocol of 1978 relating thereto (hereinafter referred to as "MARPOL 73/78"),

RECALLING FURTHER resolution MEPC.119(52) by which it adopted amendments to the International Code for the Construction and Equipment of Ships Carrying Dangerous Chemicals in Bulk (IBC Code),

CONSIDERING that the Maritime Safety Committee, at its seventy-second session, considered and approved the proposed amendments to the IBC Code with a view to adoption under the provisions of the International Convention for the Safety of Life at Sea, 1974 (1974 SOLAS Convention),

RECOGNIZING the current practices for the transport of vegetable oils in deeptanks in general dry cargo ships,

RECOGNIZING ALSO the current practices of the transport of vegetable oils in independent tanks specially designed to carry these vegetable oils on board of general dry cargo ships,

NOTING the need for the continuation of the current mode of transport of these vegetable oils on specifically identified trades, where the lack of availability of NLS tankers is demonstrated,

BEING CONVINCED that adequate precaution is needed to provide the protection of the marine environment at the level as required by Annex II of MARPOL 73/78, as amended,

1.   ADOPTS the revised Guidelines for the transport of vegetable oils in deeptanks or in independent tanks specially designed for the carriage of such vegetable oils in general dry cargo ships, the text of which is set out in the annex to this resolution;

2.   INVITES the Parties to note that the revised Guidelines supersede the Guidelines adopted by resolution MEPC.120(52) on 15 October 2004; and

3.   INVITES ALSO the Parties to note that the revised Guidelines shall take effect on 11 January 2007.

Annex
Guidelines for the transport of vegetable oils in deeptanks or in independent tanks specially designed for the carriage of such vegetable oils in general dry cargo ships

1   Preamble

1.1   The Guidelines have been developed to allow general dry cargo ships, which are currently certified to carry vegetable oil in bulk, to continue to carry these vegetable oils* on specific trades. These Guidelines only apply under the following conditions:

.1   the vegetable oils are carried in deeptanks or independent tanks in general dry cargo ships specifically designed for the carriage of such oils under an NLS Certificate issued before 1 January 2007;

.2   the products allowed to be carried are restricted to those unmodified vegetable oils (primarily triglycerides) which are listed in chapter 17 of the IBC Code, identified by a footnote (k) in *column e*; and

.3   the ship complies with all discharge requirements under Annex II to MARPOL 73/78.

1.2   The Guidelines have been developed in accordance with the provisions set forth in regulation 11.2 of Annex II to MARPOL 73/78 and in recognition of the need for standards which provide an alternative to the International Code for the Construction and Equipment of Ships Carrying Dangerous Chemicals in Bulk.

2   Carriage in deeptanks

2.1   An Administration may grant a relaxation for the carriage requirements, as required by the IBC Code, when vegetable oils are carried in deeptanks in general dry cargo ships between States for which it is demonstrated that, as a result of their geographical location, the transport of vegetable oils from the exporting State to the receiving State would not be viable using NLS tankers as required by Annex II to MARPOL 73/78. This relaxation shall be endorsed on the ship's Certificate. Such relaxation shall be communicated to the IMO by the Administration.

2.2   Every general dry cargo ship, falling under paragraph 2 of the Guidelines, shall be subject to Annex II to MARPOL 73/78 regarding the discharge requirements and the carriage of a Manual and shall be certified to carry vegetable oils by means of the issue of a certificate under regulation 10.1 of that Annex.

2.3   Before granting a relaxation, the Administration shall receive a confirmation in writing that both the Government of the country of loading and the Government of the country of unloading concur with the proposed relaxation. These confirmations shall be retained on board.

3   Carriage in independent tanks

3.1   An Administration may grant a relaxation for the carriage requirements as required by the IBC Code when vegetable oils are carried in independent tanks in general dry cargo ships specially designed for the carriage of these vegetable oils. This relaxation shall be endorsed on the ship's Certificate. Such relaxation shall be communicated to the IMO by the Administration.

3.2   The following criteria on construction and trade for such relaxation shall apply:

.1   the independent tanks shall be situated at least 760 mm from the shell plating; and

.2   such carriage of vegetable oils shall be restricted to specifically identified trades.

---

* The term "vegetable oils" is taken to mean "vegetable and fish oils and animal fats".

3.3   Every general dry cargo ship falling under paragraph 3 of the Guidelines shall be subject to Annex II to MARPOL 73/78 regarding the discharge requirements and the carriage of a Manual and shall be certified to carry vegetable oils by means of the issue of a certificate under regulation 10.1 of that Annex.

3.4   Before granting a relaxation, the Administration shall receive a confirmation in writing that both the Government of the country of loading and the Government of the country of unloading concur with the proposed relaxation. These confirmations shall be retained on board.

MEPC.1/Circ.512 of 16 May 2006

Revised Guidelines for the provisional assessment of liquid substances transported in bulk

1   Attached hereto are the revised Guidelines for the provisional assessment of liquid substances transported in bulk which were approved by the Marine Environment Protection Committee at its fifty-fourth session (20 to 24 March 2006). The present circular supersedes MEPC/Circ.265.

2   The Guidelines are revised as a consequence of the revision of Annex II to MARPOL 73/78 and the consequential amendments to the IBC Code.

3   The Guidelines provide step-by-step procedures for ascertaining the carriage requirements for all products offered for carriage in bulk.

4   Attention is drawn to the provisions of section 8 of the revised Guidelines which require that, when a provisional assessment has been made of a pure or technically pure product or mixture containing more than 1% by weight of unassessed components, the manufacturer should submit data to GESAMP/EHS. Based on the data submitted, the product will be evaluated by GESAMP/EHS. After receiving the complete GESAMP Hazard Profile, the manufacturer shall submit to the Administration a completed BLG Product Data Reporting Form including the proposed assessment for Pollution Category and Ship Type and carriage requirements. The Administration shall submit the form and a proposal for a new and complete entry in the IBC Code to IMO.

Annex
Guidelines for the provisional assessment of
liquid substances transported in bulk

Section 1: Introduction

1.1 The carriage of liquid substances in bulk is regulated by SOLAS 74 as amended and MARPOL 73/78 for safety and pollution prevention purposes.

1.2 Liquid cargoes which may be offered for shipment in bulk can be divided into the following groups:

.1 liquefied gases;

.2 oils; and

.3 noxious and non-noxious liquid substances, hereafter referred to as "products".

1.3 Liquefied gases are listed in chapter 19 of the IGC Code and their shipment is subject to the provisions of that Code.

1.4 "Oil" means petroleum in any form, including crude oil, fuel oil, sludge, oil refuse and refined products (other than those petrochemicals which are subject to the provisions of Annex II of the present Convention*) and, without limiting the generality of the foregoing, includes the substances listed in appendix I to MARPOL Annex I.

1.5 A number of products can be shipped either on gas carriers or on chemical tankers. They are included both in chapter 19 of the IGC Code, marked by an asterisk, and in chapter 17 of the IBC Code.

1.6 Each liquid substance offered for carriage in bulk should be identified as either a *liquefied gas*, or an *oil* or a *product*. These guidelines apply only to liquid substances identified as *products*.

1.7 The requirements for the carriage of products in bulk are defined in the IBC and BCH Codes. The IBC Code applies to chemical tankers built on or after 1 July 1986 and is mandatory under both SOLAS 74 as amended and MARPOL 73/78. The BCH Code applies to those built before 1 July 1986. The latter is mandatory under MARPOL 73/78 and recommended under SOLAS 74, as amended.

1.8 In the present guidelines, reference is made to the IBC Code only, for the sake of brevity; however, it implies reference to the BCH Code as well, as applicable.

1.9 The procedures described in the present guidelines are presented in diagram form in appendix 1.

Section 2: Assessed products

2.1 If a liquid substance is to be shipped as a product, the shipper should first check whether the product is listed in chapter 17 or 18 of the IBC Code, or in chapter 19 (Index of Products Carried in Bulk) or in the latest edition of MEPC.2/Circular.

2.2 A product must be shipped under the product name listed in chapter 17 or 18 of the IBC Code or in the latest edition of MEPC.2/Circular.

2.3 The products listed in the IBC Code are mainly pure or technically pure products, including their aqueous solutions.

2.4 The list of products in chapters 17 and 18 of the IBC Code will be updated in each consecutive edition.

---

* This refers to MARPOL 73/78.

2.5 The Index of Products Carried in Bulk (later referred to as "Index") gives most of the commonly used synonyms of the products listed in the IBC Code. The Index will also be updated in each consecutive edition of the IBC Code.

2.6 If the product is neither listed in chapter 17 or 18 of the IBC Code nor in the Index, the next step is to check the potential entries to chapters 17 and 18 of the IBC Code. Such a list is issued yearly (17 December) as List 1 of the MEPC.2/Circular. The same Circular also includes a list of pollutant-only mixtures classified by calculation or assessed as a mixture, List 2 (covered in section 5), a list of trade-named mixtures of assessed products with safety hazards, List 3 (covered in section 6) and a list of pollutant-only mixtures with >1% unassessed components, List 4 (covered in section 7).

2.7 If the product is neither listed in the IBC Code nor published in the MEPC.2/Circular, it is necessary to check whether the product has already been provisionally assessed by tripartite agreement by contacting the Organization.

2.8 If a product has already been assessed by tripartite agreement, any newly initiating shipping or producing country should review the basis of the previous assessment with a view to agreeing with the previous assessment. When carrying out this review, new data should be taken into account, if available, so an accurate assessment can be made in accordance with section 4.

2.9 If the shipping or producing country is already a Party to a provisional assessment of the product in question, of which one or more of the flag States and/or receiving countries are not Parties, the shipping or producing country will ask them to join in the existing agreement.

Section 3: Unassessed products

3.1 The products to be assessed can be divided into the following groups:

  .1 pure or technically pure products (see section 4);

  .2 pollutant-only mixtures containing at least 99% by weight of components already assessed by IMO (see section 5);

  .3 (trade-named) mixtures containing at least 99% by weight of components already assessed by IMO, presenting safety hazards (see section 6);

  .4 mixtures containing one or more components, forming more than 1% by weight of the mixture, which have not yet been assessed by IMO (see section 7).

3.2 The products or mixtures referred to in 3.1.1, 3.1.3 and 3.1.4 will be provisionally assessed by tripartite agreement, in accordance with regulation 6.3 of Annex II to MARPOL 73/78.

3.3 Mixtures in 3.1.2 will be assessed in a simplified manner. Due to the purely mechanical nature of such an assessment, it is not necessary for the shipping or producing country to seek the concurrence of the flag States and receiving countries (see section 5). Until the mixture is included in the MEPC.2/Circular, List 2, it is still necessary to inform the flag States and receiving countries on the assessment of the mixture. These mixtures will be shipped under the applicable generic entry to the IBC Code (i.e., Noxious Liquid (n.o.s.) or Non-Noxious Liquid (n.o.s.)).

3.4 Provisional assessments by tripartite agreement will expire after 3 years of publication in the MEPC.2/Circ. It is intended that, during this period, the product will be assessed by IMO (see section 8). After expiration of a tripartite agreement, no new tripartite agreement for the same product, even under a different name, shall be established.

3.5 It is in the best interest of the manufacturer/shipper to submit the data necessary for a provisional assessment to the Administration of the shipping or producing country well in advance of the shipment. The Administration should avoid unnecessary delays in initiating a tripartite agreement after receiving the complete set of information.

3.6 After the provisional assessment of the products in 3.1.1, 3.1.3 and 3.1.4 is completed, an addendum to the ship's Certificate of Fitness must be issued by the Administration of the flag State of the ship, before the ship sails. An example of an addendum is given in appendix 2.

3.7 Until full agreement for the provisional assessment among Governments involved has been reached, the products shall not be carried.

Section 4: Provisional assessment of pure or technically pure products

4.1   In case of pure or technically pure products, the Administration of the shipping or producing country should provisionally assess the Pollution Category, the Ship Type and the carriage requirements, on the basis of the pollution and safety data supplied by the manufacturer/shipper.

4.2   **Pollution aspects**

The following reference documents provide guidance for the Administration to assess the new product's pollution hazard:

.1   Guidelines for the Categorization of Noxious Liquid Substances (MARPOL 73/78, Annex II, appendix 1);

.2   Abbreviated Legend to the revised GESAMP Hazard Evaluation Procedure (MARPOL 73/78, Annex II, appendix 1); and

.3   Relevant parts of chapter 21 of the IBC Code: "Criteria for assigning carriage requirements for products subject to the IBC Code", from a marine pollution point of view.

4.3   The first step for the Administration is to check the latest Composite List of Hazard Profiles of substances carried by ships, issued periodically by IMO under cover of a BLG circular.

4.4   If a hazard profile can be found for the product in question, its Pollution Category should be derived from it in accordance with references 4.2.1. The Ship Type and carriage requirements, in so far as the pollution hazard is concerned, should be derived from references 4.2.3.

4.5   If no hazard profile exists, all the available data to establish a provisional one should be reviewed.

4.6   When adequate data are available, a provisional hazard profile should be derived, following the criteria developed by GESAMP/EHS (see reference 4.2.2). The provisional Pollution Category should be derived from this provisional hazard profile in accordance with 4.2.1. The Ship Type and carriage requirements, based upon its pollution hazard, should be derived in accordance with 4.2.3.

4.7   When sufficient data are not available, the Administration should make an assessment by analogy to chemically similar substances from the following sources:

.1   the IBC Code including the Index;

.2   the MEPC.2/Circular referred to in paragraph 2.5, listing the substances assessed by IMO and those provisionally assessed by tripartite agreement; and

.3   the BLG circular referred to in paragraph 4.3, listing the substances for which a hazard profile exists.

When several alternative analogies are possible, the most severe should prevail.

Safety aspects

4.8   After assessment of the pollution hazards, the possible safety hazards of the product should be assessed.

4.9   For this assessment, reference is made to the relevant parts of chapter 21 of the IBC Code: "Criteria for assigning carriage requirements for products subject to the IBC Code", from a safety point of view.

4.10   If the product to be provisionally assessed presents a safety hazard, the Administration should assign carriage requirements in accordance with the above-mentioned criteria. These requirements have to be integrated with those previously assigned for pollution prevention purposes only and the most stringent set has to be adopted. If necessary, the Administration should revise the Ship Type previously assigned for pollution considerations only.

Administrative aspects

4.11   At this point, the Administration of the shipping or producing country, having provisionally assessed the product in question, should seek the concurrence of the Administrations of the Flag State(s) and receiving countries with its evaluation, by providing information on which the provisional pollution and safety hazard assessment has been based. For this purpose, the standard format for proposing tripartite agreements for the provisional assessment of liquid substances, reproduced in appendix 3, should be used.

4.12 In the absence of an interim or final response to the notification from any of the other Parties involved within 14 days of the despatch, the proposed provisional assessment made by the Administration of the shipping or producing country should be deemed to have been accepted. In this respect it should be noted that those contact points which have not informed the Organization of their latest contact details should be deemed to have accepted the tripartite agreements whilst other contact points should still follow regulation 6(3) of Annex II of MARPOL 73/78 and these guidelines (reference is made to resolution MEPC.109(49)).

4.13 In the event of disagreement, the most severe conditions proposed should prevail to obtain the tripartite agreement.

4.14 After express or tacit agreement has been reached, the proposing Administration should inform IMO, as required by regulation 6.3 of Annex II (i.e., within 30 days but preferably as soon as possible). It is recommended to use the format, referred to in 4.11, for this purpose.

4.15 After establishing a tripartite agreement, an addendum to the relevant ship's certificate may be issued.

4.16 The manufacturer should then promptly forward to GESAMP/EHS all data necessary for a formal hazard evaluation (see section 8).

Section 5: Assignment of pollutant-only mixtures containing products already assessed by IMO

5.1 This section deals with the mixtures defined in paragraph 3.1.2, i.e. those presenting no safety hazard and containing at least 99% wt of products assessed by IMO. Those products assessed by IMO are limited to:

.1 those listed in chapters 17 and 18 of the IBC Code;

.2 those listed in List 1 of the MEPC.2/Circular without an expiry date; and

.3 those listed in List 5 of the MEPC.2/Circular.

Such a mixture may contain components with safety hazards (designated by "S" or "S/P" in *column d* in chapter 17 of the IBC Code) as long as they are so diluted that the final mixture presents no safety hazard.

5.2 The Pollution Category and the Ship Type of these mixtures are derived from the GESAMP Hazard Profiles of the components by the calculation method in 5.3 and 5.4. For the purpose of this calculation, unassessed components up to 1% should be assigned the component factor of 10,000 for pollution categorization. For the assignment of the Ship Type the component factor is 100.

5.3 **Calculation of the Pollution Category**

The first step is to establish the Pollution Category of the mixture by the following procedure:

.1 identify the revised GESAMP Hazard Profile (GHP) of each component from the latest edition of the BLG Circulars;

.2 multiply the concentration of each identified component in the mixture, expressed in percent by weight, by the factor associated with its GHP, taking the ratings resulting in the highest component factor into account, using table 1;

.3 Add the resultant multiples to obtain the value S_p

$$S_p = \Sigma \text{ (Each component \% wt)} \times \text{(Each component factor)}$$

X $S_p \geq 25,000$
Y $S_p < 25,000$ and $S_p \geq 25$
Z $S_p < 25$ unless all individual components are OS
OS a mixture where all individual components are OS

Mineral oil*: component factor for diluent mineral oil in lube oil additives = 100

---

* Most lube oil additive components are produced in mineral oil and have been assessed as produced. Sometimes more mineral oil is added to a mixture to make it pumpable. This is called "diluent mineral oil".

Table 1

Row	Rule No. (Guidelines for categorization, app. 1 to Annex II)	A1	A2	B1	B2	D3	E2	Component factor	Row
a	1	≥4	NR	≥6				100,000	a
b	1	≥4		≥6				100,000	b
c	1		NR	≥6				100,000	c
d	4	≥4	NR			CMRTNI		25,000	d
e	1			≥6				10,000	e
f	1	≥4	NR	5				10,000	f
g	1	≥4		5				10,000	g
h	1		NR	5				10,000	h
i	1			5				1,000	i
j	2	≥4	NR	4				1,000	j
k	2	≥4		4				1,000	k
l	3		NR	4				1,000	l
m	5			4				100	m
n	11					CMRTNI		25	n
o	6			3				10	o
p	7			2				1	p
q	8	≥4	NR		Not 0			1	q
r	9				≥1			1	r
s	10						Fp, F or S if not inorganic	1	s
t	12	Any product not meeting the criteria of rules 1 to 11 and 13						0	t
u	13	Any OS substance						0	u

5.4 Calculation of the Ship Type

The next step is to establish the Ship Type of the mixture by the following procedure:

.1 identify the Ship Type of each component from the IBC Code or the MEPC.2/Circular;

.2 multiply the concentration of each component in the mixture, expressed in percent by weight, by the factor associated to its Ship Type according to the following table 2;

Table 2

Ship Type	Factor
1	1,000
2	100
3	10
NA	0
Diluent mineral oil in lube oil additives	10

.3 add the resultant multiples to obtain the value "S_s";

.4 refer to the left-hand column of the flow chart for determining Ship Types and identify the row that corresponds to the value of "S_s"; and

.5 read across this row, answering the relevant questions in the middle column, to determine the Ship Type for the mixture, as shown in the right-hand column.

Flow chart for determining Ship Types

Sum of multiples	Question	Answer	Resulting Ship Type
$S_s \geq 10,000$	Is the sum of ST 1 multiples $\geq 10,000$?	Yes→ No→	1 2
$10,000 > S_s \geq 1,000$	Is the sum of ST 1 & 2 multiples $\geq 1,000$?	Yes→ No→	2 3
$1,000 > S_s \geq 100$			3
$S_s < 100$	Is the Pollution Category of the mixture X or Y?	Yes→ No→	3 NA

5.5 Examples of the calculation of the Pollution Category and the Ship Type of mixtures are given in appendix 6.

5.6 On the basis of the Pollution Category and Ship Type so calculated and of its flashpoint, a mixture is then assigned to the appropriate "Noxious (or non-noxious) liquid, n.o.s." generic entry to the IBC Code with the corresponding carriage requirements.

5.7 A mixture is designated in the shipping document by reference to the appropriate generic n.o.s. entry to the IBC Code, completed by the indication of a trade name and of one component responsible for the assigned Pollution Category. Trade names should not be such as to be confused with generally used chemical descriptions. Components should be identified by their name in either the IBC Code or the MEPC.2/Circular, List 1.

5.8 With reference to the diluent mineral oil which could be responsible for the final Pollution Category being assigned to a lube oil additive mixture, the designation of the mixture should include "contains mineral oil".

5.9 The process of assigning a pollutant-only mixture of assessed components to one of the generic n.o.s. entries to the IBC Code is of a purely mathematical nature and does not involve any assessment whatsoever. In the interest of facilitating shipments, the Administration may authorize the manufacturer to carry out the assignment on its behalf.

5.10 In this case, the obligation to inform the flag States and the receiving countries of the performed assignment falls on the delegated manufacturer. The manufacturer should also inform IMO if so requested by the authorizing Administration. Notification of the assignment by the manufacturer should be accompanied by the authorization letter indicating that the manufacturer acts under instruction and on behalf of the Administration until such authorization is recorded in the MEPC.2/Circular. After notification, the mixture shall be recorded in the next edition of the MEPC.2/Circular, List 2.

5.11 The manufacturer should inform the authorizing Administration of the assignment performed along with the details of the assignment. Upon request, the manufacturer should also provide the flag State and/or the receiving country with details of the mixture assignment.

Section 6: Assessment of trade-named mixtures presenting safety hazards containing only products already assessed by IMO

6.1 This section deals with the mixtures defined in paragraph 3.1.3, i.e. those presenting a safety hazard (one or more of the components designated by S or S/P) and containing at least 99% wt of products assessed by IMO.

Products assessed by IMO are limited to:

.1 those listed in chapters 17 and 18 of the IBC Code; and

.2 those listed in List 1 of the MEPC.2/Circular without an expiry date; and

.3 those listed in List 5 of the MEPC.2/Circular.

These mixtures contain components with safety hazards (designated by an "S" or "S/P" in *column d* of chapter 17 of the IBC Code) to such an extent that they impart a safety hazard to the final mixture.

6.2 The Pollution Category of these mixtures is calculated, as shown in paragraph 5.3.

6.3 A tentative Ship Type, for pollution prevention purposes only, is then calculated, as shown in paragraph 5.4.

6.4 The Administration should then provisionally assess the safety hazards of the mixture and assign carriage requirements. The minimum carriage requirement of each column in the Code is determined by selecting the most stringent requirement of the components present in the mixture, unless the Administration is satisfied that safe carriage is ensured by less stringent conditions. The hazards of the mixture must not exceed the hazards of any individual component (synergistic effects). If necessary, the Administration should revise the tentative Ship Type assigned in paragraph 6.3.

6.5 These mixtures, presenting safety hazards, cannot be shipped under Noxious Liquid n.o.s. generic entries in the IBC Code. Therefore, an appropriate shipping name will need to be assigned to the mixture. This will identify the principal substances responsible for the safety and pollution (if applicable) hazards of the mixture and may include its trade name.

6.6 The Administration should now proceed to obtain a tripartite agreement and to inform IMO, as indicated in paragraphs 4.11, 4.12, 4.13 and 4.14. The provisional assessment will be valid for three years.

6.7 The shipping name, Pollution Category, Ship Type and carriage requirements provisionally assigned by tripartite agreement will be evaluated by IMO based on information in the BLG Product Data Reporting Form submitted by the Administration of the producing or shipping country for final inclusion of the mixture in the MEPC.2/Circular, List 3, without an expiry date.

Section 7: Assessment of mixtures containing one or more components which have not yet been assessed by IMO

7.1 This section deals with the mixtures defined in paragraph 3.1.4, i.e., those containing one or more components, forming more than 1% wt of the mixture, which have not yet been assessed by IMO and therefore are not listed in either chapter 17 or 18 of the IBC Code, or in the MEPC.2/Circular.

7.2 There are two alternative ways of assessing these mixtures:

.1 If sufficient data are available on the mixture as a whole, it should be assessed as if it were a pure or technically pure product, as shown in section 4.

.2 If sufficient data on the mixture as a whole are not available, the producing or shipping country Administration should first provisionally assess each unassessed component according to section 4 and then assess the mixture by calculation, as shown in section 5 for a pollutant-only mixture and section 6 for trade-named mixtures presenting safety hazards.

7.3 **Mixtures presenting pollution hazards only**

7.3.1 After provisional assessment by tripartite agreement, pollutant-only mixtures containing unassessed components will be shipped under one of the "Noxious (or non-noxious) liquid, n.o.s." generic entries to the IBC Code, without the need for an addendum to the ship's Certificate of Fitness.

7.3.2 The Administration of the producing or shipping country should inform IMO on the results of the tripartite agreement within 30 days. The results will be included in the next edition of the MEPC.2/Circular, List 4.

7.3.3 The manufacturer will forward to GESAMP/EHS the available data on the mixture as a whole in the case of 7.2.1 or on each individual unassessed component in the case of 7.2.2, in order to assess the respective Hazard Profiles. This should be done as soon as possible, using the format reproduced in annex 8.

7.4 Mixtures presenting safety hazards

7.4.1 When an unassessed component shows safety hazards, the Administration of the producing or shipping country should follow the procedure set out in section 4, as if the component is to be shipped as a pure or a technically pure product.

7.4.2 When a tripartite agreement is reached for the component in 7.4.1, follow the procedure set out in section 6.

7.4.3 Provisionally assessed mixtures presenting safety hazards will be included in the List 3 of MEPC.2/ Circular with an expiry date of three years.

7.5 The manufacturer will forward to GESAMP/EHS the available data on the mixture as a whole in the case of 7.2.1 or on each individual unassessed component in the case of 7.2.2, in order to assign the respective Hazard Profiles. This should be done as soon as possible, using the format reproduced in annex 8.

Section 8: Submission of data to GESAMP/EHS and IMO

8.1 As soon as possible after a provisional assessment has been made of a pure or technically pure product or of a mixture containing more than 1% by weight of unassessed components, the manufacturer should submit to the GESAMP/EHS* Technical Secretariat the data required to develop a hazard profile of the substance or component or mixture, using the format shown in annex 7 of GESAMP Reports and Studies No. 64.

8.2 After receiving the complete GESAMP Hazard Profile, the manufacturer shall submit to the Administration a completed BLG Product Data Reporting Form based on the assessed product by GESAMP/EHS and, where possible, including the proposed assessment for Pollution Category and Ship Type and carriage requirements. The Administration should submit a proposal including the form for a new and complete entry in the IBC Code to IMO. A format of the BLG Product Data Reporting Form is shown in appendix 4 and can be downloaded from www.imo.org *click on* Marine Environment *click on* Chemicals reporting forms *click on* BLG Product Data Reporting Form.

8.3 Unless such a substance, component or mixture has been evaluated by the GESAMP/EHS and IMO in the meantime, its provisional assessment by tripartite agreement will cease to be valid three years after the date of publication in the MEPC.2/Circular. After expiration of a tripartite agreement, no new tripartite agreement for the same product, even under a different name, shall be established.

---

* The completed form should be sent to:
  The Technical Secretary of GESAMP/EHS Working Group
  International Maritime Organization (IMO)
  4 Albert Embankment
  London SE1 7SR
  United Kingdom

Appendix 1
Scheme 1

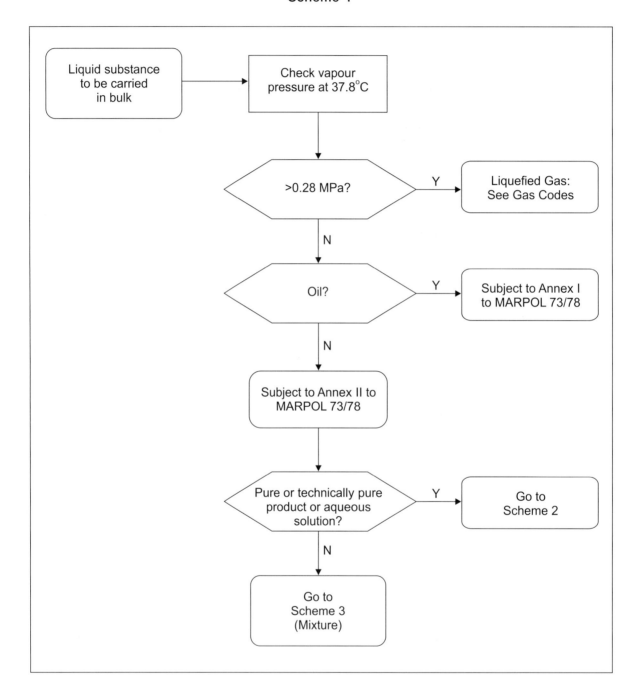

Scheme 2

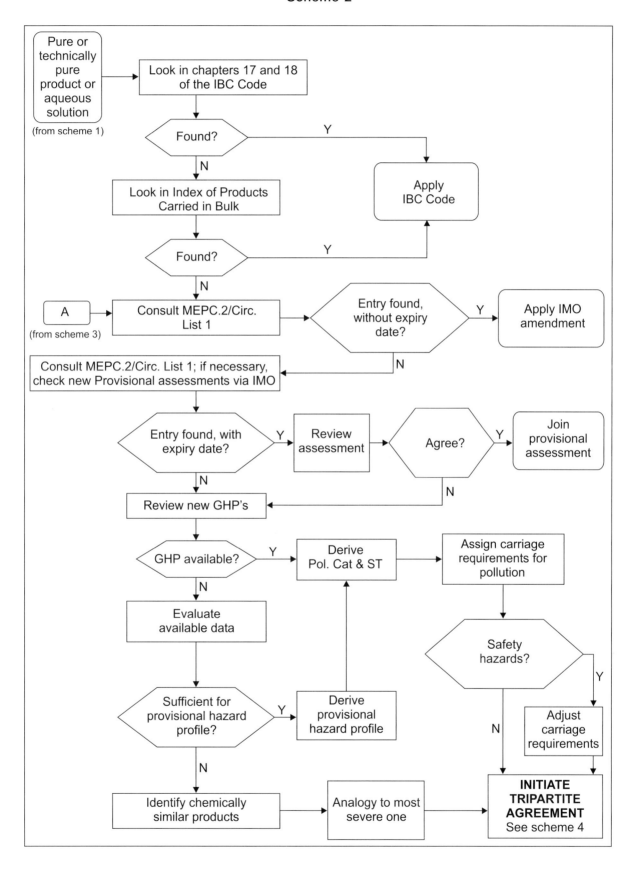

Scheme 3

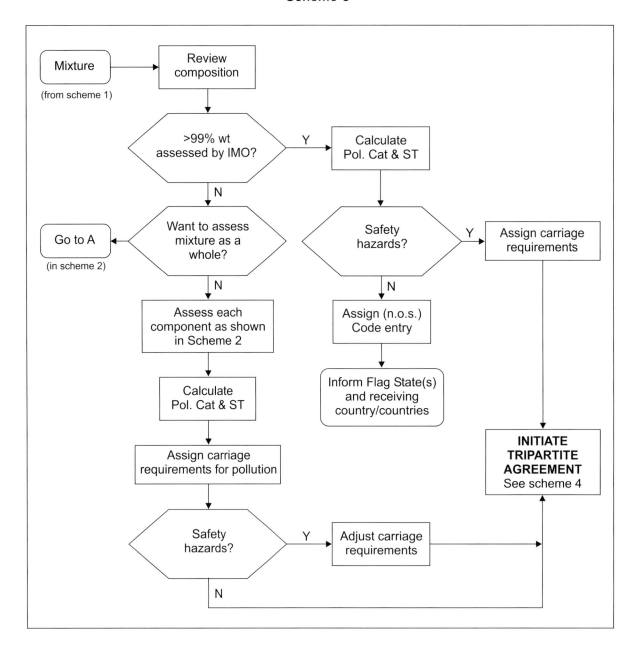

Scheme 4

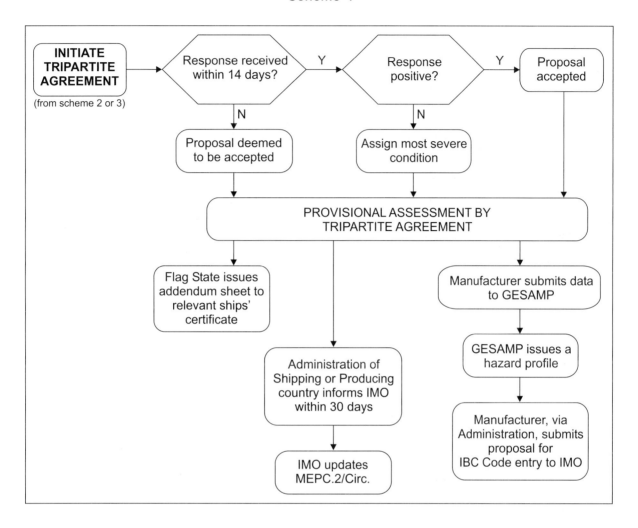

Appendix 2
*Example of an addendum to the ship's Certificate of Fitness/ International Certificate of Fitness/International Pollution Prevention Certificate for the Carriage of Noxious Liquid Substances in Bulk**

Addendum to Certificate No.: . . . . Issued at: *(dd/mm/yyyy)* . . . .

Issued in pursuance of the Code for the Construction and Equipment of Ships Carrying Dangerous Chemicals in Bulk/International Code for the Construction and Equipment of Ships Carrying Dangerous Chemicals in Bulk/Annex II to MARPOL 73/78 as amended* under the authority of the Government of:

. . . .

Name of Ship	Distinctive Number or Letters	IMO Number	Port of Registry	Gross Tonnage	Ship Type

THIS IS TO CERTIFY:

That the ship meets the requirements for the carriage in bulk of the following product(s), provided that all relevant operational provisions of the Code/Annex II of MARPOL 73/78* are observed:

Noxious Liquid Substance/Product*	Conditions of carriage (tank numbers, etc.)	Pollution Category

The transportation of this product is permitted between the following countries: . . . .

. . . .

The issuance of this Addendum is based on document: . . . .

The Tripartite Agreement for this product is valid until: *(dd/mm/yyyy)* . . . .

This Addendum will remain in force until: *(dd/mm/yyyy)* . . . .

Place and date of issue: *(dd/mm/yyyy)* . . . .

Signed . . . .
(signature of authorized official)

---

* Delete as appropriate.

Appendix 3
Format for proposing tripartite agreements for provisional assessment of liquid substances
(for insertion in lists 1, 3 or 4 of the MEPC.2/Circ.)

Name of Product: ....

proposed for inclusion in list: .... of MEPC.2/Circ. .....

Proposed pollution hazard profile:

A1	A2	B1	B2	D3	E2

Pollution hazard profile based on: .... by analogy to ....

resulting in proposed Pollution Category: .... and Ship Type (pollution hazard): ....

Additional information regarding pollution aspects:

    Melting/pour point: .... $^{\circ}$C (specify): ....

    Viscosity (mPa·s) at 20°C: ....

Safety information:

Vapour pressure (Pa): .... at .... $^{\circ}$C   Boiling point: .... $^{\circ}$C

Flashpoint (c.c): .... $^{\circ}$C

Density: .... (kg/m^3)

Relevant toxicity: Acute inhalation toxicity* (LC$_{50}$; mg/ℓ/4 h): ....

                   Acute dermal toxicity (LD$_{50}$; mg/kg): ....

                   Acute oral toxicity (LD$_{50}$; mg/kg): ....

                   Corrosivity to skin (skin necrosis): ....

Chemical properties: Solubility in water (mg/ℓ): ....

                   Autoignition temperature: ....$^{\circ}$C

                   Explosive/flammability range (% v/v): ....

                   Hazardous reaction control necessary: ....water

                   Corrosive to steel: ....

Column		Column		Column	
d		i$'$		l	
e†		i$''$		m	-deleted-
f		i$'''$		n	
g		j		o	
h		k			

---

* The criteria for inhalation toxicity are base on LC$_{50}$ data relating to 4-hour exposures: where such information is available it should be used. Where LC$_{50}$ data relating to 1-hour exposures are available, such values can be divided by 4 to be considered equivalent to LC$_{50}$ (4 h).

† Ship Type may have been overruled by safety aspects.

Appendix 4
BLG Product Data Reporting Form
(Characteristics of Products proposed for Bulk Marine Transport)

1   Product Identity

Product Name:

The product name shall be used in the shipping document for any cargo offered for bulk shipments. Any additional name may be included in brackets after the product name.

1.1   Other Names and Identification Numbers

Main Trade Name:

Main Chemical Name:

Chemical Formula:

C.A.S. Number:	Structure
EHS Number:	
BMR Number:	
RTECS Number:	

1.2   Associated Synonyms

Synonym Name	Type

1.3   Composition

Component Name	%	Type

2 Physical Properties

Property	Units	Qual.	Lower Value	Upper Value	References and Comments
Molecular weight					
Density @ 20°C	(kg/m^3)				
Flashpoint (cc)	(°C)				
Boiling Point	(°C)				
Melting Point/Pour Point	(°C)				
Water solubility @ 20°C	(mg/l)				
Viscosity @ 20°C	(mPa·s)				
Vap. Press. @ 20°C	(Pa)				
Autoignition Temp.	(°C)				
Explosion Limits	(% v/v)				
Carriage Temperature	(°C)				
Unloading Temperature	(°C)				
MESG	(mm)				

3 Relevant Chemical Properties

Water Reactivity Index   (0–2)   . . . . .

0 = No Reactivity	**Details** . . . .
1 = Reactive	. . . .
2 = Highly Reactive	. . . .

Does the product react with air to cause a potentially hazardous situation? (Y/N) ☐

If so, provide details . . . .

Reference . . . .

Is an Inhibitor or Stabilizer needed to prevent a hazardous reaction? (Y/N) ☐

If so, provide details . . . .

Reference . . . .

Is refrigeration needed to prevent a hazardous reaction? (Y/N) ☐

If so, provide details . . . .

Reference . . . .

4 Mammalian Toxicity

4.1 Acute Toxicity

	Qual.	Lower Value	Upper Value	Species	Reference/ Comments
Oral LD_{50} (mg/kg)					
Dermal LD_{50} (mg/kg)					
Inhalation LD_{50} (mg/l/4 h)					

4.2 Corrosivity and Irritation

	Qual.	Lower Value	Upper Value
Skin Corrosion time (hours)			

	Resultant observation	Species	Reference/ Comments
Skin Irritation (4 h exposure)			
Eye Irritation			

Not irritating, Slightly irritating, Mildly irritating, Moderately irritating, Severely irritating or Corrosive

4.3 Sensitization

Respiratory Sensitizer
(in humans)   (Y/N)   ☐   ....

Skin Sensitization   (Y/N)   ☐   ....

4.4 Other Specific Long-Term Effects

Carcinogen   (Y/N)   ☐   ....

Mutagen   (Y/N)   ☐   ....

Toxic to Reproduction (Y/N)   ☐   ....

Other Long-term   (Y/N)   ☐   ....

4.5 Other Relevant Mammalian Toxicity

....

....

5 GESAMP Hazard Profiles and Carriage Requirements

5.1 GESAMP Hazard Profiles

Column	Property	Value
A1	Bioaccumulation	
A2	Biodegradation	
B1	Acute Aquatic Toxicity	
B2	Chronic Aquatic Toxicity	
C1	Acute Oral Toxicity	
C2	Acute Dermal Toxicity	
C3	Acute Inhalation Toxicity	
D1	Skin Irritation/Corrosivity	
D2	Eye Irritation/Corrosivity	
D3	Specific Health Concerns	
E1	Tainting and Odour	
E2	Wildlife and Seabeds	
E3	Beaches and Amenities	
F	Remarks	

5.2 Proposed Carriage Requirements

Column in the IBC Code	Property	Value
c	Pollution Category	
d	Safety/Pollution Properties	
e	Ship Type	
f	Tank Type	
g	Tank Vents	
h	Tank Environmental Control	
i′	Electrical Equipment – Class	
i″	Electrical Equipment – Group	
i‴	Electrical Equipment – Flashpoint >60°C	
j	Gauging	
k	Vapour Detection	
l	Fire Protection	
n	Emergency Escape	
o	Special Requirements	

Appendix 5
Guidelines on the completion of the BLG Product Data Reporting Form

1   General comments applicable to all sections of the BLG Product Data Reporting Form

1.1   Most properties have the following boxes associated with them:

.1   **Qual.:** This is used to provide additional information about the reported value when required. The data used to complete this box must be selected from the following:

blank	No qualification is necessary or appropriate as it is deemed to mean '='
>	Greater than
<	Less than
~	Approximately
E	Estimated (this can be used with any of the other qualifiers)
NF	Non-Flammable (used for flashpoint, autoignition temperature and explosion limits to show that the product is not hazardous).

.2   **Lower Value:** Where only one value exists, it should be put in this box. Where there is a range of values, the lower value should be put in this box, e.g., mixtures or impure products have a boiling range rather than a boiling point and so the initial boiling point is put in the **Lower Value** and the dry point is put in the **Upper Value**. For most purposes, the **Lower Value** will be used and is normally the only one that must be completed, though for **Explosion Limits**, both the **Lower Value** and the **Upper Value** are necessary.

.3   **Reference and Comments:** This should be completed so that the source of data can be traced. This may be a reference to company information, open literature or justification for an estimated value, e.g. read across from a similar chemical.

2   Section 1: Product Identity

2.1   This section serves to provide as much identification of the product as possible. It is recognized that some of the boxes may not be relevant, such as the Chemical Abstract Services Number (C.A.S. Number) that is normally only applicable to technically pure products or process streams. However, it is advisable to complete this section as much as possible as it facilitates the classification process and provides a mechanism for checking that the product has not been processed under a different name.

2.2   **EHS Number:** This is the reference number issued and used by the GESAMP/EHS Working Group to identify every chemical in its Composite List of products that it has evaluated.

2.3   **BMR Number:** This is the reference number issued and used by IMO to identify every chemical in the IBC Code and the Tripartite Agreements listed in MEPC.2/Circulars.

2.4   **Associated Synonyms:** These are product names, other than those identified in the boxes for **Main Trade Name**, **Main Chemical Name** and **Product Shipping Name**; they tend to be less common names and should be described in the **Type of Name** section.

2.5   Synonyms in the official languages of IMO should also be included where possible.

2.6   **Composition:** This section shall be used to include components of mixtures and impurities of any product; each entry in this section should include the percentage and Type (described as either C (Component) or I (Impurity)). In situations where this information is confidential, the data should be provided separately to the Reporting State.

3   Section 2: Physical Properties

3.1   It is important to recognize that, unless otherwise indicated, **ALL** the physical properties of the product referred to in this section have to be completed in order to enable the correct carriage requirements to be assigned.

3.2   Special attention should be given to paragraph 1.1 of these guidelines when completing this section on physical properties.

3.3   The additional specific notes are applicable to the physical properties section:

.1   If the product is not flammable then put 'NF' in the **Qual.** box for flashpoint, autoignition temperature, explosion limits and maximum experimental safe gap (MESG).

.2   If the flashpoint is >200°C and the autoignition temperature has not been measured, it may safely be estimated as >200°C, which is the cut-off point for defining a product as subject to chapter 17 of the IBC Code.

.3   For products which do not have a clear melting point, the pour point is regarded as being equivalent. In these cases the reference should include the term '(pour point)'.

4   Section 3: Relevant Chemical Properties

Water Reactivity Index

4.1   This parameter is an indication of the product's reactivity with water which will result in a hazard. As there are no quantitative definitions for this property, the following guidelines are provided with examples given that can be used for purposes of comparison:

WRI = 2   Applies to any chemical which, in contact with water, may produce a toxic, flammable or corrosive gas or aerosol.

WRI = 1   Applies to any chemical which, in contact with water, may generate heat, producing a non-toxic, non-flammable or non-corrosive gas.

WRI = 0   Applies to any chemical which, in contact with water, would not undergo a reaction to justify a value of 1 or 2.

Appendix 6
Example of the calculation method

Examples of determination of Pollution Categories for mixtures

Working Method

Step 1

Determine for each component the applicable row in Table 1, by means of its hazard profile, taken from the GESAMP/EHS Composite List. This will determine the component factor.

Step 2

Multiply the component factor with the percentage of the component in the mixture. This will result in the value S_p.

Step 3

Add all resultant S_p values and determine the Pollution Category.

Example 1

Steps 1 and 2

The amount of component 1 is 11% of the mixture; its GESAMP hazard profile, taken from the GESAMP/EHS Composite List, is:

A1	A2	B1	B2	D3	E2
4	NR	6			

This leads to *row a* in Table 1. The component factor is 100,000, the multiple is 1,100,000.

The amount of component 2 is 67% of the mixture; its GESAMP hazard profile, taken from the GESAMP/EHS Composite List, is:

A1	A2	B1	B2	D3	E2
4	NR	1	1		

This leads to *row q* in Table 1. The component factor is 1, the multiple is 67.

The amount of component 3 is 22% of the mixture; its GESAMP hazard profile, taken from the GESAMP/EHS Composite List, is:

A1	A2	B1	B2	D3	E2
	R	3			

This leads to *row o* in Table 1. The component factor is 10, the multiple is 220.

Step 3

$S_p = 1,100,287$
$S_p => 25,000$
The mixture is therefore Pollution Category X

Component number	Applicable row in Table 1	Component factor (C_p)	%	Multiple ($C_p \times$ %)	Resultant Pollution Category
1	a	100,000	11	1,100,000	
2	q	1	67	67	**X**
3	o	10	22	220	
S_p				1,100,287	

Example 2

Steps 1 and 2

The amount of component 1 is 11% of the mixture; its GESAMP hazard profile, taken from the GESAMP/EHS Composite List, is:

A1	A2	B1	B2	D3	E2
		5		C	

This leads to *row i* in Table 1. The component factor is 1,000, the multiple is 11,000.

The amount of component 2 is 67% of the mixture; its GESAMP hazard profile, taken from the GESAMP/EHS Composite List, is:

A1	A2	B1	B2	D3	E2
4	NR		1		

This leads to *row q* in Table 1. The component factor is 1, the multiple is 67.

The amount of component 3 is 22% of the mixture; its GESAMP hazard profile, taken from the GESAMP/EHS Composite List, is:

A1	A2	B1	B2	D3	E2
		3			

This leads to *row o* in Table 1. The component factor is 10, the multiple is 220.

Step 3

$S_p = 11,287$
$S_p < 25,000$ and $S_p \geq 25$
The mixture is therefore category Y

Component number	Applicable row in Table 1	Component factor (C_p)	%	Multiple $(C_p \times \%)$	Resultant Pollution Category
1	i	1,000	11	11,000	
2	q	1	67	67	Y
3	o	10	22	220	
S_p				11,287	

Example 3

Steps 1 and 2

The amount of component 1 is 2% of the mixture; its GESAMP hazard profile, taken from the GESAMP/EHS Composite List, is:

A1	A2	B1	B2	D3	E2
		3			

This leads to *row o* in Table 1. The component factor is 10, the multiple is 20.

The amount of component 2 is 4% of the mixture; its GESAMP hazard profile, taken from the GESAMP/EHS Composite List, is:

A1	A2	B1	B2	D3	E2
4	NR		1		

This leads to *row q* in Table 1. The component factor is 1, the multiple is 4.

The amount of component 3 is 94% of the mixture; its GESAMP Hazard profile, taken from the GESAMP/EHS Composite List, is completely blank or zero:

A1	A2	B1	B2	D3	E2

This leads to *row u* in Table 1.

It is an OS component, the component factor is 0, the multiple is 0.

Step 3

$S_p = 24$
$S_p < 25$ and not all components are OS
The mixture is therefore category Z

Component number	Applicable row in Table 1	Component factor (C_p)	%	Multiple ($C_p \times$ %)	Resultant Pollution Category
1	o	10	2	20	
2	q	1	4	4	Z
3	u	0	94	0	
S_p				24	

Example 4

Steps 1 and 2

Component 1 is 20% of the mixture; its GESAMP Hazard profile, taken from the GESAMP/EHS Composite List, is completely blank or zero:

A1	A2	B1	B2	D3	E2
		0			

Component 2 is 80% of the mixture; its GESAMP hazard profile, taken from the GESAMP/EHS Composite List, is completely blank:

A1	A2	B1	B2	D3	E2

All components are OS, *row u* in Table 1 is applicable. The component factors and the multiples are 0.

Step 3

$S_p = 0$
The mixture consists of OS components only
The mixture is therefore OS

Component number	Applicable row in Table 1	Component factor (C_p)	%	Multiple ($C_p \times$ %)	Resultant Pollution Category
1	u	0	20	0	
2	u	0	80	0	OS
S_p				0	

Example 5

Steps 1 and 2

The amount of component 1 is 70% of the mixture; its GESAMP hazard profile, taken from the GESAMP/EHS Composite List, is:

A1	A2	B1	B2	D3	E2
		4			

This leads to *row m* in Table 1. The component factor is 100, the multiple is 7,000.

The amount of component 2 is 29% of the mixture.
It is a diluent mineral oil so *no row* in Table 1 is applicable.
The component factor, however, is 100, the multiple is 2,900.

The amount of component 3 is 1% of the mixture.
It is an unassessed component, so *no row* in Table 1 is applicable.
The component factor, however, is 10,000. The multiple is therefore 10,000.

Step 3

$S_p = 19,900$
$S_p < 25,000$ and $S_p \geq 25$
The mixture is therefore category Y

Component number	Applicable row in Table 1	Component factor (C_p)	%	Multiple ($C_p \times$ %)	Resultant Pollution Category
1	m	100	70	7,000	
2	Component is diluent mineral oil	100	29	2,900	Y
3	Unassessed component	10,000	1	10,000	
S_p				**19,900**	

Example 6

Steps 1 and 2

The amount of component 1 is 2% of the mixture; its GESAMP hazard profile, taken from the GESAMP/EHS Composite List, is:

A1	A2	B1	B2	D3	E2
5	NR			M	

This leads to *row d* in Table 1. The component factor is 25,000, the multiple is 50,000.

The amount of component 2 is 98% of the mixture; its GESAMP hazard profile, taken from the GESAMP/EHS Composite List, is:

A1	A2	B1	B2	D3	E2
			≥ 1		

This leads to *row r* in Table 1. The component factor is 1, the multiple is 98.

Step 3

$S_p = 50,098$
$S_p \geq 25,000$
The mixture is therefore category X

Component number	Applicable row in Table 1	Component factor (C_p)	%	Multiple ($C_p \times$ %)	Resultant Pollution Category
1	d	25,000	2	50,000	
2	r	1	98	98	X
S_p				50,098	

Examples of determination of Ship Types for mixtures

Working Method

Step 1

Identify Ship Type and the multiplication factor for each component using the IBC Code or the MEPC.2/Circular and table 2.

Step 2

Determine the concentration of each component and multiply the percentage by the factor found in step 1.

Step 3

Add multiples together and determine the resulting Ship Type, using the flowchart for determining Ship Types.

Step 3a

Apply the previously determined Pollution Category of the mixture if the added multiples are < 100.

Example 1

Step 1

Component 1 is Ship Type 1, the multiplication factor is 1,000
Component 2 is Ship Type 3, the multiplication factor is 10
Component 3 is Ship Type 3, the multiplication factor is 10

Step 2

Component 1 is 11% of the mixture   Multiple is 11,000
Component 2 is 40% of the mixture   Multiple is 400
Component 3 is 49% of the mixture   Multiple is 490

Step 3

$S_s = 11,890$
$S_s \geq 10,000$
The ST 1 multiples are 11,000
The ST 1 multiples are $\geq 10,000$
Therefore the Ship Type is 1

(Step 3a is not applicable since $S_s > 100$)

Component number	Ship Type	Factor (f)	%	Multiple ($f \times$ %)	Pollution Category of mixture	Resultant Ship Type
1	1	1,000	11	11,000	Not applicable in this example	1
2	3	10	40	400		
3	3	10	49	490		
S_s				11,890		

Example 2

Step 1

Component 1 is Ship Type 2 and the multiplication factor is 100
Component 2 is Ship Type 3 and the multiplication factor is 10

Step 2

Component 1 is 5% of the mixture   Multiple is 500
Component 2 is 95% of the mixture   Multiple is 950

Step 3

$S_s = 1450$
$10,000 > S_s \geq 1,000$
Sum of ST 1 & 2 multiples is $< 1,000$
Therefore the Ship Type is 3

(Step 3a is not applicable since $S_s > 100$)

Component number	Ship Type	Factor (*f*)	%	Multiple (*f* × %)	Pollution Category of mixture	Resultant Ship Type
1	2	100	5	500	Not applicable in this example	3
2	3	10	95	950		
S_s				1,450		

Example 3

Step 1

Component 1 is Ship Type "n/a", the multiplication factor is 0
Component 2 is Ship Type 3, the multiplication factor is 10
Component 3 is diluent mineral oil, the multiplication factor is 10

Step 2

Component 1 is 10% of the mixture   Multiple is 0
Component 2 is 8% of the mixture   Multiple is 80
Component 3 is 82% of the mixture   Multiple is 820

Step 3

$S_s = 900$
$1{,}000 > S_s \geq 100$
Therefore the Ship Type is 3

(Step 3a is not applicable since $S_s > 100$)

Component number	Ship Type	Factor (f)	%	Multiple ($f \times$ %)	Pollution Category of mixture	Resultant Ship Type
1	n/a	0	10	0	Not applicable in this example	**3**
2	3	10	8	80		
3	Diluent mineral oil	10	82	820		
S_s				900		

Example 4

Step 1

Component 1 is Ship Type 2, the multiplication factor is 100
Component 2 is Ship Type 3, the multiplication factor is 10
Component 3 is unassessed, the multiplication factor is 100

Step 2

Component 1 is 4% of the mixture   Multiple is 400
Component 2 is 95% of the mixture   Multiple is 950
Component 3 is 1% of the mixture   Multiple is 100

Step 3

$S_s = 1,450$
$10,000 < S_s \geq 1,000$
Sum of ST 1 & 2 multiples is $< 1,000$
Therefore the Ship Type is 3

(Step 3a is not applicable since $S_s > 100$)

Component number	Ship Type	Factor (f)	%	Multiple ($f \times$ %)	Pollution Category of mixture	Resultant Ship Type
1	2	100	4	400	Not applicable in this example	3
2	3	10	95	950		
3	Unassessed	100	1	100		
S_s				1,450		

Example 5

Step 1

Component 1 is Ship Type "n/a", the multiplication factor is 0
Component 2 is Ship Type 3, the multiplication factor is 10
Component 3 is Ship Type 3, the multiplication factor is 10

Step 2

Component 1 is 91% of the mixture   Multiple is 0
Component 2 is 7% of the mixture   Multiple is 70
Component 3 is 2% of the mixture   Multiple is 20

Step 3

$S_s = 90$
$S_s < 100$

Step 3a

Pollution Category of mixture is Y, as determined previously
Therefore the Ship Type is 3

Component number	Ship Type	Factor (f)	%	Multiple ($f \times$ %)	Pollution Category of mixture	Resultant Ship Type
1	n/a	0	91	0		
2	3	10	7	70	Y	3
3	3	10	2	20		
S_s				90		

BLG.1/Circ.17 of 24 May 2006

Use of the correct product name in offering bulk liquid cargoes for shipment

1   In order to ensure that vessel operators and crews are able to ascertain that bulk liquids offered for shipment have been evaluated for transport in bulk and apply the appropriate carriage and operational requirements as laid out in SOLAS chapter VII, MARPOL Annex II and chapters 17 and 18 of the IBC Code, paragraph 16.2.2 of the IBC Code reads:

> "Any cargo offered for bulk shipment should be indicated in the shipping documents by the correct technical name . . ."

2   In recognizing the importance of this issue and wishing to emphasize it further, paragraph 16.2.2 in the text of the amended IBC Code, adopted by MEPC 52 (resolution MEPC.119(52)) and MSC 79 (resolution MSC.176(79)), reads:

> "Any cargo offered for bulk shipment shall be indicated in the shipping documents by the product name under which it is listed in chapter 17 or 18 of the IBC Code or the latest edition of the MEPC.2/Circular or under which it has been provisionally assessed . . ."

3   Given that there is some evidence that confusion over the exact nature of a particular cargo may have contributed to a recent incident involving fatalities, Member States are urged to draw the attention of all stakeholders to the importance of fulfilling their obligation to refer to cargoes only by the product name as it appears in chapter 17 or 18 of the IBC Code or the latest edition of the MEPC.2/Circular.

*Example of an optional shipping document for the
purposes of MARPOL Annex II and the IBC Code*

1   The IBC Code requires that cargoes be referred to in the shipping document by the product name as it appears in chapter 17 or 18 of the IBC Code or the MEPC.2/Circular. The term "shipping document" has never been defined in this context in order to allow maximum flexibility for industry. However, this can sometimes lead to confusion, particularly where products are referred to by different names on various documents.

2   The Organization has developed an example of an optional shipping document that may be used where owners feel it necessary to clarify the names of products carried on board their vessels. The example is set out at annex. Columns may be completed or not at owners' discretion and the form may be amended to suit the needs of individual owners.

3   Member States are invited to bring this document to the attention of interested parties and provide feedback to the Organization on its use.

Annex

Example of an optional shipping document

(Columns may be added or amended)

For the purposes of MARPOL Annex II and the IBC Code

Name of Ship: . . . . Owner/Operator: . . . . Port of Registry: . . . .

Voyage Number: . . . . IMO Number: . . . .

Cargo Number and/or B/L ref. No.	Cargo name (as per B/L)	Product Name (as per IBC Code*)	Tanks	Date loaded (dd/mm/yyyy)	Loading port(s)	Unloading port(s)

Signature . . . .

* Product Name as it appears in the IBC Code or MEPC.2/Circular and Ship's Certificate of Fitness, NLS Certificate or an addendum.